Introduction to Creativity and Innovation for Engineers

Introduction to Creativity and Innovation for Engineers

Global Edition

STUART G. WALESH

 Pearson

Boston • Columbus • Indianapolis • New York • San Francisco • Hoboken • Amsterdam
Cape Town • Dubai • London • Madrid • Milan • Munich • Paris • Montreal • Toronto
Delhi • Mexico City • São Paulo • Sydney • Hong Kong • Seoul • Singapore • Taipei • Tokyo

Vice President and Editorial Director, ECS: *Marcia J. Horton*
Executive Editor: *Holly Stark*
Editorial Assistant: *Amanda Brands*
Acquisitions Editor, Global Editions: *Abhijit Baroi*
Program and Project Management Team Lead: *Scott Disanno*
Program Manager/Project Manager: *Erin Ault*
Project Editor, Global Editions: *K.K. Neelakantan*
Global HE Director of Vendor Sourcing and Procurement: *Diane Hynes*
Director of Operations: *Nick Sklitsis*
Operations Specialist: *Maura Zaldivar-Garcia*
Senior Manufacturing Controller, Global Editions: *Angela Hawksbee*
Media Production Manager, Global Editions: *Vikram Kumar*
Product Marketing Manager: *Bram van Kempen*
Field Marketing Manager: *Demetrius Hall*
Marketing Assistant: *Jon Bryant*
Cover Designer: *Lumina Datamatics*
Associate Project Manager, Rights and Permissions: *William Opaluch*
Full-Service Project Management: *Mohinder Singh, iEnergizer Aptara®, Ltd.*

The author and publisher of this book have used their best efforts in preparing this book. These efforts include the development, research, and testing of theories and programs to determine their effectiveness. The author and publisher make no warranty of any kind, expressed or implied, with regard to these programs or the documentation contained in this book. The author and publisher shall not be liable in any event for incidental or consequential damages with, or arising out of, the furnishing, performance, or use of these programs.

Pearson Education Limited
Edinburgh Gate
Harlow
Essex CM20 2JE
England

and Associated Companies throughout the world

Visit us on the World Wide Web at:
www.pearsonglobaleditions.com

© Pearson Education Limited 2017

The right of Stuart G. Walesh to be identified as the author of this work has been asserted by him in accordance with the Copyright, Designs and Patents Act 1988.

Authorized adaptation from the United States edition, entitled Introduction to Creativity and Innovation for Engineers, 1st Edition, ISBN 978-0-13-358707-4, by Stuart G. Walesh published by Pearson Education © 2017.

British Library Cataloguing-in-Publication Data
A catalogue record for this book is available from the British Library

ISBN 10: 1292159286
ISBN 13: 9781292159287

Typeset in 10/12 New Baskerville ITC Pro Roman by Aptara

To Jerrie

Contents

3 • PRELUDE TO WHOLE-BRAIN METHODS   101

5 • OVERCOMING OBSTACLES TO CREATIVITY AND INNOVATION

6 • CHARACTERISTICS OF CREATIVE AND INNOVATIVE INDIVIDUALS   216

8 • CREATIVITY AND INNOVATION EXAMPLES FROM VARIOUS ENGINEERING SPECIALTIES   306

Preface

I wrote *Introduction to Creativity and Innovation for Engineers* with the assumption that readers will be mostly engineering students who want to proactively acquire creativity/innovation knowledge, skills, and attitudes (KSAs) during their technically and scientifically oriented education. These KSAs will enable you to work smarter and achieve more individual and organizational success and significance in our rapidly changing world. You will be better prepared to generate and begin to develop ideas for improved or new structures, facilities, systems, products, or processes. Primarily a textbook, but also designed to be useful for practicing engineers, the text provides principles and a tool set to help you and others navigate proactively in a rapidly changing world.

Instructors might use *Introduction to Creativity and Innovation for Engineers* as the textbook or supplemental book in a first-year exploring engineering course; besides presenting critical creativity/innovation knowledge and skills, it also touches on many areas of engineering and science. It could also be the text for a creativity and innovation course and could serve as a resource for a capstone course and for many undergraduate and graduate engineering courses.

In the world of professional practice, this text could assist individuals who want to learn more about creativity and innovation. It could also be obtained by private and public engineering or similar organizations for distribution to selected personnel and as support for in-house education and training.

Achieving personal and organizational success and significance while functioning effectively as people-serving professionals will increasingly require creativity and innovation in the technical and nontechnical aspects of our work. You will find much of the material in this text immediately useful. While studying engineering, you can apply part of the presented information and techniques, and then use those and the text's other resources when you enter professional practice.

Engineering study and practice aside, the principles, ideas, knowledge, and tools offered in this text are widely applicable to other disciplines both within and outside of work. Apply them in your community, family, and other relationships and activities. For example, regardless of your profession and specialty, Chapter 2 provides an insightful introduction to that amazing instrument between your ears. Building on those brain basics, Chapters 4 and 7 offer many methods that enable you to work smarter and be more creative and innovative, no matter what you do.

THE NEED FOR A WHOLE-BRAIN APPROACH IN ENGINEERING

We engineers, beginning as students, use many tools (e.g., simulation models, computer-aided design and drafting [CADD], materials-testing devices, building information modeling [BIM], social media) that help us serve our employers, our clients and customers, and the public at large. However, your most powerful aid is that amazing three-pound entity between your ears: your brain. Because of the emphasis of our precollege formal educations, many of us rely heavily on left-brain thinking, which is verbal, analytic, logical, literal, temporal, and symbolic.

This left-hemisphere bias typically continues into our engineering education, work, and other activities.

Left-brain capabilities are valuable; lest there be any misunderstanding, nothing in this text is intended to detract from the value of left-brain capabilities. The typical engineer's critical thinking knowledge and skill is a powerful and often not fully recognized and appreciated force. However, students and their teams, while in school and beyond, are more likely to be successful if they also frequently engage in both left- and right-brain thinking; the latter is nonverbal, synthetic, intuitive, emotional, nontemporal, and real. A half-brain is good, but a whole brain is better.

Given a basic understanding of the brain—more specifically, its structure, the very different functions of the brain's left and right hemispheres, neuroplasticity, conscious and subconscious thinking, habits, negativity bias, left- and right-handedness, gender differences, brain care, and the brain's role in creativity and innovation—and given a set of thinking-enhancing methods, a group or an individual is more likely to respond successfully to challenges. The combination of brain basics and tools will enable students and their teams to more effectively define and solve a problem, execute a plan or design, identify and pursue an opportunity, or recognize and address an issue. They will work smarter, partly by being more creative and innovative. Results of this whole-brain approach will almost always be better than those produced by the common hectic, hit-or-miss, reactive, suboptimal, left-brain-dominated methods. Valuable left-brain capabilities can be supplemented with equally valuable right-brain capabilities and more focused conscious thinking can stimulate additional subconscious thought.

GOING UP TO THE NEXT LEVEL

Essentially all of us are creative and innovative. We were born that way, though formal education and experience may have taken some of it out of us. However, with knowledge, tools, and practice, each of us can be more creative and innovative. Strictly speaking, essentially all engineers are creative and innovative because whatever we design, construct, manufacture, or otherwise produce never existed before. Each result is unique, at least in some specific manner or detailed way. However, the issue here is the frequency and degree of creativity and innovation. This text argues that many more engineers, beginning as first-year engineering students and then progressing through their formal education and careers, can proactively and systematically reach for moderate to high degrees of creativity and innovation in both technical and nontechnical functions.

Yes, we could individually and collectively rely on accidental creativity and innovation, those wonderful but rare out-of-the-blue events. However, why not complement accidental creativity and innovation with the intentional kind? *Introduction to Creativity and Innovation for Engineers* shows you how to do that.

ORGANIZATION AND CONTENT

Chapter 1 defines creativity and innovation, describes the urgency of strengthening engineers' creativity and innovation, and shows the historic and linguistic connections between engineering and creativity. This is followed in Chapter 2 by insights drawing on recent neuroscience findings into how the human brain (which drives creativity and innovation) works. The chapter includes advice on how to care for and more effectively use our brains.

Building on this brain primer and Chapter 3, which introduces whole-brain tools, Chapter 4 describes and illustrates eleven basic whole-brain methods that enable you and your teams or other groups to make fuller use of your intellectual resources. Chapter 4 recognizes that although creative and innovative ideas lie within most of us, individuals and groups need mechanisms to release them.

Chapter 5 acknowledges that you and your team are likely to encounter obstacles when trying to be more creative and innovative. The chapter describes seven possible obstacles and offers ways to deal with each one. In a more uplifting mode, Chapter 6 describes seven characteristics of creative/innovative individuals; you are likely to recognize many of these attributes in yourself.

Chapter 7 builds on the basic methods described in Chapter 4 and the further knowledge presented in Chapters 5 and 6, presenting nine additional, more advanced whole-brain methods.

Chapter 8 supplements the over eighty examples of creative/innovative technical and nontechnical developments described in the preceding chapters. It presents more detailed descriptions of six creative/innovative efforts drawn from a variety of engineering specialties.

Chapter 9, the final chapter, introduces the implementation process—that is, strategies and tactics for implementing creative and innovative ideas. Appendices provide supplemental material, including abbreviations (Appendix A) and a glossary (Appendix B).

Each chapter begins with a list of learning objectives that use Bloom's taxonomy verbs to describe what the reader should be able to do after working through the chapter. Chapters include almost sixty Personal, Historic Note, or Views of Others text boxes. The first gives me an opportunity to reinforce a chapter's content with anecdotes; the other two use history and the thoughts of others to strengthen the chapter's message. The body of each chapter ends with concluding thoughts or a summary followed by a list of cited references and by exercises.

Highly varied examples of creativity and innovation and their resulting benefits appear throughout this text. Collectively, all chapters (with the exception of Chapter 2) identify and describe ninety creative/innovative ideas, products, processes, structures, facilities, systems, and approaches, to various degrees of detail. This strong examples/benefits thread is intended to inspire you to work smarter and to achieve higher levels of creativity and innovation in all aspects of your current studies and later in your professional, personal, family, community, and other activities.

Over eighty exercises, which appear at the end of all chapters, provide opportunities for further exploration of ideas, information, and techniques presented in the chapters. Most exercises are well-suited for modest to major team projects. Teamwork, especially when the teams are composed of highly diverse individuals, is conducive to creativity and innovation. Therefore, instructors are urged to assign most exercises as team projects. In that way, students will learn more about the subject matter while acquiring additional insight into the creative/innovative potential of teams and the need for team leadership.

USING THIS TEXT IN A FIRST-YEAR EXPLORING ENGINEERING COURSE

As noted near the beginning of this Preface, engineering faculty can use this text as the textbook or supplemental text in a first-year exploring engineering course. The text's design, content, and tone anticipate the varied composition of a class of freshman engineering students. That group is likely to include some students with widely varying perspectives, such as those who are:

- admirers of recent technological developments (e.g., iPhone, all-electric Tesla car) and those whose creative/innovative efforts produced them (Steve Jobs and Elon Musk, respectively);
- uncertain about engineering as a course of study and career;
- committed to making the world a better place and who think that engineering is the most appropriate profession; and
- want, or were told to want, certain employment and a comfortable income.

The perspectives of these students are markedly different, but they share an admirable characteristic: As a group, they are of above-average intelligence and offer great teaching and learning potential. How might this text be used to engage and help a group of highly intelligent first-year and perhaps second-year students with widely varying perspectives and concerns? My suggestions are as follows:

1. Use selected portions of Chapter 1 (mostly Sections 1.1 through 1.4) and some of its exercises to stimulate thinking and conversation about success and significance, each individual's desired mix, and the role of creativity/innovation in achieving that mix. Then engage students in discussing reasons that engineers in advanced countries should learn more about creativity and innovation. Plant the seed that anyone can be creative and innovative; it's mostly nurture, not nature.

2. Work through essentially all of Chapter 2, including some exercises, noting that we have learned so much about the human brain in the past decade and that use of that knowledge will enable each student and future engineer to work smarter, be more creative/innovative, and achieve his or her desired balance of success and significance.

3. Use Sections 3.1 through 3.5 of Chapter 3 and selected exercises to introduce the value of idea generation and the availability of many methods that enable an individual or group to adopt a whole-brain creative/innovative approach to solving problems, addressing issues, and pursuing opportunities. Stress the idea that these methods, which build on neuroscience, will enable them to achieve their technical, altruistic, financial, and other goals. Brain basics plus whole-brain tools will leverage their superior intelligence.

4. Work through most of the basic whole-brain methods in Chapter 4 by making heavy use of the exercises in a team mode. Note the many existing examples of creativity and innovation. Expect students to quickly understand and use the methods and begin to discover their creative/innovative selves.

5. Take time out from being creative and innovative; use Chapter 5 and some of its exercises to address the reality of obstacles to creativity and innovation and some remedies, given the many and varied benefits of being creative and innovative.

6. Assign Chapter 6, with a few exercises, primarily as a means of reinforcing the idea that anyone can be creative and innovative. The essentials are as follows: learn the basics of how the human brain functions, obtain and use whole-brain methods, overcome obstacles, and recognize and strengthen characteristics that most of us naturally possess.

7. Fit some of the Chapter 8 examples into the course, if time permits. Examine in depth some engineering marvels, the challenging circumstances motivating their development, and the engineers who led creative/innovative projects. Encourage students to anticipate participating in similar exciting efforts.

If an approach like the preceding one is used in a first-year and perhaps second-year course, faculty and students will have studied parts of Chapters 1, 3, and 8 and most of Chapters 2, 4, 5, and 6. The remaining parts of Chapters 1, 3, and 8 and all of Chapters 7 and 9 can be readily used in other parts of the undergraduate and graduate academic program and in engineering practice, as noted in the introduction to this Preface.

FITTING CREATIVITY AND INNOVATION INTO AN ALREADY FULL ACADEMIC PROGRAM

Engineering curricula tend to emphasize mathematics, science, and analysis and, as such, may be categorized as left-brain oriented. Traditional curricula also include design and its creative/innovative aspects, which draw on the right brain and left brain. However, the design experience typically occurs near the end of a student's baccalaureate program and comprises a very small part of it.

Please note that I am referring to traditional engineering curricula and basing my comments on US practice. There are curricular exceptions—engineering programs that embody design and other whole-brain educational activities earlier, if not throughout the undergraduate program.

Deferring design, and more specifically creativity and innovation, until the end of an academic program may cause the following two problems:

- Students lose interest in engineering. Some young people are drawn to engineering because they view it as being design oriented or, more fundamentally, a building profession. Engineer Florman expressed it this way: "We have an irresistible urge to dip our hands in the stuff of the earth and do something with it." These young people may lack the motivation to persist in a program that appears to be analytically focused.
- Being steeped in left-brain studies for three-plus years and then being asked to also draw heavily on the right brain—a very different mode of thinking—may be difficult. Heavy, multiyear emphasis on analysis using algorithmic, albeit sophisticated, methods may impair students' creative/innovative abilities.

There is an alternative to the traditional, heavy front-end focus on left-brain analysis. Design—or more broadly, creative/innovative activities using a whole-brain approach—can appear in all years of the curriculum. More specifically, include conceptual design in the first year. Follow this with preliminary design and detailed design in the remaining years. The left and right hemispheres can be explicitly engaged throughout all years of the curriculum.

Back to the title of this section: How can we fit creativity and innovation into an already full academic program—that is, in curricular, cocurricular, and extracurricular aspects—as advocated by this text? How can we stuff even more into that undergraduate experience?

A list of twenty curricular, cocurricular, and extracurricular tactics are available at no cost to faculty. They are part of the document "Solutions Commentary and Tactics for Fitting Creativity/Innovation into an Already Full Curriculum for Faculty Using *Introduction to Creativity and Innovation for Engineers.*" The extracurricular options are especially attractive when an engineering college is part of a diverse university environment. Perhaps some of these ideas will resonate with you and enable you, and interested colleagues, to use this text as one means of introducing more creativity/innovation into your curriculum.

Most of the preceding curricular and curriculum-related ideas and actions are not so much add-ons as they are variations on what you are doing now, in and outside of the classroom. Some of the suggested tactics can be part of advising and mentoring, including urging students to take full advantage of their campus activities, many of which offer creativity/innovation experiences. I welcome questions and suggestions from faculty in any engineering discipline about fitting creativity and innovation into your academic programs, including, but not limited to, use of this text to achieve that objective.

NEUROSCIENCE AND TEACHING EFFECTIVENESS

This text's premise is that engineers, beginning as students and then progressing through their careers, can use neuroscience and related thinking methods to achieve more creativity/innovation in both technical and nontechnical functions. Building on that idea, we might ask: If knowing brain basics makes better engineers, would knowing more brain basics make better teachers—especially teachers of engineers?

Author and biology professor Zull thinks so, as he tries to explain in his 2002 book *The Art of Changing the Brain*. He chose that title because he defines teaching and learning as the teacher and the student working together to physically change the student's brain. Therefore, if we are going to change something we need to understand it. Zull refers to the *biology of learning* as a way of encouraging teachers to study the human brain. Educator Hardiman takes a similar tact in her 2003 book *Connecting Brain Research with Effective Teaching: The Brain-Targeted Teaching Model*. She urges educators to "become better consumers of the mountains of research that have emerged since the 1990s."

I mention the brain-science-based messages of these two educators because, if you are an engineering educator and you and your students use this text, then you as the teacher are bound to learn more about the human brain. What you and they learn will help your students be more creative and innovative engineers. That introduction to neuroscience and further study of it may enable you to be an even more effective teacher, no matter what you teach.

ACKNOWLEDGEMENTS

Although I did not realize at the time, the seeds for this text were planted in 2008 when, on a whim, I took my first pencil drawing class since grade school. I appreciate the artistry and patience of art teachers Don Melander in Florida and Fred Holly in Indiana, who patiently helped me understand and apply knowledge of graphite and colored-pencil drawing supplemented with ink and acrylic paint. Their willingness to share ideas about freehand drawing and its possible connections to and roles in engineering education and practice is also valued. Listening to their drawing advice, watching them work, and trying to apply what I have learned suggests that we engineers have at least as much in common with artists as we do with scientists.

I also value the ideas, critiques, and encouragement offered by various friends and colleagues within and outside of engineering and in the business, government, academic, and volunteer sectors. This text attempts to break new ground by building enhanced creativity and innovation on a foundation of brain basics. The following accomplished and varied individuals kindly assisted me in meeting book-writing challenges by questioning some of my assertions, suggesting and/or providing resources, outlining additional key ideas and information, offering text organization and format ideas, clarifying and tightening text, and answering questions:

- Ecevit A. Bilgili, PhD, associate professor, Department of Chemical, Biological, and Pharmaceutical Engineering, New Jersey Institute of Technology, Newark, New Jersey
- Samuel G. Bonasso, PE, entrepreneur and inventor, former West Virginia secretary of transportation, Morgantown, West Virginia
- Roger D. Fruechte, PhD, former director, Electrical and Control Systems Lab, General Motors Research and Development Center, Rochester, Michigan
- John A. Hardwick, PE, former director of utilities, Valparaiso, Indiana
- Stefan Jaeger, CAE and managing director, member and corporate communications, American Society of Civil Engineers, Reston, Virginia
- Craig Kay, business manager, Ken Kay Associates, San Francisco, California
- Thomas A. Lenox, PhD, executive vice-president emeritus, American Society of Civil Engineers, Reston, Virginia
- Richard H. McCuen, PhD, professor and Ben Dyer Chair in Civil Engineering, University of Maryland, College Park, Maryland
- Paul D. Nussbaum, PhD, clinical neuropsychologist and adjunct professor of neurological surgery, University of Pittsburgh, Pittsburgh, Pennsylvania
- Peter E. Pisasale, PE, operations integrated product team lead, Seapower Capability Center, Raytheon Integrated Defense Systems, Providence, Rhode Island
- Jeffrey S. Russell, PhD, PE, vice provost for lifelong learning, dean, division of continuing studies, University of Wisconsin, Madison, Wisconsin
- Ranjit S. Sahai, PE, founder, RAM Corporation, Dulles, Virginia
- Vikram Singh, fractionation technology group head, ExxonMobil Research and Engineering, distillation, gas processes and energy section, Fairfax, Virginia
- John Steffen, PhD, PE, professor emeritus, mechanical engineering, Valparaiso University, Valparaiso, Indiana
- Ellen M. Strachota, PhD, RN, professor emeritus nursing, Grand View University, Des Moines Iowa
- Kristina L. Swallow, PE, program manager, public works, Las Vegas, Nevada
- Kim Walesh, deputy city manager, city of San Jose, California
- Elizabeth C. Wright, former systems analysis and trajectory specialist, Glenn L. Martin Company, Baltimore, Maryland
- Robert J. Wright, PE, former senior design engineer, Lockheed Missiles and Space, Sunnyvale, California

I am most appreciative of the assistance provided by the preceding professionals because it enabled me to write with what I hope is credibility and value across engineering, science, and medical topics. However, I am totally responsible for the manner in which I have used their contributions.

I acknowledge and sincerely appreciate what I have learned from and with students, faculty, practitioners, and others who participated in my creativity and innovation seminars, webinars, and workshops. Anonymous professionals who reviewed my proposal for this text and reviewed the draft manuscript also added value, for which I am indebted. My debt to other professionals is suggested in part by the many and varied sources cited in the text. I drew ideas, information, and reference materials from a wide range of sources.

Vicki Farabaugh, owner of Creative Computing, helped draft some of the graphics in this text, and her skills and responsiveness are valued. Contributions of members of the Pearson Education team are appreciated, especially Holly Stark, Executive Editor, Engineering; Scott Disanno, Program and Project Management Team Lead; Erin Ault, Program Manager; Amanda Brands, Editorial Assistant; and Melinda Rankin, Copy Editor.

Finally, Jerrie, my wife, performed some of the word processing; meticulously proofed punctuation, spelling, and grammar; critiqued content; and, as always, provided total support.

Stuart G. Walesh
Cape Haze, Florida
January 2016

ACKNOWLEDGMENTS FOR THE GLOBAL EDITION

Pearson would like to thank and acknowledge the following people for their work on the Global Edition.

Contributor
Sharmistha Banerjee, Indian Institute of Technology Guwahati, Guwahati

Reviewers
Debabrata Goswami, Indian Institute of Technology Kanpur, Kanpur
Amit Sheth, Indian Institute of Technology Gandhinagar, Gandhinagar
Vineet Vashista, Indian Institute of Technology Gandhinagar, Gandhinagar

About the Author

 Stuart G. Walesh, PhD, PE, D.WRE, Dist.M.ASCE, F.NSPE, provides management, engineering, and education/training services as an independent consultant for business, government, academic, and volunteer sector organizations. He earned his BS in civil engineering at Valparaiso University, his MSE at Johns Hopkins University, and his PhD from the University of Wisconsin–Madison. He is a licensed professional engineer.

Stu has over four decades of engineering, education, and management experience in the government, academic, and business sectors; he has served as a project manager, department head, discipline manager, author, marketer, sole proprietor, professor, and dean of an engineering college. As a member of various organizations, Stu mentored and coached junior professionals in areas such as communication, team essentials, and project planning and management.

Water resources engineering is Stu's technical specialty. He led or participated in watershed planning, computer modeling, flood control, storm water and floodplain management, groundwater, dam, and lake projects. His experience includes project management, research and development, stakeholder participation, litigation consulting, and expert witness services. Areas in which he provides management and leadership services as an independent consultant include technical and nontechnical education and training (on-site and distance learning), mentoring and coaching, corporate universities, writing and editing, speaking, marketing, meeting planning and facilitation, project planning, and team essentials.

In addition to *Introduction to Creativity and Innovation for Engineers* (2017), Stu authored *Urban Surface Water Management* (Wiley 1989); *Flying Solo: How to Start an Individual Practitioner Consulting Business* (Hannah Publishing 2000); *Managing and Leading: 52 Lessons Learned for Engineers* (ASCE Press 2004); *Managing and Leading: 44 Lessons Learned for Pharmacists* (co-authored with Paul Bush, American Society of Health-System Pharmacists 2008); and *Engineering Your Future: The Professional Practice of Engineering* (Wiley 2012; the first and second editions were published in 1995 and 2000). He also authored or coauthored hundreds of publications and presentations in the areas of engineering, education, and management and facilitated or presented hundreds of workshops, seminars, webinars, and meetings throughout the United States.

For additional information, visit www.HelpingYouEngineerYourFuture.com or contact Stu at stuwalesh@comcast.net.

1

Why Should You Learn More About Creativity and Innovation?

> In a world of forces that push toward
> the commoditization of everything,
> creating something new and different
> is the only way to survive.
> —*Geoff Colvin, journalist*

Objectives:

After studying this chapter, you will be able to:

- Articulate this text's purpose
- Explain the potential connection between your desired success and significance and this text's content
- Describe *creativity* and *innovation* and develop examples of each

- Illustrate six reasons engineers need to be creative and innovative as one way to answer the question posed by the chapter's title
- Discuss the historic and linguistic connections between engineering and creativity

1.1 PURPOSE OF THIS TEXT

The purpose of this text is to help you acquire creativity and innovation knowledge, skills, and attitudes (KSAs) so that you can work smarter and achieve more individual and organizational success and significance in our rapidly changing world. These

KSAs will enable you to develop ideas for improved or new structures, facilities, systems, products, or processes.

This is a practical book offering knowledge and tools that enable you and your teams to work smarter—partly by being much more creative and innovative—and, as a result, advance your career, strengthen your organization, and provide more effective service. Numerous exercises at the end of chapters enable you to apply knowledge gained and use new tools, often as part of a group. While studying engineering, you can apply much of the presented information and techniques, and can later use those and other resources when you enter professional practice. The book's content is also applicable outside of study and work in your personal, family, and community life and could help you develop a creative-innovative philosophy of life.

By learning and using creativity and innovation basics as a student, you are likely to acquire habitual ways of thinking and doing that will enable you to become increasingly creative and innovative as you advance in your formal education and then progress in your career. Just as we can habitually do things the way they are traditionally done, we can also instead habitually approach our studies, work, and life with a fresh perspective.

If you become more creative and innovative, are you assured personal and/or organizational success and significance? Not necessarily. A great idea not implemented is merely a novelty; an innovative concept not pursued is an opportunity lost. However, by placing more emphasis on creativity and innovation and by learning fundamentals, obtaining tools, and practicing, you can generate new ideas and follow through to earn personal and organizational benefits.

Remember the advice of lecturer and writer Ralph Waldo Emerson: "Build a better mousetrap and the world will beat a path to your door." It turns out that he didn't say it that way. He did say: "If a man has good corn, or wood, or boards, or pigs, to sell, or can make better chairs or knives, crucibles or church organs than anybody else, you will find a broad, hard-beaten road to his house, though it be in the woods" (Bartlett 1964). Not quite as catchy but still the same message—creativity/innovation can yield personal and organizational benefits.

1.2 ACHIEVING YOUR DESIRED SUCCESS AND SIGNIFICANCE

Success refers to your personal gain, such as your current high grade point average and perhaps later the money you earn, the car you drive, and the title you acquire. In contrast, "significance" refers to your positive impact on others and society during your formal education and extending throughout your career and life. Success is about "stuff"; significance is about legacy.

PERSONAL: MEANING OF SIGNIFICANCE

As an example of significance, consider this reflection. I happen to live half time near a project I managed years ago and, as a result, I frequently see "my" project serving its intended functions and adding to the quality of life in the community. Very few people remember that I had anything to do with this project. That's not important. What is important to me is the satisfaction of seeing the project work. While I and others enjoyed some personal professional successes on the project, they pale relative to observing its significant public benefit.

Another way of looking at success and significance is to think about your epitaph. Do you want it to say something like "he drove a Porsche" or "she had a prestigious title"? Or, in contrast, would you prefer an epitaph like this: "He or she left the world a better place than he or she found it"? William James, the psychologist and philosopher, tells us that "The great use of life is to spend it for something that will outlast us." I suspect that most of us want both; we want to achieve both success and significance. Where we differ is in the relative amounts.

I raise the success–significance issue near the beginning of this book because of its connection to creativity and innovation. If you embrace the success–significance idea, then whatever your desired relative portions of each, reaching your goals will be determined in part by value added in all that you do as a result of your creativity and innovation.

1.3 CREATIVITY AND INNOVATION DEFINED AND ILLUSTRATED

Because of their importance throughout this text, let's define two terms: *create* and *innovate*. Then, some examples are presented that will illustrate their meaning.

1.3.1 Definitions

While researching for this book, I found many definitions for creativity and innovation and their related verbs, create and innovate. My hope was to find some commonality among the definitions and to distill the essence of each term. However, the definitions are quite varied. Accordingly, for the purposes of this book, I offer the following definitions:

- **Create:** Originate, make, or cause to come into existence an entirely new concept, principle, outcome, or object
- **Innovate:** Make something new by purposefully combining different existing principles, ideas, and knowledge

These definitions, which were influenced by similar ones offered by engineer and educator consultant Herrmann (1996), teacher and consultant Kao (2007), consultant Nierenberg (1982), and engineering educators Beakley, Evans, and Keats (1986), suggest that *innovate* and *create* differ by degree of originality. Whereas innovation is, in effect, "integrative and aspirational" (Kao) and "grounded in already-invented products or processes" (Herrmann), creativity is "grounded in originality" (Herrmann) and "coming up with something [completely] new" (Nierenberg).

We might think of *innovate* and *create* as actions that differ by degree of newness, where to create is the ultimate. From a practical perspective, we as individuals or teams are much more likely to innovate than to create. Creativity, as defined here, is rare.

1.3.2 Examples

Next, *create* and *innovate* are illustrated with examples. Besides further clarifying the essentials of the two actions, the following historic anecdotes begin to suggest some of the characteristics of creative and innovative individuals, such as being inquisitive, being willing to experiment, and being persistent.

Creativity

As an example of creativity, consider Velcro, invented in 1948 by Swiss electrical engineer George de Mestral. This hook-and-loop fastener is made of Teflon loops

Figure 1.1
An inquisitive electrical engineer studied burrs under a microscope and creatively conceived and later developed Velcro.

(Denis Junker/Fotolia;
Fuzzphoto/Fotolia)

and polyester hooks, and the company is headquartered in Manchester, New Hampshire. De Mestral was returning from a hunting trip with his dog and cockleburs (seeds) were on his clothes and on his dog's fur (Figure 1.1). When de Mestral examined the burrs under a microscope, he saw many stiff, hooked spines that caught on almost anything. Seeing this, he thought about the possibility of repeatedly binding two materials (one with hooks and one with hoops) in a reversible manner.

De Mestral worked ten years to develop a manufacturing process, while recognizing that many people did not support his idea. He persisted and commercialized the now almost omnipresent fastener. The word *Velcro* is a combination of two other words: the French words *velour*, meaning fabric with a soft nap, and *crochet*, which is needlework in which loops of thread or yarn are interwoven with a hooked needle. The manner in which Velcro was conceived is now called biomimicry or biomimetics—that is, mimicking nature, a topic that is treated in Chapter 7 (Lee 2012; Bellis 2014).

Have you ever had a "brilliant idea" while returning from hunting, taking a shower, or walking on campus—and then failed to follow up? Or tried to follow up and failed to have people take you seriously? Ideas and information shared in this book will enhance your ability to generate creative and innovative ideas and make them happen.

Innovation

For an example of innovation, consider Johannes Gutenberg developing the reusable-type printing press (Figure 1.2), which he used to begin printing books in the 1450s, including the Bible in about 1456. He borrowed ideas from the following sources (Boorstin 1985; Murray 2009; Van Doren 1991):

- Woodblock printing, which had been used for eleven centuries in China. This process involved a sheet of paper placed on an inked block.
- Weapon and coin forging, which went back to Roman times. According to Boorstin, "Gutenberg's crucial invention was his specially designed mold for casting precisely similar pieces of type quickly and in large numbers."
- The binder's wooden screw press, which was probably an innovative adaption of the screw presses used by winemakers and olive oil producers and those used to process linen.

Figure 1.2
Gutenberg innovatively combined the screw press from wine making and olive oil production, Chinese woodblock printing, and Roman weapon and coin forging to develop the reusable-type printing press.

(Jan Schneckenhaus/Shutterstock)

Sorts, the individual letters, were produced by pouring liquid metal into the specially designed molds. The letters were arranged into type cases to make up pages, which were inked and printed. This process was a huge printing improvement over handwritten manuscripts and full-page woodblock printing.

Gutenberg was motivated mainly by trying to make a living, but his innovative reusable-type printing press transformed society and helped advance the Renaissance. "Once only the rich had been able to buy handwritten manuscripts. Suddenly, any scholar could own books," according to historian Van Doren (1991), who went on to say that those now readily accessible books "were filled with ideas that had been forgotten, ignored, or suppressed for centuries." In terms of a leap forward into access to ideas and information, Gutenberg's fifteenth-century innovative access to books was like the twentieth-century arrival of the World Wide Web accessed via the Internet.

1.4 WHY ENGINEERS SHOULD STUDY CREATIVITY AND INNOVATION AND WHY NOW

From the beginning of recorded history and all over the globe, individuals we would now label *engineers* have met the basic needs of communal society (Van Der Zee 1989; Walesh 1990; Weingardt 2005; White 1984). Going forward, that role will remain essentially the same; however, the stage on which that role is played will change dramatically. With the help of various thinkers, let's explore that new stage, with the hope that you will see the need to enhance your creative and innovative ability and thus be prepared for your role as an "actor" on that stage. In the following sections, you'll find six reasons to study creativity and innovation, starting now.

1.4.1 The Grand Challenges for Engineering

According to the National Academy of Engineering (NAE), engineering faces fourteen Grand Challenges in the twenty-first century (National Academy of

Engineering 2014). The challenges, which were announced in 2008, are listed here; note their variety, breadth, and implied depth:

1. Make solar energy economical.
2. Provide energy from fusion.
3. Develop carbon sequestration methods.
4. Manage the nitrogen cycle.
5. Provide access to clean water.
6. Restore and improve urban infrastructure.
7. Advance health informatics.
8. Engineer better medicines.
9. Reverse-engineer the brain.
10. Prevent nuclear terror.
11. Secure cyberspace.
12. Enhance virtual reality.
13. Advance personalized learning.
14. Engineer the tools of scientific discovery.

Based on the following statement, the Academy is confident that the engineering community will rise to the challenges: "The world's cadre of engineers will seek ways to put knowledge into practice to meet these grand challenges. Applying the rules of reason, the findings of science, the aesthetics of art, and the spark of creative imagination, engineers will continue the tradition of forging a better future." Note that the NAE believes that meeting the fourteen challenges will require that tomorrow's engineers possess many and varied qualities, including the "aesthetics of art" and "the spark of creative imagination."

1.4.2 After the Knowledge Age: The Conceptual Age?

As shown in Figure 1.3, advanced societies have evolved through the agricultural and industrial ages and into the knowledge age. Pink (2005, 2007) believes that the current knowledge age will be superseded in the United States and other advanced countries by what he calls the *conceptual age*, or the *engage the left and right brain age*—that is, the whole-brain age (Figure 1.3).

Conception means a new beginning or original idea. According to Pink, the conceptual age is "an era in which mastery of abilities that we've overlooked and undervalued" will be required (Pink 2007). Examples of these increasingly valued abilities, which reside partly or largely in the brain's right hemisphere, include

Figure 1.3
The knowledge age may be superseded by the conceptual age, with a premium on original ideas and concepts.

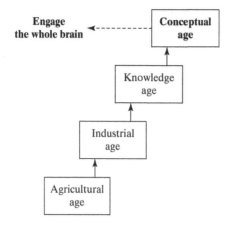

visualization, innovation, creativity, synthesis, empathy, and helping people find meaning.

Success in the knowledge age primarily requires left-hemisphere or left-brain abilities; many engineers are prime examples of knowledge workers. They logically and sequentially obtain and analyze data, calculate, and design to meet requirements. In a similar fashion, other knowledge age professionals rely heavily on their left hemispheres, such as accountants preparing tax returns, lawyers researching lawsuits, radiologists reading diagnostic data, software experts writing code, and stockbrokers executing transactions.

Pink argues that although left-brain abilities will be necessary in the looming conceptual age, they will not be sufficient. A half-brain will be necessary, but not sufficient; a whole brain will be needed if one is to succeed in the United States and other advanced countries. Work that "can be reduced to a set of rules, routines, and instructions," the functions of the left brain, is "migrating across the oceans. . . . Now that foreigners can do left-brain work cheaper, we in the US must do right-brain work better" (Pink 2007). As suggested by Figure 1.4, the Internet and a growing number of smart, ambitious, and English-speaking workers in India, China, the Philippines, Singapore, and other countries facilitate this outsourcing process.

According to columnist Brooks (2014), "Computers are increasingly going to be able to perform important parts of even mostly cognitive jobs, like picking stocks, diagnosing diseases, and granting parole." Computers also increasingly will be used in engineering to design products, processes, structures, facilities, and systems, as suggested in part by engineer and author Steiner (2012) in his book *Automate This*. In the conceptual age, leading-edge engineers will focus less on solving problems and more on resolving complex issues and finding and developing opportunities. "In similar fashion, accountants will serve more as financial advisors, lawyers will concentrate more on convincing juries and mastering the nuances of negotiation, and stockbrokers will become financial advisors to help people realize their dreams" (Walesh 2012b). Work is increasing in cognitive complexity, and our educational system (including that for engineers) must adjust. This includes placing more emphasis on creativity and innovation knowledge, skills, and attitudes (Pink 2007); knowing how to address complex issues, problems, and opportunities (IPOs); and being adept communicators (Levy and Murname 2005).

Given the material abundance enjoyed in the United States and other well-developed countries, Pink (2007) also argues that society will increasingly place

Figure 1.4
Knowledge work will increasingly move across the oceans to be done by a growing number of smart, ambitious, and English-speaking professionals in other nations.

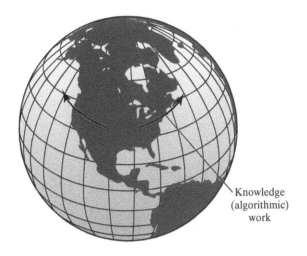

Knowledge
(algorithmic)
work

"a premium on the less rational sensibilities of beauty, spirituality, emotion. . . . Liberated by this prosperity [attributed to our very successful left-brain oriented work] but not fulfilled by it, more people are searching for meaning." These "sensibilities" also engage the whole brain. If Pink is correct, you will need a whole-brain approach to achieve success and significance in tomorrow's professional world.

1.4.3 After the Knowledge Age: The Opportunity Age?

Offering an intriguing view of the future, Naisbitt (2006) writes, "When you're looking for the shape of the future, look for and bet on the exploiters of opportunities, not the problem solvers." He claims that each of us tends to embrace one of two poles: stasis or dynamism, stability or evolution, predictability or surprise. Naisbitt suggests that problem solvers have one foot in the present and tend to have the other foot in the past (Figure 1.5). After all, today's problems originate in the past. In contrast, opportunity exploiters also live in the present and have one foot there, but tend to have the other foot in the future—the place of promise.

PERSONAL: MAINTAINER OR BUILDER?

As a follow-up to Naisbitt's "two poles" comment, I have concluded that each of us tends to be mostly a maintainer or a builder. Both outlooks are necessary to provide leadership, management, and production within our various organizations. Maintainers care for physical assets and develop and gradually improve processes, whereas builders search for opportunities, see new directions, and lead major changes.

Maintainers and builders exhibit different knowledge, skills, and attitudes (KSA) sets, especially the *attitudes* part. For example, although both appreciate what has been accomplished so far in a given organization, maintainers are generally satisfied subject to making continuous improvements in response to changing conditions. In contrast, builders are in a perpetual state of dissatisfaction and "just know" there is a better way.

Hopefully, this simplified model will help you to find your place on the maintainer–builder spectrum. Regardless of where you are, this text's creativity and innovation principles and tools will be useful. Apply the principles and use the tools if you are a maintainer and want to move toward being a builder or if you are already a builder (an opportunity seeker) and want to move further in that direction.

Figure 1.5
Problem solvers tend to look to the past while working in the present, whereas opportunity exploiters work in the present and look forward.

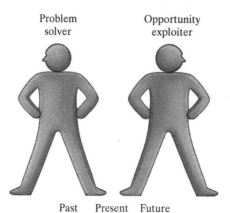

Problem solver Opportunity exploiter

Past   Present   Future

Most professions, such as engineering, law, and medicine, focus on solving problems and do a superb job. Engineering's focus on and proficiency in problem solving reflects in part engineering curricula's emphasis on problem solving and, to a lesser extent, problem prevention. Near the end of classes, I vividly recall hearing professors say things like, "For next class, solve Problems 1, 3, and 9 at the end of the chapter." Later, as a professor, I said the same thing! This approach is pedagogically sound in that principles or theories introduced, described, and discussed in lecture can be applied and further understood and appreciated by doing the homework. Furthermore, a brief discussion of the homework at the beginning of the next class period could further elucidate the topic. Understanding and applying theories and solving problems are essential aspects of engineering practice.

The teaching–learning method just described tends to be left-brained. It's linear, as in: present theory, assign problems which use the theory to reach a solution, provide students with everything needed to understand the problems, use theory to solve problems, get "the answer," and discuss how the successful students got the answer.

Engineers, beginning as students, can also perform functions besides problem solving, such as creatively and innovatively identifying and pursuing opportunities. However, rarely are students explicitly exposed to finding and pursuing opportunities, especially at the undergraduate level. This text seeks to help change that by offering creativity and innovation principles and tools that will help you be an opportunity seeker and therefore able not only to thrive in the future but also to help build it (Walesh 2012c).

1.4.4 After the Knowledge Age: The Wicked Problems Age?

Teacher, consultant, and innovation expert Kao (2007) is concerned that the United States may feel smug about its preeminence. He questions the idea that other countries will continue "to settle for being followers, mere customers, or imitators of our fabulous creations," and he asserts that "innovation has become the new currency of global competition as one country after another races toward a new high ground where the capacity of innovation is viewed as a hallmark of national success." Kao goes on to say that the security of the United States is at stake.

Continuing with the need to innovate, author Wagner (2012) states that the United States must provide "the new and better products, processes, and services that other countries want and need," and to do this "we must out innovate our economic competitors." Engineer Augustine (2011), former chairman and CEO of Lockheed Martin, says: "Innovation is the key to survival in an increasingly global economy. Today we're living off the investments we made over the past 25 years. We've been eating our seed corn. . . . We're losing our edge."

Kao's 2007 book *Innovation Nation* diagnoses the US situation, describes innovation best practices from around the globe, and explains how innovation works at the national level. Kao then proposes a US strategy to become what he calls *Innovation Nation*, "a country with a widely shared, well-understood objective of continuously improving our innovation capabilities in order to achieve world-changing goals." Innovation Nation would teach creativity and innovation to its children and young people as a matter of policy, or (to use Kao's words), would "fix the U.S. education system."

Kao envisions applying our vast resources to stimulate innovation on a huge scale. He says that America should "be in the wicked problems business," which means taking on global issues such as "climate change, environmental degradation, communicable diseases, education, water quality, poverty, population migration, and energy sufficiency." Kao believes that creative and innovative solutions to the wicked problems will be the most consequential breakthroughs of the twenty-first century. These solutions will generate "an enormous amount of social and economic value" and enable Innovation Nation—that is, the United States—to do good and do well. You can be a player in the wicked problems business if you learn and apply whole-brain principles and tools.

1.4.5 Stewardship with Aspiring Engineers and Their Gifts

As a result of working extensively in the academic and practice sectors, I've had numerous opportunities to review the credentials and accomplishments of high school and college students and observe the behavior of engineering students and engineering practitioners. You are among the brightest members of society and therefore have great potential to contribute to society. For years, I've contemplated ways to help aspiring and practicing engineers practice better stewardship with those gifts.

Now I know that one way to achieve more effective stewardship is to help student and practicing engineers gain further appreciation for the power of the right hemispheres of their brains and then show them how to engage that hemisphere to supplement their already strong left hemispheres. For this gifted group (you and your colleagues) we should settle for nothing less than a whole-brain approach, as laid out in this text.

I'm not saying that engineers are not creative and innovative—that the glass is half-empty. No, the creativity and innovation glass is half-full for most of us, but we could do more because we have the required intellect and can-do attitude. We should be more creative and innovative because of the importance of our work and because more creativity and innovation will enable us to do even more with limited resources and provide even better services. My hope is that as a result of this text and in the spirit of personal stewardship, you will at least experiment with higher levels of creativity and innovation. You have the potential within you.

HISTORIC NOTE: CONSEQUENCES OF A NATION NOT PRACTICING STEWARDSHIP WITH ENGINEERING

In his book *The Ghost of the Executed Engineer*, Graham (1993) tells the story of the Russian Engineer Peter Palchinsky. Born in 1875, Palchinsky earned an engineering degree in 1900 and went on to become "one of the best-known engineers in Soviet Russia." However, he increasingly opposed some of the positions of the Communist party because they conflicted with his intentions, which were "to assist his country by increasing its industrial strength and the welfare of its people." He believed that under socialism engineers should be major players in creating economic development plans. Increasing conflict led to Palchinsky's execution under the Stalin regime in about 1929 as a "leader of an anti-Soviet conspiracy."

In 1948, the Stalin regime arrested the twenty-two-year-old Russian inventor Genrich Altshuller and sentenced him to a twenty-five-year imprisonment in Siberia because he wrote to Stalin to criticize the Soviet Union's lack of inventive work. While in prison, he collaborated with other imprisoned intellectuals and further developed his creativity and innovation ideas. He was released from prison in 1954, after Stalin died. In 1984, he published his book about the theory of inventive problem solving known as TRIZ, which is one of the creativity and innovation tools presented in Chapter 7 (Altshuller 1996).

Graham concludes that the Soviet Union, which met its demise in 1991, failed as a modern industrialized nation even though it had a huge number of engineers and immense natural resources because of "misuse of technology and squandering of human energy," including its engineering talent. The Soviets failed to practice good stewardship with their engineering community's creative and innovative resources.

Besides offering examples of poor stewardship, the Palchinsky and Altshuller stories (which reflect very common occurrences during the Stalin era) offer another lesson. They are grim reminders that the change typically associated with creative and innovative thought and action is likely to invoke negative reactions, at least initially. Chapter 5, Section 5.5 elaborates on the often strong reluctance to change and offers remedies.

1.4.6 The Satisfaction of Doing What Has Not Been Done

Experience suggests that for most of us the magnet attracting us to engineering was excitement about creating or building something that, at least in our mind, had never existed. This pull probably started when we were children and built towers with blocks, castles with sand, and houses with cardboard boxes or drew with pencils, painted with brushes, sculpted with clay, wrote music, and modified games. These were our *originals*.

With time, study, and practice, we tended to broaden our understanding of creating and building originals. In retrospect and professionally, I value having been involved in teams that built or created original structures, facilities, systems, computer simulation models, fluid flow models, organizations within organizations, continuing education delivery methods, and approaches to engineering education.

We quietly value these professional creations and innovations because of their utility; they enhance the quality of life for many. Herbert Hoover, author, humanitarian and thirty-first US president, said this about engineering: "It is a great profession. There is the fascination of watching a figment of the imagination emerge through the aid of science to a plan on paper. Then it brings jobs and homes to men. Then it elevates the standards of living and adds to the comforts of life. That is the engineer's high privilege" (Van Der Zee 1989).

We're good at math and science, as people say, but that knowledge and skill might also prepare any of us to be productive as a banker, mathematics teacher, certified public accountant (CPA), physicist, casino manager, or auto mechanic. At a deeper level, we value the thrill of doing what has never been done, of building originals, and doing it for the benefit of many. "I do not think there is any thrill that can go through the human heart like that felt by the inventor as he sees some creation of the brain unfolding to success"; that's how the excitement of building originals was expressed by engineer Nikola Tesla, whose creative and innovative efforts include commercialization of alternating current motors, generators, and transmission lines. Therefore, my sixth and last reason for why you should study creativity and innovation and why you should start now as part of your formal education and continue on into practice is to pursue that urge to create and build originals, serve society, and enjoy the satisfaction of doing so even more proactively.

PERSONAL: ATTRACTION TO THE PROFESSION

I vividly recall my mother taking me across the highway in front of our northern Wisconsin home when I was a small boy so that I could build on the beach where a creek flowed into Lake Michigan. Near or in the creek, I constructed levees, dams, lakes, channels, and wells. Early in college, I learned that if I became a civil engineer I could continue to "play" with water, help design and build water-related facilities, have the satisfaction of being part of originals, make the world a better place, and get paid for it—which I subsequently did for over three decades.

1.4.7 Closing Thoughts about Studying Creativity and Innovation

Section 1.4 argues that you should study creativity and innovation starting now, as part of your formal education, and then continue into professional practice. Six reasons are offered: meeting the Grand Challenges; doing more conceptual work because algorithmic work is moving to increasingly capable personnel in developing countries; placing more emphasis on pursuing opportunities; addressing wicked problems; practicing better stewardship with your intellectual gifts; and experiencing the satisfaction of doing what has not been done.

Being more creative and innovative will require personal growth, including learning the basics of how the human brain functions (Chapter 2), using whole-brain tools (Chapters 3, 4, and 7), overcoming obstacles (Chapter 5), acquiring or strengthening certain personal characteristics (Chapter 6), being inspired by what others have done (Chapter 8), and learning how to implement your ideas (Chapter 9). If you make that effort, you are likely to achieve your desired success and significance, as suggested by Augustine (2009) when he said, "There will always be demand for superbly educated engineers who are capable of performing in an innovative, creative, and entrepreneurial fashion."

1.5 ENGINEERING AND CREATIVITY: THE HISTORIC AND LINGUISTIC CONNECTIONS

1.5.1 The Historic Connection between Engineering and Creativity/Innovation

As suggested by the following list and illustrated in Figure 1.6, we can note many and varied creative and innovative engineering achievements from the beginning of recorded history onward, including the following (Walesh 2012b):

- The Egyptian pyramids
- Tools developed during the Iron Age
- The Great Wall of China
- Athens' Parthenon
- The Roman Pont du Gard (in what is now France)
- China's Grand Canal
- The printing press
- The steam engine
- The telegraph system
- The transcontinental railroad in the United States
- Powered flight
- Mass production of automobiles and untold other consumer and producer products
- The Panama Canal

Figure 1.6
Engineering's accomplishments indicate that the profession's history is one of creativity and innovation.

((a) JonRob/Fotolia; (b) Windsor/ Fotolia; (c) Oleksandr Dibrova/ Fotolia; (d) Nikonomad/Fotolia)

(a)

(b)

(c)

(d)

- San Francisco's Golden Gate Bridge
- Computers
- Commercial jet aircraft
- The Eurotunnel connecting England and France
- Many electronic devices interconnected via the Internet (aka, the Internet of Things)
- Robotic prosthetics
- The International Space Station

These examples illustrate that engineering is historically connected to creativity and innovation.

1.5.2 The Linguistic Connection between Engineering and Creativity

As explained in Section 1.4.6, the possibility of creating and building attracted many of us to engineering. The words *create* and *engineer* are closely intertwined linguistically. Engineering professor Petroski (1985) and engineering practitioner Florman (1987) both explored the origins of the word *engineer*. Although they followed somewhat different routes and arrived at slightly different conclusions, they agreed that the word has its roots in *creativity*.

Petroski (1985) stated that *engineer* originally meant "one (a person) who contrives, designs, or invents." That is, *engineer was synonymous with creator*, and he noted that this use preceded by a century the idea of an engineer as one who manages an engine. According to Petroski, the association between *engineer* and *engine* began in the mid-1800s with the emergence of the railroad as the metaphor of the industrial revolution. Petroski concluded his exploration of the origins of the word *engineer* by noting that even today there is a "confusion of the contriver and the driver of the vehicle." More recently, Petroski (2011) indicated that he had moved more toward Florman's thinking, as outlined ahead, and noted that the association between *engineer* and *engine* dates to well before the 1800s.

Florman (1987) traced *engineer* back to the Latin word *ingenium*, which meant a clever thought or invention; the word was applied in about AD 200 to a military battering ram. That is, *engineer was synonymous with that which was created.* Later, in medieval times and during the Renaissance, the words *ingenieur, ingeniere,* and *ingeniero* (French, Italian, and Spanish, respectively) came into use, originally referring to those who designed and built military machines such as catapults and battering rams. In English, the word progressed from the fourth through seventeenth centuries as *engynour, yngynore, ingener, inginer, enginer,* and, finally, *engineer.*

Thus, Petroski and Florman agreed that the word *engineer* has deep roots in creativity: in contriving, inventing, designing, and creating (Walesh 2012b, 2012a). As engineers, we should be inspired to create, in part by virtue of the historic evolution of the name of our profession.

VIEWS OF OTHERS: ENGINEERS AND CREATIVITY/ INNOVATION

"Scientists define what is," according to aeronautical engineer von Karman, and "engineers create what never has been." Engineering professor Petroski (1985) refers to creativity this way: "It is the process of design, in which diverse parts of the given world of the scientist and the made-world of the engineer are reformed and assembled into something the likes of which nature had not dreamed, that divorces engineering from science and marries it to art." Engineering professor Cross (1952) said, "The glory of the adaption of science to human needs is that of engineering." According to professor Billington (1986), achieving an aesthetic result in design requires efficiency and economy plus "imagination—a talent for putting things together in unique ways that work, that are beautiful, personal, and permanent."

1.6 INTRODUCTION TO EXAMPLES OF CREATIVITY AND INNOVATION

To illustrate the creativity and innovation process and its benefits, this text contains ninety highly varied examples. The ones that I share are based primarily on my research and secondarily on my experience working on projects. In searching for and selecting examples, I sought variety in the following areas:

- **Contexts and circumstances:** For example, burrs stuck on coats and creation of Velcro; a snake bite and the invention of the Weed Eater; the Chicago stockyards and the first automobile assembly line; row crops and the creation of television; misinterpretation of two words and invention of the telephone; and the falling apple versus the "stationary" moon leading to discovery of universal gravitation.
- **Professions and specialties:** For example, creative/innovative work of individuals from various disciplines: scientists, constructors, architects, a dance instructor, biologists, a sand paper salesperson, and a road commissioner.

- **Technical and nontechnical developments and constraints:** For example, the low-tech but highly effective, like the Q-Drum; the high-tech and productive, like the moving automobile assembly line; and the useful but nontechnical, like the keystone habit—all being successful in spite of and/or fueled by various constraints.
- **Benefits:** For example, cost reduction, enhanced aesthetics, global impact, improved personal and organizational productivity, improved health and welfare, increased profit, less public impact during construction, quicker response, and reduced pollution (see Table 5.1 for many specific examples of the variety of benefits resulting from creativity and innovation).

This text draws widely from within and outside of engineering, for two reasons:

- **Many and varied process lessons to be learned:** Many of the creativity and innovation lessons learned from a variety of contexts and circumstances and widely varying professions and specialties are applicable to our work. For example, biomimicry (which is introduced in Section 7.2 and which prompted the commercial development of Velcro) can be a powerful stimulant within the engineering arena. Similarly, TRIZ, which is described in Section 7.9, is particularly powerful in technically oriented engineering work.
- **Many and varied potential applications:** Second, the potential for creativity and innovation lies within all professions and specialties and within all aspects of a given profession or specialty, including technical and nontechnical elements. When we as engineers think about being more creative and innovative, we include our technical challenges. Let's also consider being more creative and innovative within the other functions of our organizations, such as education and training, human resources, community involvement, finance, marketing, organizational structure, and simply finding ways to work smarter.

> Failure to recognize possibilities
> is the most dangerous and common mistake
> anyone can make.
>
> —*Mae Jamison, astronaut*

CITED SOURCES

Altshuller, G. 1996. *And Suddenly the Inventor Appeared: TRIZ, the Theory of Inventive Problem Solving.* Translated by Lev Shulyak from the original 1984 Russian version. Worcester, MA: Technical Innovation Center, Inc.

Augustine, N. R. 2009. "Re-engineering Engineering." *Prism,* ASEE, 18 (6): 46–47.

Augustine, N. R. 2011. "Danger: America is Losing Its Edge in Innovation." *Forbes,* January 20. Accessed July 22, 2015. http://www.forbes.com/sites/ciocentral/2011/01/20/danger-america-is-losing-its-edge-in-innovation/.

Bartlett, J. 1964. *The Shorter Bartlett's Familiar Quotations.* New York: Pocket Books.

Beakley, G. C., D. L. Evans, and J. B. Keats. 1986. *Engineering: An Introduction to a Creative Profession.* New York: Macmillan Publishing Company.

Bellis, M. 2014. "The Invention of Velcro: George de Mestral." *About.com Inventors.* Accessed August 2, 2014. http://inventors.about.com/library/weekly/aa091297.htm.

Billington, D. P. 1986. "In Defense of Engineers." *The Bridge,* National Academy of Engineers (Summer): 4–7.

Bonasso, S. 2013. Professional engineer and entrepreneur, pers. comm., April 16.

Boorstin, D. J. 1985. *The Discoverers*. New York: Vintage Books.

Brooks, D. 2014. "What Computers Can't Do." *The New York Times,* February 5.

Buzan, T. 1984. *Make the Most of Your Mind.* New York: Linden Press.

Chrysikou, E. G. 2012. "Your Creative Brain at Work." *Scientific American Mind* 23 (3): 24–31.

Cross, H. 1952. *Engineers and Ivory Towers*. Edited by R. C. Goodpasture. New York: McGraw-Hill.

Florman, S. C. 1987. *The Civilized Engineer*. New York: St. Martin's Press.

Fogler, H. S., S. E. LeBlanc, and B. Rizzo. 2014. *Strategies for Creative Problem Solving,* 3rd ed. Upper Saddle River, NJ: Pearson Education.

Graham, L. R. 1993. *The Ghost of the Executed Engineer: Technology and the Fall of the Soviet Union.* Cambridge, MA: Harvard University Press.

Herrmann, N. 1996. *The Whole Brain Business Book: Unlocking the Power of Whole Brain Thinking in Individuals and Organizations.* New York: McGraw-Hill.

Kao, J. 2007. *Innovation Nation: How America Is Losing Its Innovation Edge, Why It Matters, and What We Can Do to Get It Back.* New York: The Free Press.

Lee, D. W. 2012. "Biomimicry of the Ultimate Optical Device: The Plant." In *Biomimetics: Nature-Based Innovation,* edited by Y. Bar-Cohen, 308–330. Boca Raton, FL: CRC Press.

Levy, F., and R. J. Murname. 2005. *The New Division of Labor: How Computers Are Creating the Next Job Market.* Princeton, NJ: Princeton University Press.

Murray, D. K. 2009. *Borrowing Brilliance: The Six Steps to Business Innovation by Building on the Ideas of Others.* New York: Gotham Books.

Naisbitt, J. 2006. *Mind Set! Reset Your Thinking and See the Future.* New York: HarperCollins.

National Academy of Engineering. 2014. "Grand Challenges for Engineering," accessed November 9. http://www.engineeringchallenges.org/cms/challenges.aspx.

Nierenberg, G. I. 1982. *The Art of Creative Thinking.* New York: Barnes & Noble Books.

Petroski, H. 1985. *To Engineer Is Human: The Role of Failure in Successful Design.* New York: St. Martin's Press.

Petroski, H. 2011. *An Engineer's Alphabet: Gleanings from the Softer Side of a Profession.* Cambridge: Cambridge University Press.

Pink, D. H. 2005. *A Whole New Mind: Moving From the Knowledge Age to the Conceptual Age.* New York: Riverhead Books.

Pink, D. H. 2007. "Revenge of the Right Brain." *Public Management* (July): 10–13.

Raviv, D. 2004. "Hands-On Activities for Innovative Problem Solving." In *Proceedings of the 2004 American Society for Engineering Education Annual Conference and Exposition*, Session 1793, Salt Lake City, UT. ASEE.

Restak, R. 2009. *Think Smart: A Neuroscientist's Prescription for Improving Your Brain's Performance.* New York: Riverhead Books.

Restak, R., and S. Kim. 2010. "Creativity: The Magic Matches of Carlo Reverberi." In *The Playful Brain: The Surprising Science of How Puzzles Improve Your Mind.* New York: Riverhead Books.

Steiner, C. 2012. *Automate This: How Algorithms Came to Rule the World.* New York: Penguin.

Van Der Zee, J. 1989. "Strauss Gave Me Some Pencils." In *Sons of Martha: Civil Engineering Readings in Modern Literature,* edited by A. J. Fredrich. Reston, VA: ASCE.

Van Doren, C. 1991. *A History of Knowledge: Past, Present, and Future.* New York: Ballantine Books.

Wagner, T. 2012. *Creating Innovators: The Making of Young People Who Will Change the World.* New York: Scribner.

Walesh, S. G. 1990. "Water Science and Technology: Global Origins." In *Urban Stormwater Quality Enhancement: Source Control, Retrofitting, and Combined Sewer Technology: Proceedings of an Engineering Conference,* Davos, Switzerland. American Society of Civil Engineers.

Walesh, S. G. 2012a. "To Engineer Is To Create: To Create Is To Engineer." *Leadership and Management in Engineering,* ASCE 12 (3): 187–188.

Walesh, S. G. 2012b. "The Future and You." In *Engineering Your Future: The Professional Practice of Engineering,* 431–454. Hoboken, NJ/Reston, VA: Wiley/ASCE Press.

Walesh, S. G. 2012c. "A Half Brain Is Good: A Whole Brain Much Better." In *Proceedings of the American Society for Engineering Education Annual Conference,* San Antonio, TX, June 10–13. ASEE.

Weingardt, R. G. 2005. *Engineering Legends: Great American Civil Engineers.* Reston, VA: ASCE Press.

White, K. D. 1984. *Greek and Roman Technology.* London: Thames and Hudson.

EXERCISES

Note: These exercises are intended to gently jar you from conventional thinking.

1.1 USES OF PAPER CLIPS: This exercise (adapted from Bonasso 2013 and Buzan 1984) encourages interactive, imaginative thinking by members of a group.

  a. You have a small supply of paper clips. Give each member of your group a paper clip.

  b. For two minutes, write down all the uses your group can think of for one or more paper clips. Do this without searching the Internet.

  c. How many uses did you think of?

  d. Now do an Internet search and list additional uses. How many more did you find?

1.2 ALTERNATING GLASSES: The purpose of this exercise (adapted from Restak 2009) is to work as a team and carry out a task with a fresh perspective.

  a. As shown in Figure 1.7, six drinking glasses stand in a line. The left three are filled with water, and the right three are empty.

  b. Determine how you could get the full and empty glasses to alternate (full, empty, full, empty, full, empty) by moving only one glass.

Figure 1.7
Six drinking glasses.

1.3 **EQUATIONS:** This exercise (adapted from Restak and Kim 2010 and Chrysikou 2012) will help you see in new ways—to see what you have not seen before.

a. The equations ahead, each of which uses Roman numerals, are incorrect.
b. Think of the straight elements as equal-length match sticks, Popsicle sticks, or toothpicks.
c. Correct each equation by moving just one stick. You may not discard a stick.
d. Review the following two examples:

Example 1
Incorrect: VI = VII + I
Correct: VII = VI + I
The single move: Remove one stick from the VII on the right of the equal sign and relocate it to the VI on the left of the equal sign.

Example 2
Incorrect: IV = III − I
Correct: IV − III = I
The single move: Remove one stick from the equal sign, forming a minus sign, and add it to the minus sign on the right to form an equal sign.

e. Ten incorrect equations follow. Make each one correct with a single move.

1. III = III + III
2. IV = III + III
3. V = III − II
4. VI = VI + VI
5. VIII = VI − II
6. IV = IV + IV
7. II = III + I
8. VII = II + III
9. VI = IV − II
10. IX = VI − III

1.4 **EQUILATERAL TRIANGLES:** The purpose of this exercise (adapted from Raviv 2004) is to suggest that repeated success in one mode should not stop us from considering other modes.

a. Think of equilateral triangles and how you might create them. You have a total of six Popsicle sticks to use and need to create equilateral triangles by having the sticks touch each other only near their ends.
b. Use three sticks to create one equilateral triangle.
c. Use five sticks to create two equilateral triangles.
d. Finally, use six sticks to create four equilateral triangles.

1.5 **USES OF PAPER CLIPS WITH STIMULATION:** This exercise (adapted from Bonasso 2013 and Buzan 1984) encourages interactive, imaginative thinking by members of a group stimulated by a list of objects.

a. You have a small supply of paper clips. Give each member of your group a paper clip.
b. For two minutes, write down all the uses your group can think of for one or more paper clips. Do this without searching the Internet.
c. While thinking about uses, visualize items from the following list of objects (the words "orange" through "cat" are from Buzan 1984):

orange; watch; window; leaf; table; radio; light bulb; handbag; pen; tire; ear; potato; kitchen; pigeon; bottle; shoe; book; cup;

cloud; pepper; glass; chair; garden; Germany; wood; rain; water; holiday; dinner; garage; tea; tree; house; wine; maid; newspaper; pub; banana; mirror; cat; Christmas tree; insect; TV; GPS; shopping; lottery ticket; car

d. How many uses do you have?

e. Now do an Internet search and list additional uses. How many more did you find?

1.6 GEOMETRIC SHAPES AND EQUAL PARTITIONS OF THEM: This exercise (adapted from Raviv 2004) challenges you to visualize shapes within shapes. Think of some common geometric shapes and how we might operate on them to create smaller versions of them.

a. Draw an equilateral triangle. Partition it into four equilateral triangles.

b. Draw a symmetrical trapezoid. Partition it into four identical pieces.

c. Draw a hexagon. Partition it into eight identical pieces.

d. Draw a rectangle. Partition it into eight identical pieces.

1.7 CONNECT THE DOTS: Examine the nine dots in Figure 1.8 and then connect all of them with four straight lines. Cross each dot only once, don't lift your pen or pencil from the paper, and connect the lines only at their ends.. (adapted from Restak 2009).

Figure 1.8
Connect these nine dots with four straight lines connected end-to-end.

1.8 SHRINKING SQUARE: Use four coins to define a square, as shown in Figure 1.9.

By moving only two coins, create a square that is smaller than the original square (adapted from Restak 2009).

Figure 1.9
By moving only two coins, create a square that is smaller than the original square.

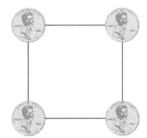

1.9 CHANGING DIRECTION: Change locations of three of the ten billiard balls (Figure 1.10) to make a triangle that points up instead of down (adapted from Fogler, LeBlanc, and Rizzo 2014).

Figure 1.10
Make a triangle that points up by changing the location of three billiard balls.

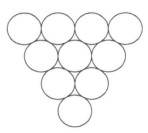

1.10 CREATIVITY/INNOVATION, NATURE OR NUTURE: Engage five to ten people (fellow students or employees, faculty, administrators, others) in a brief conversation about creativity and innovation. Without getting bogged down in the definitions of the terms, ask each person if he or she thinks creativity and innovation are mostly inborn capabilities or mostly learned capabilities—that is, mostly nature or nurture. Regardless of the answer, ask for examples or other support. Summarize your findings in a brief report. If you do this assignment, try to refer back to it later when you read Section 5.3.

1.11 SUCCESS AND SIGNIFICANCE, YOURS: The intent of this exercise is to encourage you, the aspiring student engineer or young engineering practitioner, to creatively think about what you aspire to become or achieve in the future. Imagine how you see yourself five years down the line in terms of "Success" and "Significance". The results of this exercise should be confidential, unless you want to share them with your instructor or other trusted persons. In order to do the exercise, the student can make a table and use the following questions as row headers of the table:

- What skills (or talents) do you have?
- What activities do you like to do?
- What or how do you contribute to others?
- What are the underlying values?
- Whom do you admire and why? Think of this in terms of a) your personal life and b) your professional life
- Whom do you want to be like and why? Think of this in terms of a) your personal life and b) your professional life

Now try to mix and match the points and think creatively about your success and significance goals. Then identify five actions that you need to take to move towards your goals within the next year. Try to think in a creative and innovative manner. Whatever success you have with this exercise, by the time you finish reading this text, you will be well equipped to think creatively and innovatively and to use that knowledge and skill to more effectively chart and then navigate your future.

1.12 CAPABILITIES OF TOMORROW'S ENGINEER, YOU: Although this exercise does not relate directly to the overall theme of this text, it will introduce you to or remind you of the National Society of Professional Engineers (NSPE) and its *Engineering Body of Knowledge* (EBOK), published in 2013. Furthermore, you have made a tentative choice of engineering as a profession. This bonus exercise, by describing the capabilities of tomorrow's engineer, can help you confirm or refine your choice.

Suggested tasks are as follows:

a. Search for and download the EBOK report using its name and/or NSPE.
b. Read the two-page executive summary, and note in particular the definition of the EBOK—that is, what you should *know* and *be able to do* when you enter into professional engineering practice.
c. Read Chapter 4 with an emphasis on the second and third columns in Table 1, which summarize capabilities (the *know* and *be able to do* items) and their relevance to professional engineering practice.

d. Using a paper or electronic copy of Table 1, label each of the thirty capabilities with either *Y* (for yes, this capability fits my current view of engineering) or *N* (for no, this capability does not fit my current view of engineering).

e. For the capabilities that you labeled *Y*, write a paragraph describing how seeing these expected and/or familiar capabilities may affect your choice to study engineering—for example, strengthens, weakens, or no impact.

f. For the capabilities that you labeled *N*, write a paragraph describing how being exposed to these less familiar capabilities may affect your choice to study engineering—for example, strengthens, weakens, or no impact.

g. Summarize your overall conclusions and take appropriate action.

2

The Brain:
A Primer

There is perhaps no greater untapped resource
in the universe than the human brain. . . .
The human brain is no longer
the domain of academia and medicine.
—*Paul D. Nussbaum, clinical neuropsychologist*

Objectives:

After studying this chapter, you will be able to:

- Describe the brain's features and functions and distinguish between the brain and the mind
- Demonstrate the special capabilities of the brain's left and right hemispheres
- Explain your lifelong learning potential as a result of the brain's neuroplasticity
- Contrast the workings of the conscious and subconscious minds
- Discuss the dominance of habits and explain how to change them

- Articulate why multitasking is a poor use of time and likely to cause errors
- Summarize the brain's negativity bias and explain how it could frustrate your success
- Restate the characteristics of left- and right-handedness
- Establish the value of understanding brain-related gender differences
- Illustrate how we know what we know about the human brain
- Describe exercise, diet, and mental stimulation tips for brain care

2.1 INTRODUCTION TO YOUR BRAIN

Let's consider brain basics. I suggest this on the assumption that you want to change some of your behavior. If you would like to work smarter, live smarter, replace some bad habits with good habits, and/or be more creative or innovative, then an

Figure 2.1
Just like you don't have to become an expert auto mechanic to improve your car's performance, you don't have to be a brain surgeon to more effectively use your brain.

(Stuart Walesh; Danheighton/ Fotolia)

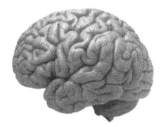

understanding of brain basics will help you. As noted by consultant Cooper (2006, 6), "It's an amazing instrument, your brain, but it's up to you to see that it plays the tune you want." Playing that tune requires a basic understanding of how the instrument works.

Scientists and medical professionals have learned much about this instrument in the last few decades. "Ninety-five percent of what we know about the capabilities of the human brain has been learned in the last twenty years," according to Gelb (2004, 3). Physician Restak (2009, 5), wrote, "We have learned more about the brain in the past decade than we did in the previous two hundred years." With the help of this text, you can immediately acquire and use that new knowledge.

You may be thinking I'm going off on a tangent. You're studying engineering and want to be a good or great engineer—not a brain surgeon. I want to help you achieve your goal. However, to be a good or great engineer, you should know a little to a lot about your brain: how it works and how to use and care for it.

Consider an analogy. You bought a classic car (Figure 2.1), and the engine ran rough. Therefore, you read about the engine, experimented with various aspects of the electrical and fuel systems, and solved the problem. You didn't have to become a certified auto mechanic to get better engine performance, and you don't have to become a brain surgeon to make better use of your brain. However, you do need to know brain basics; you need mental literacy (Gelb 2004).

The human being is the only living thing able to think about the future (Baumeister and Tierney 2011; Gilbert 2006; Medina 2008). "The greatest achievement of the human brain is its ability to imagine objects and episodes that do not exist in the realm of real," according to psychology professor Gilbert (2006, 5), "and it is this ability that allows us to think about the future." Get ready to learn more about your "thinker."

HISTORIC NOTE: BRAIN VIEWS OVER THE CENTURIES

For centuries, some societies thought that the human brain was relatively unimportant. For example, before mummifying their dead, the Egyptians—who thought that the heart was the source of intelligence and emotion—scooped out and discarded the brains (Gibb 2012). The Greek philosopher Aristotle thought that the heart was superior, while the brain was simply a radiator for cooling the blood. However, his predecessor Plato, who lived several centuries BC, had more foresight; he viewed the brain as the seat of mental processes (Carter 2009). Hippocrates, the Greek physician who lived at about the same time as Plato, was the principal author of a medical book that expressed the opinion that the brain was the body's control center (Finger 1994). Before the advent of anesthesia, the practical Romans performed a form of brain surgery called trepanation—a practice that may go back thousands of years, during which a hole is drilled in the patient's skull to relieve pressure on the brain and cure headaches (Gibb 2012; Shields 2014).

Reflecting the atmosphere of inquiry characterizing the Renaissance, Leonardo da Vinci studied brains of cadavers and then illustrated the three-dimensional form of some of the brain's structure. In 1664, Englishman Thomas Willis (who would later become a founding member of London's Royal Society) published a brain anatomy book with detailed drawings and included new words such as *neurology* and *hemisphere*. Neuroscience was born when Spanish neuroscientist Ramon y Cajal published a text in 1889 that described the human nervous system, including the role of neurons; this text led to him receiving the 1906 Nobel Prize for Medicine.

The twentieth century saw the development of various brain-imaging techniques, as described in Section 2.15.3. These techniques greatly advanced neuroscience and led to many discoveries, some of which are described in this chapter and are the basis for this text's advice to work smarter and be more creative and innovative (Gibb 2012).

2.2 SOME THOUGHTS FOR RATIONAL ENGINEERS

Student or practitioner engineers tend to be very rational (Culp and Smith 2001; Herrmann 1996). We approach our work and many other aspects of our lives in a systematic and logical manner. Our rational approach is powerful in that it enables us to define, analyze, and resolve difficult issues, problems, and opportunities (IPOs).

Although I doubt that we engineers are as fully rational as we and others think we are, many of us may be sufficiently rational to be initially suspicious of, if not turned off by, some of the content of this text. For example, this text explores topics such as brain lateralization, neuroplasticity, the subconscious mind breaking through to the conscious mind, the dominance of habits, negativity bias, gender and the brain, and whole-brain thinking, many of which may seem alien to the study and practice of engineering.

Furthermore, we will discuss many and varied thinking tools, some with strange-sounding names and unusual features, such as Borrowing Brilliance, Fishbone Diagramming, Ohno Circle, and Six Thinking Caps. Finally, I will repeatedly claim that as a result of studying brain basics and then understanding and applying whole-brain tools, you and others will be empowered to work smarter and be more creative and innovative. I welcome your healthy skepticism, provided it is balanced with your openness to new possibilities.

You may be saying, "Give us a break! We're open to new concepts, ideas, approaches, and tools." I hope you are. My experience in recent years speaking to engineering students and faculty has been neutral to receptive and, therefore, encouraging. However, during that period, I have also spoken with and written to engineering practitioners and have experienced significant lack of interest and some strong pushback.

You may be in or soon will enter that practitioner world; therefore, my experiences with it may interest you. A large fraction of engineering practitioners seem to view brain basics as irrelevant and as too academic, theoretical, philosophical, and esoteric. However, I will continue to share with practitioners what I have learned about the human brain and how that knowledge can help them, individually and organizationally, to work smarter and be more creative and innovative. Although my focus in this text is on you—tomorrow's engineers—I will continue to try to communicate with today's practitioners because I want to build a bridge from what we have recently learned about the human brain to how engineers practice their profession.

PERSONAL: PUSHBACK TO BRAIN CONVERSATION

In response to a request for topics that I could present at the annual senior managers meeting in a multioffice, engineering/science consulting firm, I proposed the topic "Working Smarter Using Brain Basics." I explained that "working smarter" meant being more effective, efficient, and innovative and was built on brain basics. The response from the firm's top executives was unanimously strongly negative. Therefore, I presented other topics, which were well received.

I asked the executives why they rejected the proposed brain-based, working-smarter topic. They said that brain talk "turned them off"; they worked in the "trenches" ten hours per day and therefore had no interest in or time for peripheral topics such as learning more about their brains and being more effective, efficient, and innovative. This incident is consistent with my negative experiences in the world of engineering practice. My view is that learning how to work smarter and be more creative and innovative could shorten the work day—leading to less time in the "trenches."

Given the considerable effort I, an engineer, have put into the creativity and innovation research summarized in this text, all I ask is that you at least temporarily set aside your perhaps overly rational nature and consider what may initially appear to be this text's irrational or strange elements. Maybe you'll think about and experiment with what initially appear to be unusual (if not irrational) concepts, ideas, and methods; as a result, maybe you'll work smarter and be even more creative and innovative.

2.3 BRAIN FEATURES

We begin our discussion of the human brain with an overview of its appearance and description of some of its elements that are essential to our later brain discussions. This initial look at the brain includes discussion of the Triune Brain Model and the structure and function of neurons.

2.3.1 Overview

About the size of a small head of cauliflower, the human brain (Figure 2.2) weighs two to four pounds, or roughly 3 percent of your weight. It is very soft, tan-gray on the outside, has a surface resembling a walnut, and is yellow-white on the inside. The brain contains one hundred billion nerve cells, called *neurons*, which can

Figure 2.2
The human brain may be
the most magnificent
mechanism in the universe.

(Adimas/Fotolia)

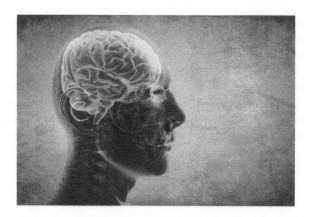

receive and send electrochemical signals stimulated by neurotransmitters. A *neu-rotransmitter* is a chemical that is released from a neuron and helps to amplify or modulate a signal that passes from one nerve cell to another or to a muscle.

A network of about one hundred thousand miles of nerve fibers, comprising what is called the *white matter*, interconnects the various parts of the brain. Each neuron has an average of ten thousand connections (*synapses*) with other neurons. To get an idea of the size of a neuron, a piece of brain tissue the size of a sand grain would contain one hundred thousand neurons. Moving deeper into this system, each neuron contains tens of thousands of molecules, and each molecule is a group of atoms. We are born with nearly all the neurons that we will have as an adult, but the neural networks—the systems of connected neurons—have yet to mature.

The adult brain receives blood through four arteries, at a rate of 0.75 to 1.0 liters per minute (up to sixteen gallons per hour), which accounts for about one-fifth of the blood pumped by the heart. The brain consumes one-fifth of the energy used by the body; it is an energy-hungry machine. The blood transports glucose (blood sugar), nutrients, and oxygen to the brain and carries away carbon dioxide and other waste products. These substances and others with similar small molecules readily pass through the blood-brain barrier, which protects the brain from many dangerous substances. Glucose is the brain's source of fuel, and it interacts with oxygen and nutrients to provide energy to brain cells. The brain cannot store glucose and therefore needs a continuous supply (Amen 2008; Baggaley 2001; Benyus 1997; Carter 2009; Freudenrich and Boyd 2014; Gibb 2012; Medina 2008; Nussbaum 2010; Pinker 2009; Wait 2009; University of Washington 2014; Zimmer 2014).

2.3.2 Triune Brain Model

Scientists use the Triune Brain Model (Figure 2.3), based on function, physiology, and evolutionary development, to describe the overall, three-part structure of the human brain (Herrmann 1996; Medina 2008; Mlodinow 2013). The first of the three parts, the *cortex*, is the most dominant and the newest part of the brain in an evolutionary sense. The cortex is the surface of your brain and covers the *cerebrum*, which is the largest part of the brain and is composed of two hemispheres.

The cortex consists of an approximately three-square-foot sheet of neural tissue (an area approximated by that of an opened newspaper) and is heavily folded so that its large surface area fits within the confines of the skull. Nerve centers for thinking, voluntary movement, the senses, and personality reside in the cortex and the rest of the cerebrum (Baggaley 2001; Carter 2009; Freudenrich and Boyd 2014; Medina 2008; Mlodinow 2013; Nussbaum 2010). More specifically, the cortex is

Figure 2.3
Scientists use the Triune Brain Model to describe the overall, three-part structure of the human brain.

Source: Adapted from Baggaley 2001; Herrmann 1996; Medina 2008.

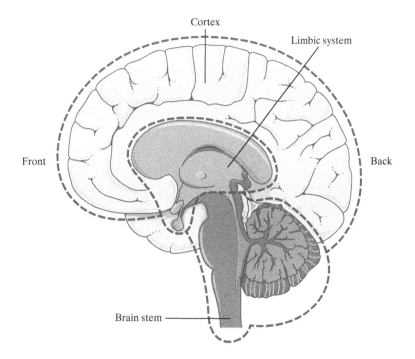

responsible for concept formation, hearing, language, memory storage, mood, voluntary movement, pain detection, planning, problem solving, seeing, spatial interpretation, speech, temperature sensing, and touch. Cortex functions are conscious and intentional (Baggaley 2001; Nussbaum 2010).

Next, working downward and as shown in Figure 2.3, you will see the portion of the brain that includes the *thalamus, amygdale,* and *hippocampus.* This area, which is also called the *limbic system,* controls fighting, feeding, fleeing, and reproductive behaviors. More specifically, the egg-shaped thalamus is the "control tower for the senses." From its position in the brain's center, "it processes signals sent from nearly every corner of your sensory universe, then routes them to specific areas throughout your brain" (Medina 2008). Regulation of emotions such as fear, rage, and pleasure and memories of the same reside in the almond-shaped and -sized amygdale, which lies beneath the thalamus. The amygdale also plays a role in formation of long-term memory (Gibb 2012; Medina 2008; Restak 2009; Wait 2009). Finally, the hippocampus is involved with learning and converts our short-term memories into long-term forms (Baggaley 2001; Medina 2008).

The final third of the human brain in the Triune Brain Model, and the oldest and lowest part, is the always-active *brain stem,* which controls basic body functions such as breathing, heart rate, blood pressure, sleeping, and being awake (Medina 2008). The *cerebellum,* or little brain, is a major part of the brain stem and responsible for involuntary movement. It occupies about one-tenth of the brain's volume while accounting for approximately half of the neurons (Gibb 2012).

The brain can't feel pain because it does not have sensory nerves. Therefore, neurosurgeons can "poke around" in a brain when a patient is alert (Wait 2009). Although the brain has no sensory receptors, it does sense pain from all parts of the body (Carter 2009), including pressure on nerve tissue or blood vessels surrounding the brain, which causes headaches. See Section 2.9 for further discussion of the cortex and the remainder of the brain and possible connections to conscious and subconscious thinking.

Figure 2.4
The most common type of neurons usually have a tree-like structure, and signals pass through them from top to bottom.

Source: Adapted from Gibb 2012; Nussbaum 2010.

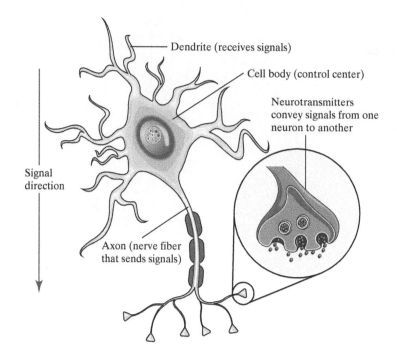

Dendrite (receives signals)

Cell body (control center)

Neurotransmitters convey signals from one neuron to another

Signal direction

Axon (nerve fiber that sends signals)

2.3.3 Neurons

Let's look a little closer at one of those one hundred billion brain cells or neurons so small that a grain-sized piece of brain tissue would contain one hundred thousand of them. As shown in Figure 2.4, the most common type of neuron has a tree-like structure and signals passing in one direction from the top to the bottom. The "foliage" portion of the neuron consists of dendrites that detect and receive chemical signals from neighboring neurons. The cell's body (its control center) composes the middle portion of the "tree." The tree's "trunk" is the *axon*, also called a *nerve fiber*, which is used to transmit signals to the dendrites of other neurons. Axons originating in the human brain vary widely in length, ranging from those that transmit from neuron to neuron within the brain to those that transmit from the brain to the ends of our toes.

For a given neuron, chemical signals from the axons of other neurons are received at the ends of the dendrites of the neuron. The signals are sent within the dendrites in the form of an electrical charge (charged ions) to the cell body, where they are processed. The cell body produces new signals that are sent down the axon as an electrical charge and transmitted in the form of chemicals called *neurotransmitters*, released from the axon's end to the dendrites of other neurons. The site of communication between neurons, which is a minute gap where neurons don't touch, is called a *synapse* (Baggaley 2001; Gibb 2012). For discussion of neurotransmitters, see Section 2.14.3.

2.4 BRAIN FUNCTIONS

Having reviewed the brain's features and essential elements, let's now explore its functions. We'll note the body processes controlled by the brain and stress the dominance of vision among our six senses.

2.4.1 Overview

As suggested by the preceding information, and mostly without us having to think about it, various parts of the human brain fulfill the following roles:

- Control body processes such as temperature regulation, blood pressure, heart rate, and breathing.
- Accept and act on information received from our six senses—that is, vision, hearing, smell, taste, touch, and proprioception. The last term means "sensing of body position, movement, and posture" (Carter 2009).
- Manage physical motion such as walking, talking, standing, and sitting.
- Enable us to dream, think, plan, create, and innovate.

In my view, the human brain is the universe's most engaging entity, intriguing instrument, and magnificent mechanism.

VIEWS OF OTHERS: TRYING TO DESCRIBE THE BRAIN

Individuals from a variety of professions and specialties have tried to capture the essence of the brain's appearance, structure, or functions. For example, journalist Rita Carter (2009) wrote that the brain is "three pounds or so of rounded, corrugated flesh with a consistency somewhere between jelly and cold butter." According to brain imaging expert Daniel G. Amen (2008), "the brain is comprised of 80 percent water and is the consistency of soft butter or custard" and is the "most complicated organ in the universe." Continuing that theme, marketing consultant Neale Martin (2008) calls the brain "the most complicated complex object in the cosmos." Neuroscientist Jill B. Taylor (2009) says, "The focused human mind is the most powerful instrument in the universe." As viewed by neuropsychologist Paul D. Nussbaum (2010), even with all of the technology at our disposal, the human brain is "the most impressive portable and wireless system."

2.4.2 Vision Dominates

Before leaving this introductory discussion of brain functions, consider further the brain and the six senses. In any given learning or human interaction situation, many of the senses are engaged. For example, they are used by each of us as we try to understand someone or learn something and by others as they strive to understand our message.

However, vision is the most important of the six senses, as stressed by biologist Medina (2008) when he says that "vision trumps all other senses" and states that vision is the most dominant of the six senses, "taking up half of our brain's resources." He mentions one research study that concluded that when information was presented only orally, individuals remembered about 10 percent when tested seventy-two hours later. However, remembering jumped to 65 percent when images were also used to present the information.

Recognizing the major role of vision in learning, educator Zull (2002) urges teachers to "make extensive use of images to help people learn," and Hardiman (2003), another educator, advocates "visually stimulating environments." Consider the dominance of vision from the perspective of a presenter trying to convey ideas and information to an audience. Many presentation slides consist of a statement followed by bullet points. However, research reveals that the most effective slide contains a declarative statement with a supporting image. Audience members tend to learn and remember better from words and pictures than from words alone (Atkinson 2010; Medina 2008).

You, as an engineering student and later as a practitioner, will be offered many learning and presenting opportunities. Therefore, leverage the fact that "vision trumps all other senses." For example, when you or your group is trying to understand a process or mechanism, make one or more freehand sketches (see Section 7.4 for an in-depth discussion of freehand drawing). The next time you or your team prepares a presentation, get beyond communicating with just words. Use supplemental photographs, props, graphs, and other visual elements. Also recognize that although the audience will listen to your words and look at your visual aids, your expressions, gestures, grooming, and overall appearance are also part of your message.

2.5 BRAIN AND MIND

Before going on, let's distinguish (as suggested by Figure 2.5) between the brain, our principal topic in this chapter, and the mind. The brain "is an organ of the body, a collection of cells and water, chemicals and blood vessels, that resides in the skull," according to neuroscientist Levitin (2006). In contrast, he goes on to say, "The word mind refers to that part of each of us that embodies our thoughts, hopes, desires, memories, beliefs, and experiences." Pinker (2009), a psychologist, writes that the mind is "the generator of human behavior: the package of information-processing and goal-pursuing mechanisms." Levitin (2006) continues this theme, noting that "activity in the brain gives rise to the content of the mind." Simply stated, the brain is the organ and the mind is what we do with it.

Our focus now is on the brain, recognizing that the brain and mind are related. In other words, knowledge of our brain and how we use that knowledge can influence our mind—our "thoughts, hopes, desires, memories, beliefs, and experiences" and our creativity and innovation. Although your brain looks similar to others, you as defined by your mind are probably unique.

We mentioned memories; very few of our experiences are encoded as brain memories, where a *memory* is a reactivation of neurons involved in the original

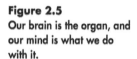

Figure 2.5
Our brain is the organ, and our mind is what we do with it.

experience. Memories are not exact replays of that original experience. Some aspects may be left out, added, or changed. "Memories are dynamic and must be reconsolidated each time we remember them" (Restak and Kim 2010). "We generally retain only those experiences that are in some way useful" and our recall of the past is "selective and unreliable" (Carter 2009). As part of a discussion of memories, author and journalist Jonah Lehrer (2008) observes that "our recollections are cynical things, designed by the brain to always feel true, regardless of whether or not they actually occurred." In using your memory to understand yourself and interact with others, forewarned is forearmed.

2.6 HEMISPHERES AND SYMMETRY

When the brain (minus the skull) is viewed from above, as illustrated in Figure 2.6, we see the cerebrum, which is the brain's largest part and includes nerve centers for thought, personality, the senses, and voluntary movement. It has symmetrical left and right halves or hemispheres. Specific areas of the halves are connected by a band or bridge of about two hundred million nerve fibers, called the *corpus callosum* (Baggaley 2001; Carter 2009; Freudenrich and Boyd 2014). "Every fiber is a neuron's axon, the long, spindly protrusion that connects brain cells" (Wolf 2013).

Each of the brain's hemispheres interacts with the opposite side of the body. Imagine being above the body and brain and looking down at it, as shown in Figure 2.7. Lateralization means that, in general, the left side of the brain interacts

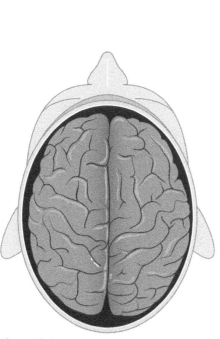

Figure 2.6
The cerebrum has symmetrical halves or hemispheres.

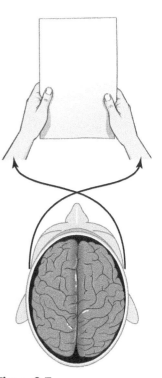

Figure 2.7
Lateralization of functions means that the left side of the brain interacts with the right side of the body and vice versa.

with the right side of the body and vice versa (Restak and Kim 2010). For example, if you inadvertently touch this text with your right hand, the result is sensed in your brain's left hemisphere. If you want to pick up the text with your left hand, the command comes from your right hemisphere. Therefore, just as the two hemispheres are symmetrical in appearance, they are also largely symmetrical in function.

Why does the brain exhibit lateralization? We don't know. According to neuroscientist and medical doctor Restak (Restak and Kim 2010), "No one has satisfactorily explained the brain's odd anatomical arrangement whereby information to and from one side of the body is processed on the opposite side of the brain."

2.7 ASYMMETRICAL CAPABILITIES: AN EXCEPTIONAL EXCEPTION

Although your brain exhibits some symmetry, as just discussed, it is also asymmetrical. That asymmetry leads us to left- and right-brain capabilities and the resulting powerful potential of whole-brain thinking.

2.7.1 Left- and Right-Hemisphere Capabilities

As you may have concluded from the preceding section, there are exceptions to functional symmetry. These exceptions, which are very relevant to this text, are presented in summary form in Table 2.1. The two sides of the brain tend to be specialized with respect to their capabilities and the tasks they perform.

Note the first comparison: The left hemisphere is *verbal* and the right hemisphere is *nonverbal.* Assume you are recalling an afternoon at the beach with your significant other. You were there on a Saturday in August from about 2:00 p.m. to 4:30 p.m., the air temperature was in the low 80s, and there was a light breeze off the sea. That part of your memory is courtesy of your left hemisphere. As you recall that afternoon, you also feel the sand on your feet, taste the salt air, and experience the pleasure of just being with your loved one. That part of the memory is provided by your right hemisphere. Total recollection of the wonderful afternoon requires your whole brain.

Recall that the purpose of this text, as stated at the beginning of the preceding chapter (Section 1.1), is to help you acquire creativity and innovation knowledge,

Table 2.1 The brain's two hemispheres are asymmetrical with respect to some capabilities.

Left Hemisphere	Right Hemisphere	Source
Verbal	Nonverbal	Edwards; Taylor
Analytic	Synthetic	Edwards
Logical	Intuitive	Edwards
Literal	Emotional	Taylor
Temporal	Nontemporal	Edwards; Taylor
Linear processor	Parallel processor	Taylor
Symbolic	Actual; real	Edwards
Abstract	Analogic	Edwards
Digital	Spatial	Edwards
Judgmental	Nonjudgmental	Taylor

Sources: Edwards 1999; Taylor 2009.

skills, and attitudes so that you can work smarter and achieve more individual and organizational success and significance in our rapidly changing world. Doing that requires use of your whole brain (left and right hemispheres), just like you use your whole brain when you happily recall that afternoon at the beach. Using your whole brain to recall a special emotional event is natural, but using your whole brain in study and work is not necessarily so. Therefore, you may need help such as that offered in this text.

Jill Taylor, a brain scientist, suffered a stroke and needed eight years to completely recover all physical and mental functions. That intense experience provided her with a unique opportunity to learn even more about the brain. Taylor shared her stroke and recovery experience in her book *My Stroke of Insight: A Brain Scientist's Personal Journey* (Taylor 2009). To reinforce the previous reference to using the whole brain in recollecting the memorable afternoon at the beach, Taylor says that "both of our hemispheres work together to generate our perception of reality on a moment-by-moment basis."

Let's elaborate on the comparisons in Table 2.1. Do this as follows by using the insights of Taylor and others:

- Relative to the first comparison in the table, according to Taylor (2009), *verbal* means that we "use words to describe, define, categorize, and communicate about everything," whereas *nonverbal* means that one "thinks in collages of images."
- Consider the *analytic* and *synthetic* entries in the table. The left brain is good at "figuring things out step-by-step and part-by-part," states Edwards (1999), whereas the right brain's strength is "putting things together to form new wholes." "You need your left brain to order and analyze things," according to Elizabeth Miles (1997), an ethnomusicologist (i.e., someone who studies music in cultural context), "but you need an ongoing relationship between the left and right side if you ever expect to contribute anything new to the process."
- Edwards sees *logical* capability as "one thing following another" based on theories, facts, and well-stated arguments. In stark contrast, the *intuitive* capability is described by her as "making leaps of insight, often based on incomplete patterns, hunches, feelings, or visual images."
- The *literal* versus *emotional* pair in Table 2.1, according to Taylor, indicates that the left hemisphere receives the literal content of a message (the facts), while the right hemisphere receives the emotional content. Therefore, the entire brain is needed to fully benefit from the message.
- According to Edwards, the *temporal* capability includes "keeping track of time" and "doing first things first," whereas *nontemporal* means to be "without a sense of time." Similarly, Taylor says that the left hemisphere's *temporal* capability partitions moments into "past, present, and future," whereas for the right hemisphere's *in the now* capability, "no time exists other than the present moment."
- Taylor says that the left brain's *linear processor* capability takes each of those moments and "strings them together in timely succession." In contrast, the right brain's *parallel processor* creates a collage of the present moment, including its "sounds, tastes, aromas, and feelings."
- The left brain's *symbolic* capability, as explained by Edwards, means that it uses symbols to represent things or processes. For example, a plus sign stands for the addition process. In contrast, the right brain's *actual/real* capability means that it experiences or sees things as they are right now.
- According to Edwards, the left hemisphere's *abstract* capability means "taking out a small bit of information and using it to represent the whole thing." The

right brain's *analogic* capability means "seeing likenesses among things; understanding metaphoric relationships."

- *Digital* capability refers to "using numbers, as in counting," as explained by Edwards. In contrast, *spatial* capability means "seeing where things are in relation to other things and how parts go together to form a whole."
- The left hemisphere is *judgmental* in that it "defines boundaries and judges everything as right/wrong or good/bad," as viewed by Taylor. In contrast, the *nonjudgmental* right hemisphere "takes things as they are" and is empathetic, compassionate, and peaceful.

HISTORIC NOTE: SPLIT-BRAIN STUDIES

In the middle of the last century, as a last resort to help individuals severely disabled by epileptic seizures involving both hemispheres, surgeons severed their corpus callosums in an operation called *commissurotomy*. These operations on humans, which were first performed in 1963, occurred after neurobiologist Sperry had performed similar surgeries on cats and monkeys (Shlain 2014).

As noted in Section 2.6, a person's corpus callosum connects the two hemispheres. Therefore, after the surgery, each of a patient's hemispheres was isolated from the other; they were disconnected. Surprisingly, especially given its large size and strategic location, scientists determined that when the corpus callosum is severed, the two hemispheres functioned independently, and "the patients' outward appearance, manner, and coordination were little affected" (Edwards 1999).

In the 1970s, seeing an opportunity, researchers at the California Institute of Technology conducted "split-brain" studies. They worked with the "split-brain" individuals using specially designed tests. These experiments revealed that each hemisphere "perceives reality in its own way" (Edwards 1999), as suggested by the previous discussion of Table 2.1. According to Taylor (2009), "When surgically separated, the two hemispheres function as two independent brains with unique personalities." This historic account begins to tell us how scientists know how the two sides of the human brain function.

Roger W. Sperry, who was awarded the Nobel prize for medicine along with two colleagues for his leadership of this research, said this during his 1981 Nobel lecture: "The same individual can be observed to employ consistently one or the other of two distinct forms of mental approach and strategy, much like two different people, depending on whether the left or right hemisphere is in use" (Taylor 2009). Sperry also said that each hemisphere of the human brain is "a conscious system in its own right, perceiving, thinking, remembering, reasoning, willing, and emoting, all at a characteristically human level" (Gibb 2012). Commissurotomy ceased in the 1970s because new drugs successfully controlled epilepsy (Shlain 2014).

2.7.2 Practical Applications of Hemisphere Knowledge

Of course, the two halves of the brains of most of us are connected, and "when normally connected, the two hemispheres complement and enhance one another's abilities" (Taylor 2009). This text recognizes that each of us uses both hemispheres, and we each tend to be dominated by one—typically the left brain for engineers and most others. Having a dominant side of our brain should not surprise us; our bodies naturally exhibit other types of dominance, such as being left- or right-handed (Herrmann 1996).

We can be more effective if we seek better brain balance. For engineers, that improved relationship between the two hemispheres usually means making more use of the right hemisphere while not diminishing the role of the left hemisphere. Accordingly, this chapter provides a brain primer that describes the brain's asymmetric capabilities and the tendency of most of us to be dominated by the left side. Chapters 4 and 7 provide many methods for proactively engaging both hemispheres. This is part of a whole-brain approach, with the other part being to engage the soon-to-be discussed conscious and subconscious minds.

2.8 NEUROPLASTICITY: A MUSCLE—NOT A MACHINE

Up to several decades ago, the human brain was viewed as "a rigid, fixed, and essentially degrading system from birth" (Nussbaum 2010). Hardwiring of the brain was a metaphor suggesting that the brain was like "computer hardware, with permanently connected circuits, each designed to perform a specific, unchangeable function" (Doidge 2007). Although this hardwired view of the brain (as suggested by Figure 2.8) was first proposed in the seventeenth century and may still find a few adherents, a newer, more accurate view of the brain is that it exhibits neuroplasticity.

2.8.1 The Evolving Brain

As explained by medical doctor Doidge, a researcher and author of *The Brain That Changes Itself* (2007), "neuro is for neuron . . . plastic is for changeable, malleable, modifiable." He goes on to say, and illustrates with examples in his book, that "the damaged brain can often reorganize itself so that when one part fails, another can

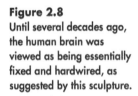

Figure 2.8
Until several decades ago, the human brain was viewed as being essentially fixed and hardwired, as suggested by this sculpture.

(Stuart Walesh)

Source: Pam Reithmeier, sculptor.

often substitute . . . thinking, learning, and acting can turn our genes on or off, thus shaping our brain anatomy and our behavior."

He cites neuroplasticity examples such as the woman who felt like she was perpetually falling, and often fell, because of total damage to the balancing apparatus in her ears. After working with an artificial sensor, she eventually regained her balancing ability because her plastic brain reorganized itself. Earlier (Section 2.7.1), I mentioned Jill Taylor (2009), a brain scientist who suffered a stroke. At the outset of the stroke in the left hemisphere of her brain, she "could not walk, talk, read, write, or recall any of [her] life." Over eight years, she completely recovered all physical and mental functions. She describes her neuroplasticity story of recovery as being "about the beauty and resiliency of our human brain."

As another neuroplasticity example, consider drivers of London's black cabs. Research reveals that they have differently shaped hippocampi, which (as noted in Section 2.3.2) is that part of the brain involved with learning and converting short-term memories into long-term forms. This hippocampi effect is thought to be caused by each driver's need to navigate central London's complex street system (Gibb 2012; Restak and Kim 2010). Perhaps you can begin to imagine how some of your oft-repeated skills have reshaped or are reshaping your brain.

Hemispherectomy is a surgery in which either the entire left or right half of the brain is removed to treat intractable epilepsy. According to neuroscientist Eagleman (2012), as long as this surgery is performed on children before they are eight years old, they will be fine. Patients "can eat, read, speak, do math, make friends, play chess, love parents, and everything else that a child with two hemispheres can do." The plastic brain amazingly adjusts.

When stimulated, the brain can grow. According to Doidge (2007), "Mental training or life in enriched environments increases brain weight. . . . Trained or stimulated neurons develop 25 percent more branches and increase their size, the number of connections, and their blood supply." He goes on to note that this kind of brain growth occurs late in life, although the rate of change slows.

Neurons form in our minds until the very end of life, according to Doidge, and he states, as suggested by Figure 2.9, that "the idea that the brain is a muscle that grows with exercise is not a metaphor." Generation of new brain cells is also cited by engineer and consultant James Adams (2008) and neuroscientist William Skaggs (2014), with the latter referring to the process as *neurogenesis* and noting that the hippocampus is one place it occurs. Restak and Kim (2010) reinforce the idea of

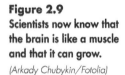

Figure 2.9
Scientists now know that the brain is like a muscle and that it can grow.

(Arkady Chubykin/Fotolia)

lifelong changes in the human brain, noting that the changes are more profound when the experiences are richer. The impact of experiences and related activities on neuroplasticity and other aspects of the brain are discussed in detail in Section 2.16.

2.8.2 Significance

Neuroplasticity means that certain uses of the brain can change its physical structure (anatomy) and functional organization (physiology). The significance of neuroplasticity, as summarized here, is the suggestion that we engineers, as students and as practitioners, can change the way we think—that is, change our brains. We can expand understanding of our brains, engage more of our neurons and grow new ones, and, as a result, become more creative, innovative, and effective.

As you age, neurons are lost and impulses are transmitted more slowly, which can lead to slowed thought processes, memory problems, and balance and movement problems (Carter 2009). Your brain's neuroplasticity means that you can offset some of those aging effects. You ignore neuroplasticity at your peril. If you fail to practice self-directed neuroplasticity, your brain will respond to other forces. According to neuropsychologist Hanson (2013), examples of those forces include "pressures at work and home, technology and media, pushy people, [and] the lingering effects of painful past experiences," and we should add aging. Mold your evolving brain, or other people and forces will. Refer to Section 2.16 for tips on how to use your brain's neuroplasticity.

2.9 CONSCIOUS AND SUBCONSCIOUS THINKING

In this section, we'll discuss two modes of thinking—conscious and subconscious—and how each comes into play in your day-to-day life. Let's begin our look into these two modes with an examination of the cortex and subcortex.

2.9.1 Cortex and Subcortex

As explained in Section 2.7, your brain has left and right parts, or hemispheres, that each have very different characteristics. Although the two halves assist each other's abilities, one hemisphere is dominant for you. Further engaging the less dominant hemisphere is likely to enhance your effectiveness.

Another way to partition your brain is to look at conscious and subconscious thinking processes. This text uses the word *subconscious* to refer to brain processes that are below what professor Rollo May (1976) calls our *level of awareness*. Other terms for the subconscious are *unconscious* and *preconscious*.

Discussing conscious and subconscious thinking processes requires considering the cortex and subcortex. As explained by neuropsychologist Nussbaum (2010), we can think of the brain divided from top to bottom with the cortex above and the subcortex below as generally illustrated earlier in Figure 2.3.

To expand on some of the brain structure description provided earlier in this chapter, Nussbaum (2010) says that the cortex "is a convoluted mass of cells, with folds and flaps that sits snug within your skull." He explains that "the cortex is primarily responsible for the most complex thinking abilities, including memory, language, planning, concept formation, problem solving, spatial representation, auditory and visual processing, mood, and personality." Cortex processing is conscious; it is intentional.

Positioned beneath the cortex, the more primitive subcortex processes mostly rote skills and procedures with most of the processing being subconscious (Nussbaum 2010). Examples of subconscious activities are word processing, tying your shoes, and driving—things we do habitually. The cortex and subcortex are connected in many ways and work very effectively together.

Although there is widespread agreement about the existence of conscious and subconscious thinking processes, the location of the processes is somewhat uncertain. For example, although some experts (Clayman 1991; Mlodinow 2013) generally support Nussbaum's cortex–subcortex model, biologist and researcher Medina (2008) says, "We don't know the neural location of consciousness, loosely defined as that part of the mind where awareness resides." Nussbaum (2014) says there is "no real conflict" because "the brain does work in harmony, yet it can also maintain regional specialization." He goes on to explain that "awareness and conscious processing are a cortical specialization. However, such a specialization requires input from more primitive and older subcortical structures."

2.9.2 Workings of the Conscious and Subconscious Minds: Overview

Psychiatrist Peck (1997) says, "The conscious mind [drawing on information from our senses and memory] makes decisions and translates them into actions." As an example of using your conscious mind, you define a problem, develop alternative engineering solutions, compare them, select one, and recommend it. You're aware of the cognitive processing required for that process. With your conscious mind, you're thinking and you know it.

In contrast, the cognitive processing in the subconscious mind occurs without our being aware of it. "The [subconscious] mind resides below the surface"; according to Peck, "it is the possessor of extraordinary knowledge that we aren't naturally aware of." In the case of your subconscious mind, you're thinking and don't know it. During that conscious engineering process described in the previous paragraph, we can be certain that the subconscious mind is influencing the process, unbeknownst to us.

One indication of the functioning of your subconscious mind: That great idea that "pops into your head" or "comes out of the blue." The subconscious mind, if we can more effectively use it, has great potential, as suggested by anthropologist Lagace (2012), who said: "Our conscious mind is pretty good at following rules, but our unconscious mind—our ability to think without attention—can handle a larger amount of information. Studying the unconscious mind offers exciting new avenues for research, including creativity, decision making, and sleep."

Considering further the relative impact on us of our conscious and subconscious minds, neuroscientist Eagleman (2012) writes that "consciousness is the smallest player in the operations of our brain. Our brains run mostly on autopilot." The biggest player is our subconscious mind (Peck 1997). As summarized metaphorically in Figure 2.10, the conscious mind is the tip of the iceberg; the subconscious mind is its bulk. "It is the rule of thumb among cognitive scientists that unconscious thought is 95 percent of all thought," according to academics Lakoff and Johnson (1999), who go on to say, "That may be a serious underestimate." Many of the whole-brain tools described in Chapters 4 and 7 engage or prime our very active subconscious mind. They facilitate collaboration between conscious and subconscious thinking (Irvine 2015).

The following metaphors are intended to help you understand your conscious and subconscious minds and how they complement each other and work together. They also suggest how you can cause them to work even better together. All of the following are from Murphy 1963, except as otherwise noted:

- The conscious mind is the camera and the subconscious mind is the digital image, so point your "camera" at the things you want to capture.
- The conscious mind sees reality, whereas the subconscious mind cannot tell the difference between reality seen by the conscious mind and that which is imagined by the conscious mind (Tice 2002). Therefore, consciously imagine and

Figure 2.10
The working of the conscious mind is the tip of the iceberg, whereas the much greater cognitive processing of the subconscious mind is hidden.

(Adimas/Fotolia)

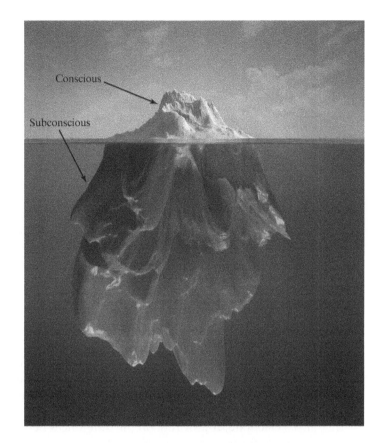

visualize those good things you desire, and your subconscious mind will accept and work on them as though they were an evolving reality.

- The conscious mind selects and plants seeds, and the subconscious mind germinates and grows them. Select seeds for the crop you want to harvest.
- Your conscious mind is the cause; your subconscious mind is the effect. Choose your causes carefully.
- The conscious mind is a part-time worker, while the subconscious mind works full-time; it never sleeps (Gibb 2012). Use the limited time available with your conscious mind to direct and fully utilize the 24-7 efforts of your subconscious mind.
- The conscious mind is the ship's captain; the subconscious mind is a fast ship and with an excellent crew.

For additional ideas, see the Views of Others feature in Section 2.9.3.

On learning about our powerful subconscious mind, we might ask how scientists know it exists if we are not aware of its mental activity. This question was first answered in the 1980s by cognitive scientist Libet, who monitored the electrical activity of research subjects. He asked them to press a button whenever they felt like it. "He could see that movement-controlling brain regions became active about a quarter of a second before subjects said they'd consciously decided to push the button. Some subconscious part of the brain decided well before the conscious mind did" (McGowan 2014). The subconscious acts before the conscious (Koch 2012).

Another argument for the existence of the subconscious mind is research that indicates that we often follow, without conscious thought, preset behavioral scripts (Mlodinow 2013). Also recall the reference in Section 2.9.2 to that great idea that "pops into your head" or "comes out of the blue."

HISTORIC NOTE: FREUD STARTED IT

Sigmund Freud, who started his career as a neuroscientist, became the originator of psychoanalysis in the 1890s. His theory included identifying the subconscious mind as the source of powerful impulses that are censored and repressed before we become aware of them. Today, experts say that Freud "underestimated the power and sophistication of unconscious thought. . . . The nature of unconscious thought that emerges from contemporary experiments is radically different from what Freud posited so many years ago: It looks more like a fast, efficient way to process large volumes of data and less like a zone of impulses and fantasies" (McGowan 2014). Freud was correct in the broad sense that "the mind was not simply equal to the conscious part we familiarly live with; rather it was like an iceberg, the majority of its mass hidden from sight" (Eagleman 2012). To this day, we know that much of the behavior of humans is controlled by mental processes outside of our awareness (Mlodinow 2013).

2.9.3 Comparing the Conscious and Subconscious Minds

Let's explore further differences between the conscious and subconscious minds and the thinking that occurs within them by considering the contrasts summarized in Table 2.2. The differences are great, and leveraging them by using the tools described in Chapters 4 and 7 can enhance creativity and innovation. Furthermore, understanding gained from contrasting the conscious and subconscious minds helps us change our habits, as will be described in Section 2.10.

Let's elaborate, row by row, on the differences between conscious and subconscious minds as summarized in Table 2.2.

- Comparison 1: Both minds think, but we are only aware of the conscious. Engineer Bonasso (1983) refers to the work of the subconscious as unconscious simmering, whereas journalist Goleman (2013) says that it is "purring away in quiet to solve our problems." He adds that the subconscious mind "learns voraciously," much of which is outside of our awareness.
- Comparison 2: We sometimes turn off our conscious mind, as when we are sleeping. In contrast, the subconscious mind is going 24-7, which means that it functions even when we are sleeping (Adams 1986; Hill 1960; Restak 2009).

Table 2.2 The conscious and subconscious minds are very different, and leveraging those differences can enhance creativity and innovation.

	Conscious	Subconscious
1.	When thinking, we know it	When thinking, we don't know it
2.	Intermittent	24-7
3.	Linear processor	Parallel processor
4.	Slow	Fast
5.	Prefers complete information in order to decide/do	Can work with pieces
6.	Sees, or thinks it sees, what can be accomplished	Believes that what is imagined by the conscious mind can be achieved and goes to work on it
7.	Does not control dreams	Controls dreams
8.	Can change habits	Source of habits

- Comparison 3: The conscious mind can think of only one topic or thing at a time, but the subconscious mind is a parallel processor (Adams 1986; Medina 2008; Taylor 2009).
- Comparison 4: Engineer and consultant Adams (1986) says that "conscious thinking proceeds in real time" as it draws on information from our memory and senses. Conscious thinking, which is linear, is very slow compared to subconscious thinking, which uses parallel processing.
- Comparison 5: The conscious mind wants complete information (always seeks to know more) so that it can even more rationally decide and act. In contrast, the subconscious mind can work with incomplete information (Adams 1986). Imagine that you are consciously planning a project, a vacation trip, or a night out. You would like to know more but recognize that what you don't know now you will figure out as you go along; now you know that your subconscious mind will help you because it knows what you want to do.
- Comparison 6: The conscious mind sees reality, whereas the subconscious mind cannot tell the difference between reality seen by the conscious mind or that which is imagined by the conscious mind (Hill 1960; Tice 2002). Therefore, if you consciously imagine and visualize the levels of success and significance you desire in your career, your subconscious mind will accept and work toward them as though they were an evolving reality. "A [person] cannot directly choose [his or her] circumstances, but [he or she] can choose . . . thoughts," according to author James Allen (1987), "and so, indirectly, yet surely, shape [his or her] circumstances." That's a positive reality of your powerful subconscious mind; you tend to become what you think. However, be careful; the process also works the other way. Think negatively and you will accomplish little.
- Comparison 7: The subconscious mind is the immediate source of dreams, but "many of us have dreams that reflect previously conscious experience" (Adams 1986).
- Comparison 8: The conscious mind can cause the subconscious mind to create new habits or replace "bad" with "good" habits. The formation and changing of habits are discussed in the next major section of this chapter.

VIEWS OF OTHERS: THE MYSTERIOUS AND POWERFUL SUBCONSCIOUS MIND

Consider the views of others about the subconscious mind. Motivational author Hill (1960), who devoted decades to studying people who achieved success and significance, says that "your subconscious mind works continuously, while you are awake, and while you sleep." He also states, based on his studies, that you can direct your subconscious mind to work for you—that is, "the subconscious mind will translate into its physical equivalent, by the most direct and practical method available, any order which is given to it in a state of belief, or faith that order will be carried out." "Your subconscious mind is like a bed of soil that accepts any kind of seed, good or bad," notes scientist and theologian Murphy (2000). He goes on to claim that the seeds—your thoughts—"will emerge and take shape as an outer experience that corresponds to their content." Gladwell, whose book *Blink* (2005) focuses on snap judgments, writes, "Our unconscious reactions come out of a locked room and we can't look inside the room."

According to Carlson (1997), the subconscious mind is the back burner of your mind and uses a process that "mixes, blends, and simmers ingredients into a tasty meal." He advises us to feed our always-available back burner with a "list of problems, facts, and variables, and possible solutions," let them simmer, and expect a pleasing result. In a similar manner, physician Maltz and consultant Kennedy (Maltz and Kennedy 2001) say that "you can give problem-solving and idea-getting tasks to your [subconscious] mind, send it off on a search while you do other things, even while you sleep, and have it return with useful material you didn't know you knew and might never have obtained through conscious thought or worry." Eagleman (2012) calls the subconscious "the giant and mysterious factory that runs below [the conscious mind]." Finally, introducing what we do in times of crises, scientist Mlodinow (2013) says, "Conscious thought is a great aid in designing a car or deciphering the mathematical laws of nature, but for avoiding snake bites or cars that swerve into your path or people who may mean to harm you, only the speed and efficiency of the unconscious can save you."

I suspect, especially if you are an engineering student or practicing engineer, that you are very aware of the capabilities of your conscious mind. It drives your engineering studies and practice. My hope is that you will, as a result of reading this section about conscious and subconscious thinking, more proactively engage your subconscious mind. Many of the whole-brain tools presented in Chapters 4 and 7 will help you do that.

2.10 HABITS

We turn now to habits, a powerful force in our lives. Let's explore how habits work and then use that understanding to change or replace unwanted habits.

2.10.1 Dominance of Habits in Our Lives

The preceding discussion of conscious and subconscious thinking mentioned habits. A *habit* is an involuntary behavior, a behavior controlled by the subconscious mind. Nussbaum (2014) says that a habit, or what he also calls our *default*, is "an overly-used and very rapid electrical connection between two or more neurons."

How much of what we think, say, and do is habitual? Studies by psychologists suggest that about half of human behavior is habitual (Duhigg 2012; Neal, Wood, and Quinn 2006; Verplanken and Wood 2006). Recall the mention in Section 2.9.2 of subconscious thought being 95 percent or more of all thought. Recognize that much of that subconscious activity is focused on the basic body processes listed in Section 2.4, not on habits as defined here. As suggested by Figure 2.11, let's proceed conservatively, assuming that we are on automatic pilot at least half the time.

We use our conscious mind for new situations, while our subconscious mind— our habits, good or bad—takes care of routine activities. For example, while eating breakfast today, you consciously decide to attend an off-campus meeting later today. While driving to the meeting, your conscious mind thinks about the meeting while your subconscious mind drives your car. You drove your car a few blocks and suddenly realized you couldn't recall having done so. Your driving was largely habit, and your subconscious mind was "at the wheel."

2.10.2 Habits: Good and Bad

When you hear *habits*, what's the first thing you think of? Negative thoughts? "Bad" habits, such as drinking, smoking, drugs, or worse? Or do you think of "good" hab-

Figure 2.11
We are on automatic pilot at least half the time in that our involuntary actions— our habits—dominate what we think, say, and do.

(ID1974/Fotolia)

its, like regularly working out, watching your diet, and saying "please" and "thank you?" Clearly, habits can be good or bad, and both kinds sneak up and capture us. The English writer Samuel Johnson said, "Chains of habit are too weak to be felt until they are too strong to be broken." That observation can be good news or bad news, depending on whether we are referring to good habits or bad habits.

Duhigg (2012) explains that habits are "the choices that all of us deliberately make at some point, and then stop thinking about but continue doing, often every day." In other words, you learned any of your habits—good or bad—and you can unlearn them or, better yet, replace them. Let's explore this promising idea of unlearning and/or replacing habits.

2.10.3 Cue-Routine-Result Process

Duhigg (2012) suggests how habits work when he says that "a habit is a formula our brain automatically follows." The "formula" by which our subconscious mind directs our behavior is illustrated in Figure 2.12 and works as follows:

1. We see or experience a *cue*, such as feeling thirsty.
2. We initiate a *routine*, such as buying a soft drink.
3. We receive a *result*, such as feeling good—which may or not be good for us.

Another example of this automatic process, as also illustrated in Figure 2.12, is that a person meets someone (the cue), starts talking about herself/himself

Figure 2.12
The subconscious mind experiences a cue, initiates a routine, and generates a result.

Thirsty	**CUE**	Meet potential client
Buy soft drink	**ROUTINE**	Tell client about me/us
Feels good	**RESULT**	The client smiles and seems to listen
(But not good for you)		**(But nothing happens)**

(routine), and experiences a frustrating indifference (result). The cue-routine-result process, which is essentially controlled by the subconscious mind, is the key to understanding habits and their results. If we are not pleased with some of the results, such as consuming too much sugar or failing at marketing, that three-step process enables us to change our habits.

2.10.4 Opportunities Offered by Habit Change

You may be thinking further about being on automatic pilot (being governed by habits) most of the time. Maybe it's true for routine activities, but certainly not for serious matters such as studying, working part time, and making important decisions because then you are concentrating and focused, right? Research says no! As succinctly stated by consultant Martin (2008), "Because the workings of the habitual [subconscious] mind are unconscious, the executive [conscious mind] thinks it is in control of most of our behavior." If you believe the research, almost everything you do (including many of your serious activities) is likely to be heavily driven by habits.

So what? Think about this: If so much of what we do is habitual, then improving any aspect of our life, such as roles (e.g., son, daughter, friend, student, employee, service provider) or activities (e.g., studying, analyzing, designing), means that we should examine and maybe change some of our habits. Mandino (1968), in his small but powerful book *The Greatest Salesman in the World*, says this about the power of habits: "In truth, the only difference between those who have failed, and those who have succeeded lies in the difference of their habits. Good habits are the key to all success. . . . I will form good habits and become their slave."

Consider the story of a wise Indian grandfather (Osteen 2007). He said to his grandchild: "A battle rages inside of you between two wolves. One wolf is evil, that is, angry, jealous, unforgiving, and lazy. The other wolf is good, that is, loving, kind, forgiving, and ambitious." The grandchild asked, "Which wolf will win?" Grandfather said, "Whichever one you feed." The grandchild might have asked, "Which wolf will lose?" And the grandfather would probably have answered, "The one you starve."

This story suggests the wisdom of replacing bad habits, which impact whatever aspects of life are most important to you, with good habits; feed the good habits and starve the bad habits. The story implies that each of us has the opportunity to improve our lives, including our likelihood of achieving our desired success and significance, by moving toward a more productive set of habits. Listen again to Mandino (1968): "As a child, I was a slave to my impulses; now I am a slave to my habits. . . . My bad habits must be destroyed and new furrows prepared for good seed. . . . For it is another of nature's laws that only a habit can subdue another habit."

My suggestion: Inventory your habits. Look at relevant portions of, and/or activities in, your daily routine as a student, practitioner, or other. Compare your habitual behavior with your goals and aspirations, your desired mix of success and significance. Are your habits aligned with what you want to achieve? If not, consider applying the process described in the next section.

2.10.5 Method for Changing Habits

Destroying a bad habit or subduing it with another, to use Mandino's terminology, is not easy. This is where basic brain knowledge assists us. Psychiatrist, psychoanalyst, and researcher Doidge (2007) says: "Most of us think of the brain as a container and learning as putting something in it. When we try to break a bad habit, we think the solution is to put something new into the container." He goes on to explain that as we learn a bad habit, it takes over a brain map or processing area. As we repeat the bad habit, it gradually occupies more of that processing area, which prevents

Figure 2.13
This cyclical method, based on neuroscience, will enable you to replace a "bad" habit with a "good" habit.

Source: Adapted from Duhigg 2012 and Martin 2008.

The conscious mind, when wanting to replace a "bad" with a "good" habit, starts by recognizing the cue, then introduces a new routine and tests it.

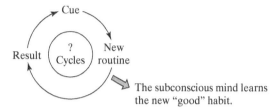

The subconscious mind learns the new "good" habit.

use of that area for good habits. In other words, unlearning is typically more difficult than learning (Doidge, 2007).

Consider a method that you might use for unlearning what you consider a "bad" habit and replacing it with a desired "good" habit. The technique is based on neuroscience and uses the previously mentioned cue-routine-result process. New habits are developed through the process of repetitive cue-routine-result cycles.

Assume you have the bad habit of putting off doing your homework until late at night and you want to replace that habit with doing it earlier and better. Consider what happens now: You come back to your dormitory room after your last class and the *cue* is the television. Your *routine* is to turn it on, and your *result* is to relax and catch up on things. This leads to your next *cue*, which is hunger; your *routine* is to go out for a quick meal; your *result* is feeling good. Other cues probably occur, initiating other routines, none of which move you toward doing your homework. Late that night, you finally get to work on some homework, probably due tomorrow. The work you do is difficult, given the late hour, and the quality reflects neither your ability nor your desire. Therefore, you decide to use the method shown in Figure 2.13 to replace your bad homework habit with a good one.

Starting today, when you come back to your dormitory room after your last class, the *cue* is still the television. However, your new *routine* is not to turn it on. Instead, you enter a new *routine*: do one homework assignment that is due the next day of class, no matter when that day is. Having done that on this, your first day of your new "habit," your *result* is to relax, knowing that your homework is done in a manner that reflects your ability. Now you can watch television and catch up on things.

That one-time change may have been easy, provided you knew, recognized, and acted on the cue. However, you are very far from replacing your old habit with a new habit. You must persist. Next time you experience the cue, you repeat the new routine, or refine it, and follow through. I don't know how many cycles will be needed, but it will be many. Eventually, your subconscious learns the new habit. The payoff is that you reduce your stress and improve your academic performance.

The cyclical habit-change process could also be used to replace the previously posed "thirsty" and "meet a new person" scenarios. In the former, the cue could now lead to buying a bottle of water, and in the latter the cue could now involve asking questions about the other person. If these habit changes are successful, the result could be improved health and making more friends or gaining more clients and customers.

2.10.6 Necessary Number of Cycles

As suggested, no one can predict the number of new cue-routine-result cycles needed for a specific person's subconscious mind to implement a particular new habit. However, my experience suggests that dozens of cycles will be needed, and therefore we must persist. More specifically, my rule of thumb is that thirty days of successful repetitions will enable my subconscious mind to learn a new habit. One study (Jabr 2011) concluded that nine weeks to several months were needed for habit formation, whereas Connellan (2011) suggests twenty-one to thirty days. All of this suggests that the necessary number of cycles is highly variable and you will have to figure it out.

A century ago, philosopher and psychologist James (1917) offered this habit-forming advice, which seems relevant today: "Never suffer an exception to occur till the new habit is securely rooted in your life. Each lapse is like the letting fall of a ball of string which one is carefully winding up; a single slip undoes more than a great many turns."

2.10.7　There Must Be an Easier Way

You may be thinking, "I like this good habit idea. Habitually practicing productive behaviors—being on smart automatic pilot—appeals to me. However, learning a habit by this tedious cyclical process seems burdensome. It reminds me of how I learned how to use a keyboard, play the trombone, or drive a car. Therefore, I'm going to circumvent the cycle and simply think myself or talk myself out of some bad habits and into some good habits."

Sorry, it won't work. Your subconscious mind is illiterate; you can't talk to it. As stated by Martin (2008), author of the book *Habit:* "The habitual mind is nonverbal, so it doesn't learn by reading or listening to an explanation. It learns unconsciously through associating an action with an outcome." He also says, as illustrated by the cue-routine-result cycle, that "the habitual mind learns through cause and effect, reward and repetition."

2.10.8　The Long View

If the possibility of habit creation and/or change interests you, then consider the long-term potential for you and those you might influence. James (1917) explains the potential this way: "Small, seldom-seen habits have the power to bear us irresistibly toward our destiny." Because of what you now know about one aspect of the workings of your brain, you have the ability to form positive "small, seldom-seen habits" that will profoundly affect your life and the lives of others. You can also assist receptive individuals in changing their habits. Habit change is one example of brain basics at work for you, and (as will become very apparent as you work through this text) the applications of brain basics offered so far are just the tip of the applied-neuroscience iceberg.

PERSONAL: A HABIT CHANGE

Early in my career, one of my responsibilities was marketing water resources engineering services. Our firm made heavy and effective use of digital computer hydrologic-hydraulic models. Whenever I had the opportunity, I would habitually talk to potential clients about how our computer models worked. This was not effective—as indicated, in part, by the way clients' eyes glazed over.

I eventually learned from a marketing professional in our firm that instead of stressing *how the models worked*, I should habitually stress the *benefits the models provided.* I focused on benefits, did it enough that describing benefits became habitual, and my marketing effectiveness improved. Although I no longer market modeling-related services, the habit of focusing on benefits, not features, stuck and has served me well in a variety of positions and situations in the business, government, and academic sectors.

2.11 TAKING MULTITASKING TO TASK

Are you a multitasker? Do you, like the grasshopper in Figure 2.14, jump from task to task? You text, email, tweet, Google, blog, and talk—and you did all that in just the last few minutes! You are certainly busy, but are you effective and efficient? That is, are you doing the right things—and are you doing them right?

2.11.1 Costs of Multitasking

If you believe that activity, no matter how energetic, is progress, consider the contrary, neuroscience-based view of multitasking. Brain researcher John Medina (2008) writes, "It is literally impossible for our brains to multitask when it comes to paying attention." Multitasking, which is really jumping or toggling from thinking task to thinking task, is very inefficient because of the time, perhaps unnoticed, needed to resume a task.

Medina goes on to describe the "50-50" negative consequences of multitasking: "Studies show that a person who is interrupted takes 50 percent longer to accomplish a task . . . and he or she makes up to 50 percent more errors." Psychologists Strayer and Watson (2012) report research that concluded that "our performance [on any given task] deteriorates drastically when we attempt to focus on more than one task at a time." Somewhat optimistically, for some diehard multitaskers, Strayer and Watson's research suggests that a very small percent of us may be able to truly multitask, but they indicate that more study is needed.

Moving away from results of neuroscience research, business coach Joe Robinson (2010), in an intriguing and informative article titled "E-mail Is Making You Stupid," says, "People may be able to chew gum and walk at the same time, but they can't do two or more thinking tasks simultaneously." In a similar vein, Publilius Syrus, the Latin writer of maxims, said two millennia ago, "To do two things at once is to do neither."

2.11.2 The Valued Kind of Multitasking

The just-described negative multitasking is characterized by spending a short period, a minute or less, on a task, setting it aside unfinished, and haphazardly jumping to another task, and then to another, and so on. Before going on, briefly consider a very positive type of multitasking.

Let's personalize it. Assume that you are developing a knowledge-skills-attitude (KSA) set that enables you to plan and successfully complete many different kinds of tasks and sometimes groups of tasks that constitute projects. Some of these tasks and projects are design-oriented, whereas others focus on planning, research, experimentation, writing, speaking, and other functions. Some you finish in an hour, but most require elapsed times of days, weeks, or months. In this admirable form of multitasking, you juggle many and varied tasks, eventually finishing all of them—and you are increasingly respected and valued for your contributions. You

Figure 2.14
Multitasking means
frequently jumping, in
grasshopper fashion, from
task to task.

(Natara/Fotolia)

are proficient at the constructive kind of multitasking. You possess the KSAs needed to take on and complete a wide variety of tasks and projects.

2.11.3 The Interruption Rationale

As noted, the negative type of multitasking increases the absolute amount of time needed to complete a task and increases the likelihood of errors. Perhaps you might argue that you multitask because you are frequently interrupted. Who is interrupting whom? Pattison (2008) reports that half of the interruptions experienced by US office workers in high-tech companies are self-interruptions—that is, "jumping from task to task." We frequently interrupt ourselves! He also notes, as did Medina, that a significant time period is needed to get back "on task." For a similar message, see Jackson's (2008) book, *Distracted: The Erosion of Attention and the Coming Dark Age*. How's that for an ominous message?

2.11.4 Benefits of Not Multitasking

What if, as an experiment, we stopped multitasking for a while? Bregman (2011), a consultant, describes a one-week experiment in which he tried to not multitask. He largely succeeded and realized the following five benefits:

- Noticed more things and interacted more effectively with people
- Made significant progress on projects
- Experienced a dramatic drop in stress
- Lost patience with things that were not a good use of his time
- Gained patience for things that were useful and enjoyable

Bregman reported that there were no downsides to not multitasking. Perhaps his experience will motivate you to conduct a similar experiment or move away from multitasking in some other manner.

2.11.5 Moving Away from Multitasking

Given the costs of multitasking and the benefits of not multitasking, how might you reduce your multitasking? Consider some productive antimultitasking habits that you could develop. First, prioritize your tasks. Then, commit to studying, analyzing, or writing for an hour; calculating for half an hour; or emailing for half an hour. Attempt to stick with a task, or well-defined portion of it, until finished. Try to ignore everything else during these periods or while performing these tasks.

When the task, or a series of tasks, is finished, reward yourself! Kick back, grab a soft drink or cup of coffee, enjoy one of those candy bars hidden in your backpack, or take a walk around the block. "Stressed spelled backwards is desserts! Offset some of that intense and productive work, during which you avoid multitasking, with one or more well-earned and pleasurable desserts" (Walesh 2013).

By the way, try not to take a break (or too many breaks) during a task that you consider unpleasant, like cleaning your room, filling out your timesheet, or doing your taxes. Take the break after the task! Why? Research suggests that the irritating or boring job will seem even worse when you return to it after the break. "Instead of thinking about taking a break as a relief from a chore, think about how much harder it will be to resume an activity you dislike." The opposite is true for pleasant tasks; that is, taking breaks makes them more pleasurable (Ariely 2010). All of this may seem counterintuitive; you'd think that we would want to take breaks from unpleasant tasks and not do so during pleasant ones. However, that isn't how our brains work.

By reducing multitasking, we address how we use one of our most valuable gifts: our time, an essence of our life. To reiterate, brain science supports our antimultitasking efforts in two ways. First, it reveals that the brain cannot perform two thinking tasks at once. Second, it indicates that we can help our subconscious mind acquire antimultitasking habits.

2.12 NEGATIVITY BIAS

Now, let's turn to an aspect of your brain that can prevent you from achieving your desired mix of success and significance. Without basic brain knowledge, you may not even know that it's happening to you.

2.12.1 Origin

As suggested by Figure 2.15, our ancestors lived in a harsh environment, whether on the largely open savanna or in the densely vegetated jungle. These hunter-gatherers frequently faced the threats of predation and starvation. On any given day, they knew they could either be *eating* lunch or *be* lunch.

Therefore, our predecessors learned to be very cautious when considering short-term actions and their possible consequences, to frequently see danger or potential danger in a variety of common daily circumstances, and to act defensively. Sure, some good things happened to them, but our ancestors learned to think mostly negatively in order to survive, to remember what went wrong the last time they were in similar situation, and to not let it happen again. That is, they had a negativity bias (Hanson 2013). A variation on negativity bias is the anger superiority effect (Restak and Kim 2010), which means that we are more likely to see an angry face in a crowd or audience when we are about to speak than a friendly, approving face. Brain expert medical doctor Cohen (2005) says, "This basic brain imbalance between our reason and our emotions leads to all sorts of trouble."

2.12.2 Our Unfortunate Inheritance

The human negativity bias, although not needed anywhere near the extent to which our ancestors needed it, is still with us today. It is in our brain and is not our fault. More specifically, we are seeing the results of the almond-sized and -shaped

Figure 2.15
Our ancestors faced a harsh environment that caused them to focus on possible negative outcomes.

(Stuart Walesh)

amygdale, which, as noted in Section 2.3.2, lies near the center of our brain and regulates emotions such as fear, rage, and pleasure and memories of the same.

Our evolution reflects the past. Our brains are still, to some extent, like our ancestor's brains. As explained by neuropsychologist Hanson (2013), your brain is "like Velcro for bad experiences but Teflon for good ones." Of course, most of us have many more positive than negative experiences. However, because of evolution, we are still subject to our ancestors' negativity bias. Hanson also says, "The brain is good at learning from bad experiences, but bad at learning from good ones." He goes on to add, "The 'soil' of your brain is more fertile for weeds than for flowers."

Some people claim (e.g., Sharot 2011) that humans tend to be overly optimistic about the future, which may seem to be at odds with negativity bias. When asked to imagine hypothetical broad and long-term future conditions, such as finding a great job, having a happy family life, and avoiding illness, Sharot says that we tend to be optimistic. This observation does not conflict with negativity bias or the anger superiority effect discussed in this section. Negativity bias and the anger superiority effect pertain to immediate, actual situations demanding quick or prompt responses, not to hypothetical, far-off future happenings requiring no commitment now.

2.12.3 Negative Consequences of the Negativity Bias

If you allow the negativity bias or anger superiority effect of your brain to prevail, you will miss out on many rewarding professional and personal experiences. You will be less likely to achieve your desired combination of success and significance, as introduced in Section 1.2. "The greatest mistake you can make in life," according to writer Elbert Hubbard, "is to continually fear you will make one." More specifically, ignorance of the negativity bias or inability to deal with it can have unfortunate consequences, such as the following, the cumulative effect of which is to set you up for major late-life regret:

- As a student, you are asked to speak about your coop experience at the next meeting of the student chapter of your professional society, but you decline because of an earlier speaking disaster.
- A professor offers you the opportunity to work on an especially challenging senior project, but you defer because of an unfortunate project failure during your sophomore year.
- Shortly after earning your professional engineering license, you are asked to manage a construction project, but don't accept the challenge because of an earlier project management setback.
- As a young practitioner, you are about to speak at an engineering society meeting and have just been introduced. The floor is yours. You look at the audience. Because of the brain's negativity bias or anger superiority effect, you are much more likely to see disapproving or angry faces in the audience than supportive or friendly faces. You are intimidated; as a result, your presentation falls far short of what you expected. (Although unfriendly faces will automatically "pop out" because of the anger superiority effect, by looking more intently you are very likely to find friendly faces, and usually there are many more of them. Please remember, the audience wants you to succeed, if for no other reason than that they are investing valuable time in your presentation.)
- You are invited by friends to take a month off and bike across Europe, but you defer because of things that went wrong during an earlier group bike trip across your state.

- In your early thirties, you think about a long-held dream: starting your own business. However, you decide not to follow through after vividly recalling a failed part-time business while in college.

In personal situations like those just described, you immediately remember an event or experience that steers you away from the stated opportunity. You do this essentially without thinking (largely under the control of your subconscious mind) because of negativity bias. With some conscious thought, you probably could also recalled one or more positive events or experiences. This leads us to our next topic: what you can do about the potentially destructive negativity bias.

2.12.4 Offsetting Negativity Bias

When you are initially presented with a special opportunity, don't react. Instead think—think about why, in knee-jerk fashion, you may be about to decline the attractive proposition. Remember the Velcro versus Teflon nature of your brain. It will automatically cause you to recall some negative event or circumstance that is counter to you pursuing this opportunity. Next, consciously recall one or more of your goals, in support of your desired success (Section 1.2), that would be advanced by this opportunity. Also, remember and celebrate some positive experiences consistent with that goal and this opportunity. Then, and only then, decide. Going forward, create a success file and one way of doing this is to develop the habit of asking yourself what is the best thing that happened to me today (Kleon 2012).

The preceding process requires a special effort. However, the payoff is a greatly increased likelihood of you achieving your desired mix of success and significance. "We must all suffer from one of two pains," according to motivational speaker Rohn, "the pain of discipline [now] or the pain of regret [later]. . . . Discipline weighs ounces while regret weighs tons."

PERSONAL: NIX NEGATIVITY BIAS

In my mid-thirties, I was one of several scheduled speakers sitting on a platform in a hotel conference room and facing about two hundred professionals. As the person chairing the session stepped up to the microphone and began to welcome the audience, I fell, with my chair, off the end of the platform and onto the floor. Very embarrassing! While some audience members laughed and others showed concern, I got up, put my chair back on the platform, climbed up onto the platform, and sat down. When my turn to speak came, I self-consciously and nervously gave a presentation that was acceptable, but not one of my best.

Since then, I have been presented with hundreds of opportunities to speak and have taken on most of them. Early on after the "falling" event, when learning about a speaking situation, I would recall falling off the platform and, consistent with the negativity bias, was tempted to decline the opportunity. However, I kept in mind my goal, the formation of which preceded the embarrassing event: to become an effective speaker and realize the related benefits. Accordingly, I consciously recalled and drew on a series of positive speaking experiences, which offset the one disaster, and accepted many speaking opportunities. As a result, I grew and continue to grow as an effective speaker.

Bottom line: Don't let your brain's negativity bias frustrate your personal and professional growth. Don't risk major late-life regrets. Instead, use your conscious mind to overcome that negative force or anger superiority effect and move you toward your desired mix of success and significance.

2.13 LEFT- AND RIGHT-HANDEDNESS

Our earlier discussion of the brain's left and right hemispheres may cause you to think about possible connections to left- and right-handedness. About 10 percent of us are left-handed. In the spirit of first things first, tests indicate that there is no difference in intelligence between left- and right-handers (Carter 2009; Edwards 1999; McManus 2012).

2.13.1 How Handedness Affects Behavior

Our handedness can influence our bias and metaphors. One study (Hutson 2012) concluded that our dominant side can influence our worldview. More specifically, "right-handers associate right with good and left with bad and . . . left-handers make the reverse association."

Studies by psychologist Cassanto (Hutson 2012) observed that presidential candidates George W. Bush, John Kerry, John McCain, and Barack Obama gestured with their dominant hands when making positive points and their weak hands to stress negatives. He also noted that "lefties hold higher opinions of their flight attendants when [the lefties are] seated on the right side of a plane." Presumably, the passengers arrive at this conclusion because the flight attendants are on the passenger's left. Cassanto also learned that children thought that similar cartoon animals on their dominant side "looked nicer or smarter."

2.13.2 Advantages of Being Left-Handed

Recall the discussion of lateralization—that is, the strong tendency of the human brain's hemispheres to be specialized with respect to certain capabilities. Right-handed people are more lateralized than left-handers. For example, "Language is mediated in the left hemisphere in 90 percent of right-handers and 70 percent of left-handers" (Edwards 1999). In other words, left-handers are slightly more whole-brained than right-handers.

"Lefties" have a slight edge on creativity. "Left-handers' brains are structured differently from right-handers' in ways that can allow them to process language, spatial relations and emotions in more diverse and potentially creative ways" (McManus 2012). Or, as already noted, left-hander's brains are less lateralized. Although only about 10 percent of the general population is left-handed, art school enrollments include 30 to 40 percent of left-handers (Shlain 2014).

Left-handers also have a slight edge in music and mathematics. According to McManus (2012), "A slightly larger number of left-handers than right-handers are especially gifted in music and math." This source reports that there are a greater proportion of left-handers in professional orchestras, even among musicians who play instruments like violins that appear to be designed for right-handers. Studies reveal that mathematically gifted adolescents are more likely to be left-handed. The observation that mathematicians are frequently musically inclined is probably not a coincidence. And, for the sports-minded, a left-handed batter is closer to first base when he or she hits the ball.

2.13.3 Advantages of Being Right-Handed

"Righties" are less likely than "lefties" to have learning difficulties, dyslexia, and to stutter. Furthermore, language and custom favor right-handers. For example, the honored guest traditionally sits on the host's right side, we shake our right hands when greeting or meeting someone, and a "left-handed compliment" is anything but (Edwards 1999; McManus 2012).

2.13.4 Closing Thoughts about Handedness

As engineering students and aspiring engineers, you may want to be aware of ways in which your handedness, and that of others, influences bias and behavior. That awareness can provide more self-understanding as well as insight into what others say and do. Depending on your handedness, you may have certain advantages and liabilities and can be prepared to act accordingly.

2.14 GENDER AND THE BRAIN

Having considered many aspects of the human brain in this chapter, your brain may begin to think about gender, which has not been mentioned even once! For example, are female and male brains different? If so, are they different in ways that influence characteristic gender-specific behaviors? The short answer is that if we (metaphorically) remove the tops of adult heads and look down at female and male brains, they look essentially the same. However, they have small internal differences, and those variations may influence some markedly different female and male behavior, and you ought to know about such differences.

This topic warrants your attention because, whatever your gender, the ideas and information offered can help you work smarter and be an even more effective communicator and collaborator with females and males. Relative to creativity and innovation, you will soon see why gender is an important consideration when forming and working with teams. As explained in the Medici Effect discussion (Section 4.6), diverse teams, including gender-diverse teams, tend to deliver highly creative and innovative results. This contrasts with homogenous teams, which typically produce results largely void of creativity and innovation.

PERSONAL: SENSITIVE TOPIC IN SCIENCE

When I proposed this text to an acquisitions editor at a publisher (not Pearson) a few years prior to this text's publication and he realized that I intended to write about gender aspects of the human brain, the editor reacted negatively. He said, "You'll have to take care with gender and the brain. We risk getting clobbered." Later, I encountered biologist John Medina's statement that "characterizing gender-specific behaviors has a long and mostly troubled history," but he went on to address the topic (Medina 2008), and some of his information is cited in this gender section. That "troubled history" probably included discrimination or disparate treatment of women.

After considering the matter, and given what I was learning about the brain and how the basics can help student and practicing engineers work smarter and be more creative and innovative, I knew that the gender aspects of the brain needed to be included in this chapter. Omitting a gender discussion in this brain basics chapter would have created a serious gap, whereas including it will enhance your communication effectiveness, support productive team formation and work, and contribute to creative and innovative results. Leaving gender out of this chapter would be like excluding other basics such as lateralization, neuroplasticity, and habits.

Accordingly, I combed through my large collection of neuroscience-related books and other sources and found that the gender topic was largely omitted. Neuropsychiatrist Brizendine (2010) explains that, until recently, "large areas of science and medicine used the male as the 'default' model for understanding human brain biology and behavior, and only in the past few years has that really begun to change." In other words, gender and the brain is a relatively new science and medical topic; we won't find broad and deep literature. However, I found enough current facts and information to construct this section of the chapter for your benefit.

2.14.1 Caveats

As you read about gender and the brain, please keep these four points in mind:

1. When reference is made to the female versus male brain structure, neurotransmitters, hormones, and pathologies, the intent is to convey tendencies and "averages." Clearly, you and others can readily find individuals of both genders who are exceptions.
2. I report only what appears to be based on scientific research and try to avoid conjecture, whether it be mine or others.
3. Neuroplasticity (Section 2.8) prevails; that is, our brains change throughout our lives as a result of formal education and experiences.
4. Finally, and to reiterate a point made at the beginning of this section, I am sharing this information with you so that you can work more effectively with others, including being more creative and innovative, regardless of your or their gender.

2.14.2 Brain Structure

Let's begin our discussion of the brain and gender with an overview of the female and male brains' structures. The overall volume of adult men's brains is about 10 percent larger than that of women, even after accounting for body size (Brizendine 2006; Gibb 2012; NHS Choices 2014). However, let's not simplistically assume that this larger volume means that men are more intelligent or more creative and innovative. For example, elephant brains weigh three times that of humans, but humans have the intelligence edge, and Albert Einstein's brain weighed about 88 percent of that of the average human brain (Gibb 2012).

Many factors influence male and female thinking effectiveness, including the number of brain cells, the connections between them, and the relative sizes of various parts of the brain (Gibb 2012; NHS Choices 2014). For example, men and women have the same number of brain cells; they are just packed closer together in the females' smaller skulls. There is no overall intelligence difference between genders as measured by IQ tests (Brizendine 2006; Gibb 2012; Stover 2014).

When neuroscientists and medical doctors examine the interiors of adult brains, they find differences in the sizes of certain parts of female and male brains (Stover 2014), which, as we will see in Section 2.14.6, help explain differences in men's and women's behavior. The following are some examples of size differences:

- The amygdale "registers fear and triggers aggression" (Brizendine 2010), "drives emotional impulses," and is larger in men than in women (Brizendine 2006, Stover 2014).
- The prefrontal cortex, the CEO of the brain that resides behind our foreheads and which (among other functions) keeps emotions from running wild, is larger in women than in men (Brizendine 2006). Interestingly, visual stimulation

travels faster to the amygdale than to the cortex, so we are primed for an emotional response before we can produce a cognitive one (Hardiman 2003).

- Women have a larger and more active hippocampus than men (Brizendine 2006; Gibb 2012; Stover 2014). As explained in Section 2.3, this part of the brain is involved with learning and converts our short-term memories into long-term forms.
- Women's brains have greater connectivity between hemispheres via the corpus callous than men's. In contrast, men's brains have greater connectivity within each hemisphere than women's. This is based on a study of one thousand females and males between ages eight and twenty-two, and the results are thought to apply to adults (Paddock 2013). As summarized by Nussbaum (2010), "females tend to utilize both sides of their brains more to process than men, who tend to rely primarily on one side, the dominant hemisphere." "Women tend to use both hemispheres when speaking and processing verbal information. Men primarily use one," according to Medina (2008), who goes on to say that "Women tend to have thick cables connecting their two hemispheres. Men's are thinner."

2.14.3 Brain Chemistry: Neurotransmitters and Hormones

The brain contains one hundred billion nerve cells or neurons, as explained in Section 2.3, which receive and send electrochemical signals. A neurotransmitter is a chemical that is released from a neuron and helps to amplify or modulate a signal that passes from one nerve cell to another or to a muscle. The following are some examples of neurotransmitters (Baggaley 2001; Gibb 2012):

- Serotonin: influences mode, memory, temperature regulation, and sleep
- Dopamine: stimulates bodily movement, feeling good, and excitement
- Noradrenaline: activates the automatic functions of the nervous system

Hormones are chemicals produced by glands and transported by the body's circulatory system to produce effects on cells and organs remote from the point of origin (Hormone Health Network 2014; MedicineNet 2014). Brizendine (2006) explains that hormones help determine what the brain is interested in doing right now—that is, behavior such as being nurturing or aggressive, or social or withdrawn. Four examples of hormones are as follows:

- **Oxytocin:** Tends to settle and calm both women and men (Baggaley 2001; Brizendine 2010).
- **Cortisol:** Rising levels indicate increased stress (Brizendine 2006).
- **Estrogen:** A female sex hormone. It also promotes, for women, neuron growth and maintenance of brain function with age (Brizendine 2006; Stover 2014).
- **Testosterone:** Drives focused, assertive, fast, and unfeeling behavior. Throughout adulthood, male testosterone levels are ten to one hundred times that of females (Brizendine 2006).

2.14.4 Pathology

Consider a highly factual area: brain pathology—that is, brain-related disease. The following pathologies are more common in males than females: alcoholism and drug addiction, antisocial behavior, dyslexia, autism, mental retardation, and schizophrenia (Medina 2008; NHS Choices 2014). The following pathologies are more common in females than males: depression, by a factor of two to one; anorexia, by a ten to one ratio; and anxiety, by a factor of four to one (Brizendine 2006; Gibb 2012; Medina 2008; NHS Choices 2014; Stover 2014).

Consider strokes, episodes in which oxygen-rich blood stops flowing to one or more parts of the brain. Within minutes, brain cells begin to die. Women recover from stroke-induced verbal impairment better than men. This and other medical issues suggest differences in the normal brain functions of men and women. Because women tend to use both hemispheres when speaking and processing information, females have a more robust backup system.

2.14.5 Nature versus Nurture

Recent scientific evidence clearly points to physiological, neurotransmitter, hormonal, and pathology differences in the female and male brains and beyond. There is disagreement, however, on the role nature versus nurture plays in leading to those differences in adults. Arguing for a nature plus nurture position, Brizendine (2010) says, "Certain behaviors and skills are wired and programmed innately in boys' brains, while others are wired innately in girls' . . . These differences are reinforced by culture and upbringing, but they begin in the brain." Brizendine (2006) also declares that "there is no unisex brain" and that "male and female brains are different from the moment of conception" (Brizendine 2010). Male and female brain differences "arise before a baby draws its first breath" (Stover 2014). In strong contrast, and in what appears to be a minority position, neuroscientist Rippon (Knapton 2014) says that the differences in adult male and female brains "are tiny and are the result of environment, not biology."

Although the nature versus nurture debate may be of interest, it does not affect our pragmatic treatment of gender and the brain. Based on the preceding discussion, we now understand some typical differences between the brains of adult men and women. That background enables us to explore the practical significance of brain differences—that is, the possible influence on male and female behavior and what it may mean for each of us.

2.14.6 Examples: How Differences in Female and Male Brains May Influence Behavior

How might differences in female and male brains influence typical female and male behavior and/or help us understand that behavior? To answer this practical question, consider a series of observations of women's and men's behaviors and how their brain characteristics may explain some of the dissimilar results. Although some behavior differences are not readily explained by specific brain dissimilarities, they are probably attributed to one or more of the many structural, neurotransmitter, and hormonal variations between male and female brains. Some suggestions are provided for how to use understanding of brain gender differences to enhance female-male interaction, including creative and innovative collaboration in professional work and beyond.

Recall the caveats in Section 2.14.1, including the statement that I report only what appears to be based on scientific research and try to avoid conjecture. Although the following observations are based on the science presented in Section 2.14, the observations are generalized and recognize that both women's and men's behaviors are on a continuum. In other words, there will be exceptions. With that in mind, the following are my science-based observations of women's and men's behaviors and some related suggestions:

- **Expressing emotions with facial expressions and voice tone:** Men tend to subconsciously suppress showing emotions on their faces, whereas women tend to do the opposite. Research reveals that although both genders immediately experience emotions in stimulating situations, males typically and quickly adopt a "poker face" and corresponding voice tone, whereas female faces and voices tend to practice extended communication of the emotion (Brizendine 2010). Male masking of emotion is often interpreted as not having any. This, of course, is incorrect and is further discussed in the "response to a problem" discussion later in this list.

Suggestions: Men—Try to be a little more expressive of your emotions, with facial expressions and voice, in order to improve your communication with women. Women—Remember that men are feeling much of what you are feeling but not expressing it the way you do.

- **Reading facial expressions and voice tone:** Women do this much better than men. More specifically, women are more likely than men to read nonverbal clues in order to recognize and feel another person's pain (Brizendine 2006; Stover 2014). Recent studies (Woolley, Malone, and Chabris 2015) underline the importance of "emotion-reading skills" in that some teams worked smarter than others because their members communicated effectively, participated equally, and possessed "emotion-reading skills."

Suggestions: Women—Set the standard for these important modes of communication, mainly to benefit the men. Men—Learn from women and your own experience how to more effectively read expressions, not just see them, and how to listen, not just hear.

- **Reacting angrily:** "A woman is slower to act out of anger" than a man, but can express just as much anger with time and if needed. The difference is the female tendency to exert more up-front control (Brizendine 2006); in comparison, males tend to be aggressive (Stover 2014). Women have more initial control partly because of their larger prefrontal cortex (the brain's CEO), whereas men have a larger amygdale, the brain's fear, anger, and aggression center.

Suggestions: Women—Continue to set a self-discipline example. Men—Strive to benefit from women's example. One benefit is that you are less likely to say or do something you will regret.

- **Emotional memory:** "Research shows that women typically remember emotional events . . . more vividly and retain them longer than men" (Brizendine 2006). This difference is explained, in part, by the female use of both of the brain's hemispheres when responding to emotional experiences; men tend to use just one (Medina 2008; Nussbaum 2010; Paddock 2013). Another reason for the stronger emotional memory of females is their larger hippocampus. Retaining strong emotional memories of negative events can be a mixed blessing. Although it can prevent repeat mistakes, it can also lead to unproductive rumination about past failures, which in turn can lower confidence (Kay and Shipman 2014).

Suggestions: Men—Appreciate women's emotional memories and the richness it can add. You may have forgotten that temporary but intense disagreement about the team's project, but she probably hasn't. Women—Patiently remind men about what happened, how it felt, and what they can learn from it.

- **Three-dimensionality:** Males tend to have a better understanding of how an object occupies space and are more adept at mentally rotating that object. This male spatial perception ability shows up early, at about age five. Interestingly, when boys were asked to explain this cognitive ability, they did not answer with words. "Instead they squirmed, twisted, turned, and gestured with their hands and arms to explain how they got the answer. The boys' body movements were their explanations." Researchers then taught a group of girls to use physical explanation, and within six weeks they solved mental rotation problems as quickly as the boys (Brizendine 2010). This research finding may suggest a new, more kinesthetic way to teach and learn engineering and other disciplines requiring three-dimensional abilities.

Suggestions: Men—Quietly celebrate the three-dimensional visualization capability that you bring to joint efforts and diligently apply it. Women—Persist in developing this three-dimensional attribute.

* **Response to a problem:** On learning about a serious problem, both men and women tend to immediately experience emotional empathy. However, while females continue to feel and express emotional empathy, males quickly shift to cognitive empathy. They get analytic sooner; they want to get on with solving the problem, as in "the male is a lean, mean, problem-solving machine" and "is structured to seek solutions rather than continue to empathize." This quick testosterone-driven male shift to cognitive empathy should not be taken as indicating lack of concern but rather the opposite. Concern is just being expressed in a typical male manner (Brizendine 2010). Although men and women tend to show different emotional responses to serious problems and use different means to solve them, both genders are equally adept at problem solving (Gibb 2012).

Suggestions: Women—Recognize that the men feel empathy but reflect it by acting, perhaps too quickly. Men—Hesitate a little longer and think empathetically about the challenge to more fully understand it.

2.14.7 Application of Gender and the Brain Knowledge

Having worked through this section, you now have more insight into why you exhibit certain behaviors. Equally important, you may more fully understand why others, female and male, say what they say and do what they do. Gender and the brain warrants your attention, as noted at the beginning of this section, because the ideas and information offered can help you work smarter—that is, be a more effective communicator and collaborator with females and males. In doing so, this knowledge can enable you and your team to be more creative and innovative. Because of brain-driven behavior differences and the value they offer, both genders should be represented in teams and groups that take on challenging IPOs. That is one aspect of the Medici Effect (Section 4.6) in action.

2.15 HOW DO WE KNOW WHAT WE KNOW?

The preceding discussion of brain basics is, obviously, just the tip of the iceberg of a vast and growing field of knowledge. Even so, the limited material may cause you to ask: "How we know, from a scientific and medical perspective, what we know?" I am not about to provide a detailed answer to that question in this text; to do so would take us way off topic. However, on the assumption that some readers may want to pursue that "how" question on their own, I offer an introductory discussion that may motivate you to dig deeper. More specifically, let's touch briefly on split-brain studies, studies of large groups over time (cohort studies), and brain-imaging techniques.

2.15.1 Split-Brain Studies

The Historic Note appearing earlier in this chapter (Section 2.7.1) introduced the split-brain studies conducted at the California Institute of Technology in the 1960s.

Figure 2.16
One type of test concluded that the human brain's two hemispheres are very different with respect to some capabilities.

Source: Adapted from Funnell, Colvin, and Gazzaniga 2007.

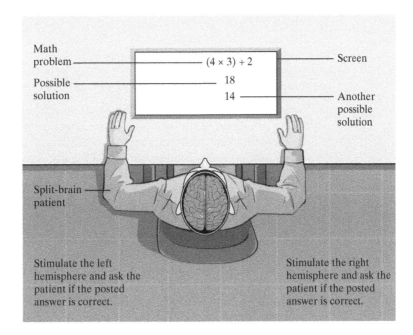

This research showed that the human brain's two hemispheres are very different with respect to some capabilities. The results of these investigations were so profound that the study leader Roger W. Sperry and two colleagues received the Nobel Prize for Medicine in 1981.

To further appreciate their experimental process, consider one of many tests involving split-brain patients. Imagine a vertical blank screen with a split-brain person seated in front of it, as shown in Figure 2.16. A mathematics problem is projected on the screen, and then a possible solution is also projected on the screen. The patient's left hemisphere is gently stimulated, via a probe, and the patient is asked if the answer is correct. Then another possible solution is shown, the patient's right hemisphere is stimulated, and the patient is asked if the answer is correct.

The preceding process is repeated many times. Analysis of the data revealed that the left hemisphere was correct 90 percent of the time. In contrast, right hemisphere results were random. The conclusion: The left hemisphere is much more proficient in mathematics (Funnell, Colvin, and Gazzaniga 2007). See Edwards (1999) and Gibb (2012) for more examples.

2.15.2 Studies Over Time of Large Groups of Similar People

Excellent examples of cohort studies as a means of discovering brain characteristics include the Nun Study and the Rush University Medical Center Study, both of which are described later in this chapter (Section 2.16.3). The decade-long Nun Study found that lowered risk of dementia and higher probability of long life correlated with early language ability, a positive outlook, and ongoing mental and physical activity. Similarly, the Rush University research concluded that more frequent brain activity throughout one's life correlates with slower late-life cognitive decline.

2.15.3 Brain-Imaging Techniques

Brain knowledge improved rapidly over recent decades because of the creative and innovative development of various brain-imaging techniques. Although the functions of many human organs and "parts" (e.g., our limbs) can be readily observed, the brain's electrochemical processes could not be seen by the naked eye prior to the arrival of brain-imaging devices. Before access to these tools, scientists would need to perform an autopsy and relate predeath injuries or malfunctions to the site and extent of brain damage. Now, we can see the brain's workings in real time (Brizendine 2006; Carter 2009). Today's imaging devices include the following:

- Powerful microscopes (Carter 2009; Chin and Upson 2011).
- X-rays: Shadings of the resulting image indicate denseness of various parts of the imaged object, with bone appearing light and tissue dark (Hardiman 2003).
- Computerized Axial Tomography (CAT) scans: A major X-ray advance for investigating brain structure and detecting tumors and nodules that cannot be seen with the traditional X-ray. Output images include slices through the brain in various planes and three-dimensional representations (Davis 2014; Hardiman 2003)
- Electroencephalography (EEG): "A graphic record of the electrical activity of the brain, made by attaching electrodes to the scalp that pick up the underlying brain waves" (Carter 2009). The brain is "awash with electrical activity, miniscule electrical pulses generated by individual neurons" and EEG "massively amplifies them" so that they can be traced over time (Gibb 2012).
- Magnetic Resonance Imaging (MRI): "A brain-imaging technique that provides high-resolution pictures of brain structures" (Carter 2009; Chin and Upson 2011). This device uses a magnetic field and the body's resonating water molecules to generate radio signals that are combined in an image (Hardiman 2003).
- Functional Magnetic Resonance Imaging (fMRI): "A brain scan that uses powerful magnets to look at brain blood flow and activity patterns" (Amen 2008). This imaging device is called *functional* because it identifies brain regions recruited during a specific mental task in three dimensions, via the slight waxing and waning of blood flow, which includes metal ions (Chin and Upson 2011; Gibb 2012; Mlodinow 2013; Zimmer 2014).
- Positron Emission Tomography (PET): "A brain scan that uses isotopes to look at glucose metabolism and activity patterns in the brain" (Amen 2008). Radioactive glucose is injected into a person, who is placed in a PET scanner and asked to do mental tasks. The resulting images show brain areas with the greatest activity for each task (Hardiman 2003).
- Single Photon Emission Computed Tomography (SPECT): "A brain scan that uses isotopes to look at blood flow and activity patterns in the brain" (Amen 2008).
- Magnetoencephalography (MEG): "A non-invasive neurophysiological technique that measures the magnetic fields generated by neuronal activity of the brain. . . . MEG is a direct measure of brain function, unlike functional measures such as fMRI, PET, and SPECT that are secondary measures of brain function reflecting brain metabolism" (MIT 2014).

Imaging devices are listed here to stress why and how we have learned so much about the human brain in recent decades. If any of them interest you, learn more about them. For example, Chin and Upson (2011) provide examples of fascinating detailed images produced by microscopes, MRI, fMRI, and MEG.

2.16 CARE AND FEEDING OF YOUR BRAIN

The entire chapter to this point is a brain primer. It describes, in basic terms, what is probably the most magnificent mechanism, the most amazing assembly, or the most engaging entity in the universe. You have been introduced to the human

Figure 2.17
This chapter discusses many features of the human brain, all of which are relevant to working smarter and enhancing creativity and innovation.

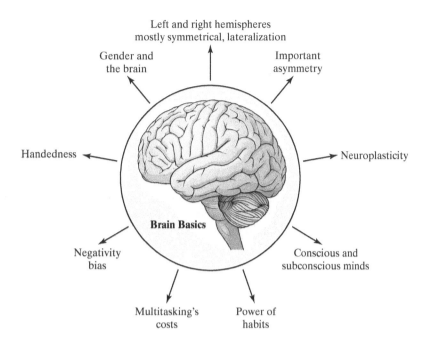

brain's features and functions and the distinction between the brain and the mind. More specifically, as illustrated in Figure 2.17, you learned about the brain's symmetrical hemispheres and related lateralization and the asymmetrical exception, with our formal education's focus on the left side. You also learned about neuroplasticity and its potential for maintaining lifelong cognitive functions, conscious and subconscious minds, the power of habits and the ability to replace them, the wastefulness of multitasking, built-in negativity bias, the vagaries of handedness, the value of understanding gender differences, and how we know what we know about the human brain.

All of this suggests that the trajectory of your entire professional and personal life—the extent to which you achieve your desired mix of success and significance—will be heavily influenced by

- what you know about your brain,
- how you apply what you know, and
- how you take care of your brain.

Let's address the third item now; the previous portions of this chapter have discussed the first two. Going forward, whether you are twenty years old or several or more decades beyond that, how can you care for that three-pound marvel in your head? In support of knowing about your brain and taking care of it, neuroscientist and psychiatrist Amen (2008) says, "The lack of brain education is a huge mistake, because success in all we do starts with a healthy brain."

2.16.1 Exercise

We exercise for various reasons, such as weight control, stress reduction, participating in our favorite sports, and enjoying the outdoors. Exercise also benefits the brain and does so by increasing the following:

- **Number of blood vessels in the brain:** Brain cells receive more oxygen, glucose, and other nutrients (Medina 2008; Restak 2009).

- **Density of neuron connections:** We think better and faster and also offset brain cell loss (Restak 2009).
- **Number of neurons (neurogenesis):** Occurs in some portions of the brain, such as the frontal lobes (also known as the executive system), the corpus callosum, and the hippocampus (the region that controls learning and memory) (Medina 2008; Nussbaum 2010).
- **Flow of oxygen to the brain:** "Physical activity is helpful, not only because it creates new neurons," according to Doidge, "but because the mind is based in the brain and the brain needs oxygen" (Doidge 2007). Oxygen's main function is to carry away potentially damaging excess electrons that are produced as glucose is consumed by brain cells, according to Medina (2008). He goes on to emphasize the importance of oxygen to the brain by noting that we can live for about thirty days without food and about a week without drinking water, but "cannot go without oxygen for more than five minutes without risking serious and permanent damage" to our brain.
- **Level of neurotransmitters:** This means that the person will be more focused, less stressed, and less impulsive (Costa 2010). As noted in Section 2.14.2, a neurotransmitter is a chemical released from a neuron, creating a signal that passes from one neuron to another or to a muscle (Baggaley 2001). Serotonin, dopamine, norephinephrine, and noradenaline are examples of neurotransmitters (Medina 2008; Restak 2009) associated with mental health.

Clearly, regular physical exercise has many benefits. This leads us to consider what kind of exercise is needed, how much, and when during our life. We do not need extreme measures. Nussbaum (2010) suggests options such as performing aerobic exercise three times per week or walking for thirty minutes or ten thousand steps (which you can measure with a pedometer) each day. Medina (2008) recommends a twenty-minute walk each day or three thirty-minute aerobic exercises per week. Most of us, regardless of our stage in life, can exercise at these moderate levels for the sake of our brain, and we should exercise throughout our life, as indicated by Nussbaum (2010), who, recognizing neuroplasticity, said "I do not believe in a critical period of brain development unless it is defined as life."

2.16.2 Diet

We can also care for and "tune up" our brain by watching our diet. We should adopt what Restak (2009) calls a "brain diet" or what Nussbaum (2010) refers to as a "healthy brain diet." For starters, a brain-friendly diet should achieve the following:

- **Avoid trans fats:** Trans fats are "formed when liquid oils are transformed into solid fats by adding hydrogen to vegetable oil." They "clog arteries in the brain and heart, leading to cognitive decline . . . and heart attacks. . . . In general, foods that come from nature (unprocessed) don't contain trans fats" (Restak 2009).
- **Control weight:** While we have long known that obesity causes heart disease, hypertension, and diabetes, "the effect of obesity on brain function has only recently been uncovered" and "as tests of cognitive performance in humans indicate, obesity is more often associated with cognitive impairment than with age, gender, education, or IQ." We need to restrict calories by reducing "protein, carbohydrates, and unhealthy (trans) fat content of food without [reducing] the nutrient content" (Restak 2009).

Moving from "don't" to "do," consider the following advice on what we should include in our diet:

- **Eat vegetables and fruits:** Particularly green leafy vegetables and tomatoes. Green leafy vegetables provide more vitamin E than other vegetables. This vitamin is an antioxidant and boosts the body's immune system so that it can fight invading bacteria and viruses. Fruits and vegetables contain other chemicals that are antioxidants. Oxidants injure or destroy membranes in the interior of cells (National Institutes of Health 2014; Restak 2009), whereas antioxidants are like a broom "that helps to sweep the toxins out of our bodies" (Nussbaum 2010). How many servings of fruits and vegetables should you consume? Restak (2009) suggests drinking fruit or vegetable juice at least three times per week.
- **Consume "good" fats:** That is, omega-3 fatty acids (Nussbaum 2010). This substance lowers the incidence of depression and, more relevant to our discussion, will "improve memory and the clarity of one's thinking." The brain is 60 percent fat by volume (it may be the fattest part of our bodies), and that fat "insulates our nerve tracts and cells and helps the brain process information rapidly" (Nussbaum 2010). Restak (2009) explains that fish, especially tuna, salmon, herring, mackerel, sardines, sablefish, and trout, are "loaded with . . . omega-3 fatty acids" and recommends two servings per week. Nussbaum suggests unsalted nuts, such as almonds and walnuts.
- **Eat some protein:** Protein is the building block of body tissue in that it is used to grow and repair cells (Baggaley 2001; Costa 2010; Nussbaum 2010). According to Nussbaum (2010), proteins supportive of brain health are found in fish containing good fats, turkey and chicken, lean beef and pork, eggs, and low-fat and fat-free dairy products.
- **Consume some carbohydrates:** The body uses carbohydrates to make glucose, the fuel that gives us energy. Excessive carbohydrate intake can result in high blood sugar levels, which, if not managed by natural insulin response, can damage some organs, including the brain. Some specific carbohydrate sources include whole grains with fiber, oats, dried beans and lentils, nuts, and barley (Baggaley 2001; Nussbaum 2010).
- **Get some caffeine:** From coffee, tea, or soft drinks. "New evidence shows that caffeine can be beneficial to brain function" (Restak 2009). However, you should probably limit it to what is contained in two or three servings per day. Excessive caffeine can restrict blood flow to the brain, resulting in dehydration, which interferes with thinking (Adams 2008).
- **Drink moderately and selectively:** Red wine in moderate amounts enhances brain function. Scientists are not sure why, but the key may be a substance in grape skins; red wine is fermented with the skins and white wine without (Restak 2009). Wine is optional; water is essential. Recognize that about 75 percent of your brain, by weight, is water (USGS 2014) and "anything that dehydrates you makes it harder to think," according to Amen (2008). Water helps your brain produce neurotransmitters and hormones; get glucose, nutrients, and oxygen; and remove waste products (USGS 2014).

Additional brain diet advice is readily available. For example, sociobiologist Costa (2010) provides a list of foods associated with higher brain functioning. Nussbaum (2010) identifies many specific foods needed for a healthy brain diet and provides recipes for many soups, dishes, breads, and desserts.

Figure 2.18
Nourish your brain with a
Mediterranean diet.

(Snyfer/Fotolia)

In summary, the "brain diet" described here is similar to the Mediterranean diet (Figure 2.18), which is described as "rich in fruits, vegetables, legumes, and cereals. Olive oil and other unsaturated fatty acids are preferred. . . . fish is eaten more often than poultry or meat. Dairy consumption is low to moderate. Alcohol is taken in mild to moderate amounts in the form of wine with meals" (Restak 2009).

2.16.3 Mental Stimulation

Let's take a look at ways to stimulate your brain and why it's beneficial to do so. We'll review two scientific studies centered on mental stimulation and then discuss how you might benefit from such research in your own life.

The Nun Study

We begin this last portion of the Care and Feeding of Your Brain topic with a review of the Nun Study (Belluck 2001; Snowdon 2001), one of the most unique and revealing investigations ever of the human brain. Starting in 1990, 678 nuns in seven US convents within the School Sisters of Notre Dame order agreed to participate in a groundbreaking study that focused on their brains. The study's purpose was to determine who gets dementia (and especially Alzheimer's disease, which is the principal type of dementia), and why, and what factors affect life expectancy.

The nuns offered an ideal situation for scientific study because they led similar lives, had access to similar health care, ate well, didn't smoke, hardly drank alcohol, and didn't experience physical changes caused by pregnancy. The research process included tracking each nun's writings and other activities beginning in their twenties and extending to death, conducting annual cognitive and physical tests on each participant, and removing and studying the brain of every deceased study participant. Because of the similar lifestyles of its participants, the study was ideal, but the project's leaders also realized that the study's results may not represent the population at large.

The study reached a decade milestone in 2001, which saw the publication of *Aging with Grace*, authored by epidemiologist Snowdon, the principal investigator. The book noted that 383 nuns had passed away. Although the study continues to this day, the comprehensive findings presented thus far in Snowdon's book are highly relevant to our brain care discussion.

The study concluded that early language ability, a positive outlook, and ongoing mental and physical activity correlated with lowered risk of dementia, including Alzheimer's, and also correlated with longer life. The reasons for this correlation are not fully understood. However, that does not significantly diminish their potential value for you, assuming you govern your life accordingly.

The Rush University Medical Center Study

This cohort study, led by neuropsychologist Wilson, started with 294 older persons with, at the beginning, an average age of eighty. Base data on participants included early-life and late-life (current) participation in "cognitively-stimulating activities such as reading, writing, visiting museums, playing challenging card games, doing puzzles, and the like." Somewhat similar to the Nun Study, participants in this investigation participated in annual cognitive function testing until death (a mean of 5.8 years since the beginning of research), when their brains were autopsied. The autopsies enabled the researchers to adjust the data for cognitive diseases such as Alzheimer's (Hughes 2013). The researchers concluded, consistent with the Nun Study, that "more frequent activity across the life span has an association with slower late-life cognitive decline that is independent of common neuropathologic conditions" (Wilson et al. 2013).

The researchers' view of their work: "We have proved for the first time that increased cognitive activity has an association with reduced cognitive decline independent of cognitive-related pathology." The reference to "independent of cognitive-related pathology" means that the researchers analyzed the data to remove the effects of diseases. The researchers' advice: "Start doing some sort of cognitive activity every day if you're not already doing it" (Hughes 2013).

In other words, if you are running mainly on habit and what is comfortable and routine, stop. If you are a successful engineering student or young practitioner, you may react by saying, "I live most days around cognitive activity; I have to in order to survive." That may be true, but I have observed many middle- and advanced-career professionals who have gotten into a rut. For every five years, they have one year of cognitive experience five times instead of five years of cognitive experience. That "in-a-rut thinking" may extend into their personal lives. Avoid that with a vengeance, if for no other reason than to practice faithful stewardship of your gift of a superior intelligence and the opportunities it offers for achieving success and significance.

Other Views

We can readily find many experts who urge us to regularly stimulate our brains. "The human brain operates best when it is regularly subjected to new challenges," according to Costa (2010), "because whenever we learn something new we are burning new biological 'circuits' in the brain that challenge the old circuits we have relied on over and over and over again. . . . We are creating more options and more pathways for the brain to select from." "We can all work to develop our writing and speaking abilities early in life as one means of building a healthier brain," according to Nussbaum (2010), "and perhaps a resistance to neurodegenerative disease later in life." Doidge (2007) states that, based on postmortem examinations, the complexity of interneuron connections increases with level of education. Finally, some say that an idle mind is the devil's workshop. Perhaps that devil's name is dementia.

The principal implication of the preceding studies and views is that we should stay mentally stimulated and physically active throughout our life. Use that amazing muscle called your brain, and leverage its plasticity by giving it many and varied workouts. The sky is the limit on how you might do this; your choices are highly subjective. However, to stimulate your thinking, consider options throughout your life such as the following:

- Earn another degree
- Master a new dance step
- Play brain games, such as crossword puzzles, Sudoku, poker, board games, and solitaire, and experiment with Internet-based services that claim to improve brain capabilities
- Seek speaking opportunities
- Take art lessons
- Request job assignments different than your norm
- Travel to new places
- Join a book club
- Plant and nurture a vegetable or flower garden
- Learn another language
- Engage in a new sport
- Take different routes in your daily travels
- Walk or ride your bicycle instead of driving
- Design and build a boat
- Lead an ad hoc task committee
- Participate in an archeological dig
- Read articles and books from outside of your discipline and/or specialty
- Start a part-time business
- Learn to play an instrument
- Write that book!

2.16.4 Care and Feeding of Your Brain: The Essentials

To reiterate, care for your brain first by regularly exercising because a healthy body tends to mean a healthy brain. Second, watch what you eat and drink. Finally, seek lifelong mental stimulation. Recall this chapter's discussion of habits (Section 2.10). Strive to develop habits that enable you to care for your brain by automatically exercising your body, eating smart, and exercising your brain.

2.17 THE REST OF THE STORY

I began this chapter by stating that if you want to work smarter, live smarter, replace some bad habits with good habits, be more creative and innovative—in short, achieve your desired levels and balance of success and significance—then you need to understand some brain basics. Therefore, I selected, researched, and wrote about, and hopefully you read about, some neuroscience topics. Recall the used car story, in which I argued that you don't need to become a certified automobile mechanic to get better performance out of your car. Analogous with that story, I selected topics that would help you get better performance out of your brain—not make you a brain surgeon. In subsequent chapters, we will draw on that brain primer.

However, knowing some students (and still being one), I suspect that the brain primer may motivate a few of you to delve deeper into neuroscience. You might do so out of simple interest, or maybe you see a possible connection to your formal studies (e.g., senior project, graduate research) or your career (e.g., seeking engineering employment in the neuroprosthetic field). Given that I have touched on only the tip of the brain iceberg in this very introductory treatment, you could dive further into many interesting and fruitful neuroscience topics. Furthermore, given that we have much more to learn about the human brain, your efforts might someday lead to valuable new knowledge. Perhaps one or more of the following topics will entice you as the focus of your research paper, independent study, or capstone course project, which could meld engineering, neuroscience, medicine, and/or other disciplines:

- Functions of various parts of the brain (in the process, the foolishness of the claim that we use only 10 percent of our brains)
- Improved teaching and learning (start with books by Zull [2002] and Hardiman [2003])
- The promise embodied in neuroplasticity for the struggling student who views his or her brain as inferior and fixed
- The structure and electrochemical aspects of neurons
- The fact that seeing and hearing occur in the brain and not in the eyes or ears (Section 8.4.2) and how that reality holds promise to help the blind see and the deaf hear
- Artificial intelligence: Where is it now, how far could it go, and would it encourage or discourage creativity and innovation?
- The new diagnostic and surgery-guidance tools that might be developed because the brain's absence of sensory nerves means that it cannot feel pain (Section 2.3.2)
- Impacts, if any, of brain-training software and websites on thinking ability and IQ
- Ways magicians use brain basics to fool us
- Use of lie detectors and brain-imaging devices in legal proceedings
- Applying brain basics to improve memorization ability
- Telepathy—that is, mind-to-mind communication (e.g., see Rao and Stocco 2014 for an intriguing Internet-based version)
- Effects of the tools and toys we use, such as smartphones, video games, and the Internet, on our brains
- Clairvoyance—that is, gathering information about an object or place using means other than our six senses (Section 2.3.1) of vision, hearing, smell, taste, touch, and proprioception

2.18 LOOKING AHEAD TO CHAPTERS 3, 4, AND 7

After studying Chapters 1 and 2, especially Chapter 2, and because of your practical tendency, you may be tempted to ask, "So what?" That is, you may wonder how you could use your new brain knowledge to help you be more creative and innovative. The partial answer is that I have already offered you some practical tips based on brain basics. For example, because of neuroplasticity, you can continue to maintain your brain, just like you can continue to maintain your muscles. Also if you are willing to work at it, you can use your conscious and subconscious minds to replace bad habits with good ones.

However, those examples are just the tip of the iceberg. Chapter 3 introduces and Chapters 4 and 7 describe and illustrate the use of twenty methods intended to stimulate you and, more powerfully, your group (such as a project, planning, design, research, experimental, marketing, or other team) to think more deeply and widely—to generate more ideas. Deep understanding and effective use of each of the whole-brain tools requires knowledge of brain basics, as offered in this chapter. You now have the necessary foundation to proactively learn about and use those tools.

> Ninety-five percent of what we know about the human brain
> has been learned in the past twenty years.
> Our schools, universities, and corporations are only beginning
> to apply this emerging understanding of human potential.
> —*Michael J. Gelb, author of the 2004 book*
> *How to Think Like Leonardo da Vinci*

CITED SOURCES

Adams, J. L. 1986. *The Care and Feeding of Ideas: A Guide to Encouraging Creativity.* Reading, MA: Addison-Wesley Publishing Company.

Allen, J. 1987. *As a Man Thinketh.* White Plains, NY: Peter Pauper Press.

Amen, D. G. 2008. *Magnificent Mind at Any Age: Natural Ways to Unleash Your Brain's Maximum Potential,.* New York: Three Rivers Press.

Ariely, D. 2010. *The Upside of Irrationality.* New York: HarperCollins Publishers.

Atkinson, C. 2010. *Beyond Bullet Points: Using Microsoft PowerPoint 2007 to Create Presentations that Inform, Motivate, and Inspire.* Redmond, WA: Microsoft Press.

Baggaley, A., ed. 2001. *Human Body: An Illustrated Guide to Every Part of the Human Body and How It Works.* London: Dorling Kindersley Limited.

Baumeister, R. F., and J. Tierney. 2011. *Willpower: Rediscovering the Greatest Human Strength.* New York: Penguin Press.

Belluck, P. 2001. "Nuns Offer Clues to Alzheimer's and Aging." *The New York Times,* May 7.

Benyus, J. M. 1997. *Biomimicry: Innovation Inspired by Nature.* New York: Harper Perennial.

Bonasso, S. 1983. "Can We Become More Creative?" *Civil Engineering–ASCE 53* (1): 70–72.

Bregman, P. 2011. "How (and Why) to Stop Multitasking." *Harvard Business Review,* December 4.

Brizendine, L. 2006. *The Female Brain.* New York: Broadway Books.

Brizendine, L. 2010. *The Male Brain.* New York: Three Rivers Press.

Carlson, R. 1997. *Don't Sweat the Small Stuff . . . And It's All Small Stuff: Simple Things to Keep the Little Things from Taking over Your Life.* New York: Hyperion.

Carter, R. 2009. *The Human Brain Book: An Illustrated Guide to Its Structure, Function, and Disorders.* New York: DK Publishing.

Chin, A., and S. Upson. 2011. "Head Shots." *Scientific American Mind,* November/December: 42–47.

Clayman, C. B., ed. 1991. *The Brain and the Nervous System.* Pleasantville, NY: Readers Digest Association.

Cohen, G. C. 2005. *The Mature Mind: The Positive Power of the Aging Brain.* New York: Basic Books.

Connellan, T. 2011. *The 1% Solution for Work and Life.* Chelsea, MI: Peak Performance Press.

Cooper, R. K. 2006. *Get Out of Your Own Way: The 5 Keys to Surpassing Everyone's Expectations.* New York: Crown Business.

Costa, R. D. 2010. *The Watchman's Rattle: Thinking Our Way out of Extinction.* Philadelphia: Vanguard Press.

Culp, G., and A. Smith. 2001. "Understanding Psychological Type to Improve Project Team Performance." *Journal of Management in Engineering,* ASCE 17 (1): 24–33.

Davis, L. M. 2014. "CT Scan." *eMedicineHealth.* Accessed November 13. http://www.emedicinehealth.com/ct_scan/article_em.htm.

Doidge, N. 2007. *The Brain That Changes Itself: Stories of Personal Triumph from the Frontiers of Brain Science.* New York: Penguin Books.

Duhigg, C. 2012. *The Power of Habit: Why We Do What We Do in Life and Business.* New York: Random House.

Eagleman, D. 2012. *Incognito: The Secret Lives of the Brain.* New York: Vintage Books.

Edwards, B. 1999. *Drawing on the Right Side of the Brain.* New York: Jeremy P. Tarcher/Putnam.

Finger, S. 1994. *Origins of Neuroscience: A History of Explorations into Brain Function.* New York: Oxford University Press.

Freudenrich, C., and R. Boyd. 2014. "How Your Brain Works." *HowStuffWorks.* Accessed November 10. http://science.howstuffworks.com/life/inside-the-mind/human-brain/brain2.htm.

Funnell, M. G., M. K. Colvin, and M. S. Gazzaniga. 2007. "The Calculating Hemispheres: Studies of a Split-Brain Patient." *Neuropsychologia* 45 (10): 2378–2386.

Gelb, M. J. 2004. *How to Think like Leonardo da Vinci: Seven Steps to Genius Every Day.* New York: Bantam Dell.

Gibb, B. J. 2012. *A Rough Guide to the Brain: Get to Know Your Grey Matter.* London: Rough Guides Ltd.

Gilbert, D. 2006. *Stumbling on Happiness.* New York: Vintage Books.

Gladwell, M. 2005. *Blink: The Power of Thinking without Thinking.* New York: Little, Brown and Company.

Goleman, D. 2013. *Focus: The Hidden Driver of Excellence,* New York: HarperCollins Publishers.

Hanson, R. 2013. *Hardwiring Happiness: The New Brain Science of Contentment, Calm, and Confidence.* New York: Harmony Books.

Hardiman, M. M. 2003. *Connecting Brain Research with Effective Teaching: The Brain-Targeted Teaching Model.* Lanham, MD: Rowman & Littlefield Education.

Herrmann, N. 1996. *The Whole Brain Business Book: Unlocking the Power of Whole Brain Thinking in Individuals and Organizations.* New York: McGraw-Hill.

Hill, N. 1960. *Think and Grow Rich.* New York: Fawcett Crest.

Hormone Health Network. 2014. "Hormones and Health." Accessed October 4, 2014. http://www.hormone.org/hormones-and-health.

Hughes, S. 2013. "An Active Brain throughout Life Slows Cognitive Decline." *Medscape Medical News.* Accessed July 3. http://www.medscape.com/viewarticle/807290#2.

Hutson, M. 2012. "Right Hand, Right Choice." *Scientific American Mind,* July/August: 11.

Irvine, W. B. 2015. *Aha! The Moments of Insight that Shape our World,* Oxford, UK: Oxford University Press.

Jabr, F. 2011. "How to Form a Habit," *Scientific American Mind,* January/February: 7.

Jackson, M. 2008. *Distracted: The Erosion of Attention and the Coming Dark Age.* Amherst, NY: Prometheus.

James, W. 1917. "Habits." In *Selected Papers on Philosophy.* New York: E. P. Dutton & Co.

Kay, K., and C. Shipman. 2014. "The Confidence Gap." *The Atlantic,* May.

Kleon, A. 2012. *Steal Like an Artist,* New York: Workman Publishing Company

Knapton, S. 2014. "Men and Women Do Not Have Different Brains, Claims Neuroscientist," *The Telegraph—Science News*, March 8. Accessed October 4, 2014. http://www.telegraph.co.uk/science/science-news/10684179/Men-and-women-do-not-have-different-brains-claims-neuroscientist.html.

Koch, C. 2012. "Finding Free Will." *Scientific American Mind*, May/June: 22–27.

Lagace, M. 2012. "The Unconscious Executive." *Harvard Business School Working Knowledge*, July 9. Accessed November 10, 2014. http://hbswk.hbs.edu/item/6872.html.

Lakoff, G., and M. Johnson. 1999. *Philosophy in the Flesh: The Embodied Mind and Its Challenge to Western Thought*. New York: Basic Books.

Lehrer, J. 2008. *Proust Was a Neuroscientist*. New York: Houghton Mifflin Company.

Levitin, D. J. 2006. *This Is Your Brain on Music: The Science of Human Obsession*. New York: Plume-Penguin Group.

Maltz, M., and D. S. Kennedy. 2001. *The New Psycho-Cybernetics*. New York: Prentice Hall Press.

Mandino, O. 1968. *The Greatest Salesman in the World*. New York: Bantam Books.

Martin, N. 2008. *Habit: The 95% of Behavior that Marketers Ignore*. Upper Saddle River, NJ: Pearson Education.

May, R. 1976. *The Courage to Create*. New York: Bantam Books.

MedicineNet. 2014. "Definition of Hormone." MedicineNet.com. Accessed October 4, 2014. http://www.medicinenet.com/script/main/art.asp?articlekey=3783.

Medina, J. 2008. *Brain Rules: 12 Principles for Surviving and Thriving at Work, Home, and School*. Seattle: Pear Press.

MIT. 2014. "Basic Principles of Magnetoencephalography." Accessed August 4. http://web.mit.edu/kitmitmeg/whatis.html.

McGowan, K. 2014. "The Second Coming of Sigmund Freud." *Discover*, April: 54–61.

McManus, C. 2012. "Ask the Brains." *Scientific American Mind*, May/June: 70.

Miles, E. 1997. *Tune Your Brain: Using Music to Manage Your Mind, Body, and Mood*. New York: Berkley Books.

Mlodinow, L. 2013. *Subliminal: How Your Unconscious Mind Rules Your Behavior*. New York: Vintage Books.

Murphy, J. 1963. *The Power of Your Subconscious Mind*. Englewood Cliffs, NJ: Prentice Hall.

Murphy, J. 2000. *The Power of Your Subconscious Mind*, rev. New York: Bantam Books.

National Institutes of Health. 2014. "Vitamin E." Accessed July 16. http://ods.od.nih.gov/factsheets/VitaminE-Consumer/.

Neal, D. T., W. Wood, and J. M. Quinn. 2006. "Habits: A Repeat Performance." *Current Directions in Psychological Science* 15 (4): 198–202.

NHS Choices. 2014. "Men's and Women's Brains found to be Different Sizes." February 14. Accessed October 4, 2014. http://www.nhs.uk/news/2014/02February/Pages/Mens-and-womens-brains-found-to-be-different-sizes.aspx.

Nussbaum, P. D. 2010. *Save Your Brain: Five Things You Must Do to Keep Your Mind Young and Sharp*. New York: McGraw-Hill.

Nussbaum, P. D. 2014. Personal communication to author. August 13.

Osteen, J. 2007. *Become a Better You: 7 Keys to Improving Your Life Every Day*. New York: Free Press.

Paddock, C. 2013. "Brain Wired Differently in Men and Women." *Medical News Today*, December 4. Accessed October 4, 2014. http://www.medicalnewstoday.com/articles/269652.php.

Pattison, K. 2008. "Worker, Interrupted: The Cost of Task Switching." *Fast* Company.com, July 28. Accessed July 20, 2015. http://www.fastcompany.com/944128/worker-interrupted-cost-task-switching.

Peck, M. S. 1997. *The Road Less Traveled and Beyond: Spiritual Growth in an Age of Anxiety.* New York: Simon & Schuster.

Pinker, S. 2009. *How the Mind Works.* New York: W. W. Norton & Company.

Rao, R. P. N., and A. Stocco. 2014. "When Two Brains Connect." *Scientific American Mind,* November/December: 36–39.

Restak, R. 2009. *Think Smart: A Neuroscientist's Prescription for Improving Your Brain's Performance.* New York: Riverhead Books.

Restak, R., and S. Kim. 2010. *The Playful Brain: The Surprising Science of How Puzzles Improve Your Mind.* New York: Riverhead Books.

Robinson, J. 2010. "E-mail Is Making You Stupid." *Entrepreneur,* March: 60–63.

Sharot, T. 2011. "The Optimism Bias." *Time,* June 6.

Shields, R. 2014. "Skeleton Reveals Ancient Greek Brain Surgery." *The Independent,* London, March 14.

Shlain, L. 2014. *Leonardo's Brain: Understanding da Vinci's Creative Genius.* Guilford, CT: Lyons Press.

Skaggs, W. 2014. "New Neurons for New Memories." *Scientific American Mind,* September/October: 49–53.

Snowdon, D. 2001. *Aging with Grace: What the Nun Study Teaches Us about Leading Longer, Healthier, and More Meaningful Lives.* New York: Bantam Books.

Stover, E., ed. 2014. *His Brain, Her Brain.* New York: Scientific American.

Strayer, D. L., and J. M. Watson. 2012. "Supertaskers and the Multitasking Brain." *Scientific American Mind,* March/April: 22–29.

Taylor, J. B. 2009. *My Stroke of Insight: A Brain Scientist's Personal Journey.* New York: Penguin Group.

Tice, L. 2002. "Winners Circle Network with Lou Tice." E-newsletter from *The Pacific Institute,* April 25. http://www.thepacificinstitute.com.

University of Washington. 2014. "Brain Facts and Figures." Accessed November 9. https://faculty.washington.edu/chudler/facts.html.

USGS. 2014. "The Water in You." *USGS Water School, US Geological Survey.* Accessed September 16, 2014. http://water.usgs.gov/edu/propertyyou.html.

Verplanken, B., and W. Wood. 2006. "Interventions to Break and Create Consumer Habits." *Journal of Public Policy and Marketing,* American Marketing Association 15 (1): 90–103.

Wait, M. 2009. *No More Brain Drain: Proven Ways to Maintain Your Mind and Memories.* Pleasantville, NY: The Reader's Digest Association.

Walesh, S. G. 2013. "Taking Multi-Tasking to Task," *Leadership and Management in Engineering,* ASCE, January: 61–62.

Wilson, R. S., P. A. Boyle, L. Yu, L. L. Barnes, J. A. Schneider, and D. A. Bennett. 2013. "Life-Span Cognitive Activity, Neuropathologic Burden, and Cognitive Aging." *Neurology,* July 3.

Wolf, C. C. 2013. "The Mystery of the Missed Connection." *Scientific American Mind,* January/February: 54–57.

Woolley, A., T. W. Malone, and C. F. Chabris. 2015. "Why Some Teams are Smarter than Others." *The New York Times,* January 16.

Zimmer, C. 2014. "Secrets of the Brain." *National Geographic,* February.

Zull, J. E. 2002. *The Art of Changing the Brain: Enriching the Practice of Teaching by Exploring the Biology of the Brain.* Sterling, VA: Stylus Publishing.

EXERCISES

Notes:

1. The goal of the exercises is to provide students, usually working alone, with the opportunity to think about and use the ideas, principles, and information offered in the chapter.

2. However, many circumstances and corresponding teaching/learning opportunities may arise. For example, a stated situation may be altered to meet specific concerns or needs. Rather than work with the largely hypothetical situation described in a particular exercise, an individual or team may wish to take on an actual issue, problem, or opportunity facing the team or one or more of its members. These and similar variations are encouraged, subject to the concurrence or direction of the instructor.

2.1 **BOOK REVIEW:** The purpose of this exercise is to provide you with an opportunity to study, in depth, one book about the human brain and identify the book's key ideas/information, summarize the book, critique it, and determine the book's relevance to your study and work. In so doing, you will be further introduced to the broad range of neuroscience literature, with the hope that you will continue to read critically in this area as one means of growing professionally. Suggested tasks are as follows:

   a. Tentatively select one neuroscience book. Some possible sources are books listed in the Cited Sources sections of this text's chapters, books reviewed in newspapers and magazines, books recommended by others, and books you find by searching for "brain," "neuroscience," "innovation," or similar words.

   b. Request approval of the book from your instructor.

   c. Read the book and prepare a review in which you do the following: a) Cite your book (e.g., name, author, publisher, date), b) describe some of the key information/ideas and/or theses presented in the book, c) identify the supporting evidence, d) indicate whether or not you agree with the key ideas/theses, and e) comment on the relevance, or lack thereof, to your study and work.

2.2 **ORIGINS OF A FAVORED FACILITY/PRODUCT OR SERVICE:** Have you come across or used an interesting or appealing facility, product or service? In this exercise, you will identify two creative and innovative endeavors of others.

   a. The first one will be a well-documented and commercially successful product like the iPhone, WhatsApp, Kickstarter, Fab Labs and so on. Conduct your research, and write a short report that cites all sources (e.g., websites, reference books, published articles or papers, experts) and answers questions such as the following:

   • Why do you admire the selected facility, product or service?
   • Who (an individual or a team) is credited with the original idea?
   • What motivated the creative or innovative effort? What were the circumstances? Stated differently, what issue, problem, or opportunity (IPO) was being addressed?

- How did the creative or innovative idea arise? For example, did the individual or team follow some systematic process (like those described in Chapters 4 and 7 of this text), or did the idea simply "appear?"
- What obstacles were encountered, and how were they overcome?
- What was needed (expertise, finance, legal advice, prototyping, testing) to implement the creative or innovative idea?

b. Once the first product analysis is complete, you should go around into your surroundings, trying to identify creative and innovative endeavors by common people around you. These will be undocumented innovations.

These innovations or creative solutions have come up mostly because no standard solution existed in the market and hence people tweaked available solutions or created ideas of their own. These solutions need not be huge or commercially viable. Now repeat the research answering the questions from section (a). Identify the difference between the first and second development situation and context.

2.3 RESEARCH PAPER (INDIVIDUAL STUDENT VERSION): The intent of this exercise is to provide you with a means of studying, in depth, a neuroscience-related topic largely of your choice. This can broaden and deepen your knowledge, increase your awareness of neuroscience literature and other resources, and strengthen your research and writing abilities. Suggested tasks are as follows:

a. Select a neuroscience-related topic. To get you started, but at the risk of unintentionally confining your thinking, drill down into one of the brain basics discussed in this chapter or refer to the topics listed in Section 2.17.

b. Request approval of the topic by the instructor.

c. Research your topic by drawing on a variety of sources. Consider using one or more personal sources that you contact in person or by telephone, e-mail, or letter. If you use a personal contact, cite that contact at the end of your paper using this format: Smith, J. A., 2015. Director of Engineering, XYZ Company, Chicago, IL. Personal communication via email. October 27.

d. Write the paper. Assume your principal readers are engineering or other technical profession students who know little about your topic.

2.4 EXPLORING GENDER AND THE BRAIN: Diverse teams, including gender-diverse teams, tend to deliver highly creative and innovative results. Repeat exercise 2.2 (b) in teams. Form three types of team: a. Male only; b. Female only; c. Gender-mixed. As a class, discuss the similarities and differences in approach (if any) within teams.

2.5 MUCH MORE THAN A COMPUTER: Think of your favorite material possession. Now consciously imagine how you would destroy it. Describe the destruction process you would use and your likely emotions during the process. (Adapted from Adams 1986.)

2.6 ONE AT A TIME: Take one minute and think about as many things as possible that you did yesterday. Make a note for each one and count them when you finish. Then reflect on and answer this question: Regardless of how many things you identified, were you ever thinking of two or more at the same time—that is, in parallel? (Adapted from Adams 1986.)

2.7 HABIT CHANGE: Do you waste food, water, electricity, gasoline, money, time, health or any other resource for that matter? Identify one such bad habit, where you waste a resource, and which you would like to change. Next, identify the cue which triggers you into this habit. Commit for one month to recognizing the cue, trying a new routine in response to the cue, assessing the "reward," recognizing the cue the next time it occurs, and refining the new routine as needed. This process takes great self-discipline, but it works, based on my experience and (more importantly) neuroscience.

Document your experience each time you go through the cue-routine-result cycle. Depending on the nature of the bad habit selected and the cue-routine-reward cycle, you can choose to share it or not with the instructor.

After a month-long commitment, you can also discuss the cue-routine-result cycle that you followed with a friend and see if the same works with your friend as well. Suggestions on improving the cycle can also be sought. This part of the exercise is optional and can be taken up at the discretion of the student.

2.8 **TAKING MULTITASKING TO TASK:** Multitasking is a matter of habit as well. Carefully observe yourself for a week and identify the cues that trigger multitasking in you. For the next one week, use the cue-routine-result cycle as mentioned in exercise 2.7. Did the habit change method help you in avoiding or reducing multitasking? Did focusing on one task at a time improve your efficiency and reduce your error rate? Prepare a brief summary of your experience.

3

Prelude to Whole-Brain Methods

> Begin with the end in mind.
> —*Stephen R. Covey, leadership expert*

Objectives:

After studying this chapter, you will be able to:

- Illustrate the universality of the divergent-convergent thinking process when resolving an issue, solving a problem, or pursuing an opportunity
- Explain how whole-brain methods enable intentional creativity and innovation
- Articulate the importance of method selection
- Discuss the value of using a series of multiple methods on many types of projects

- Show the limiting consequences of relying solely on the Einstellung Effect
- Report how we know that methods work
- Demonstrate the potential value of errors and accidents
- Summarize why a few methods are only good for individual or group use
- Review the fundamentals of facilitation

3.1 THE MORE IDEAS, THE BETTER

When faced with a well-defined issue, problem, or opportunity (IPO), we typically begin by developing a list of ideas or options. This is divergent thinking, as shown at the top of Figure 3.1. Then, we explore the pros and cons of each idea or option, make a decision, and act on it. This is convergent thinking, also shown at the top of Figure 3.1.

The quality of any of our decisions at any point in an endeavor, whether arrived at individually or as a team, is likely to be better when we consider more ideas (more

Figure 3.1
The useful divergent-convergent thinking process can generate even more ideas or options to define and resolve a challenge when it is enhanced with whole-brain tools.

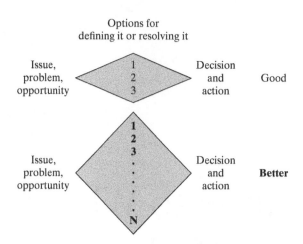

options), as shown in the bottom of Figure 3.1. The value of more ideas is widely applicable in engineering; it enhances our ability to address challenges we face with structures, facilities, systems, products, and processes as well as nontechnical challenges. We want the divergent thinking effort to be rich and varied. In the world of idea generation, more is usually better! Scientist Pauling said, "The best way to have a good idea is to have lots of ideas." American writer Steinbeck put it this way: "Ideas are like rabbits. You get a couple, and learn how to handle them, and pretty soon you have a dozen."

This *early on, more is better* concept applies whether we are striving to *define* an IPO or endeavoring to *resolve* one. For example, some of the whole-brain tools described in this text will enable you and/or your team to generate many more ideas about the possible causes of a problem in the divergent portion of the divergent-convergent process and then zero in on the most likely cause in the convergent portion. Similarly, some tools will help you generate options for solving the problem within the divergent portion of the divergent-convergent process and then select the best solution in the convergent portion.

Whether you are attempting to define or resolve an IPO, separate your and/or your group's divergent and convergent thinking to maximize idea generation. Do the divergent part thoroughly before even thinking about the convergent part. Don't mix the two cognitive processes, and don't rush through either of them, lest you fail to do either one well. Furthermore, remember what you learned about the subconscious mind in Section 2.9 and try to practice both divergent and convergent thinking intermittently to engage and benefit from the 24-7 subconscious thinking of all participants.

3.2 THE TOOLBOX

Let's introduce and begin to explore a toolbox with contents that will enable you to take a whole-brain approach. Although these are just tools, recognize that in the right hands—yours and those of your teammates—they can help you be creative and innovative.

3.2.1 Many Methods

Fortunately, many methods are available to help you engage both cranial hemispheres, whether working alone or in collaboration with others. You can employ your conscious and subconscious minds and make use of other brain basics

Table 3.1 Twenty whole-brain methods are described in this text.

Method	Applicability		User		
	Definition of an Issue, Problem, Opportunity	Resolution of an Issue, Problem, Opportunity	Individual	Team	Highly Visual?
In Chapter 4					
Ask-Ask-Ask	X	X	X	X	No
Borrowing Brilliance	X	X	X	X	No
Brainstorming	X	X	X	X	No
Fishbone Diagramming	X	–	X	X	Yes
Medici Effect	X	X	–	X	No
Mind Mapping	X	X	X	X	Yes
Ohno Circle	X	–	X	–	Yes
Stream of Consciousness Writing	X	X	X	X	No
SWOT	X	–	X	X	Yes
Taking a Break	X	X	X	X	No
What If?	X	X	X	X	No
In Chapter 7					
Biomimicry	–	X	X	X	Yes
Challenges and Ideas Meetings	X	X	–	X	No
Freehand Drawing	X	X	X	X	Yes
Music	X	X	X	–	No
Process Diagramming	X	X	X	X	Yes
Six Thinking Caps	X	X	X	X	Yes
Supportive Culture and Physical Environment	X	X	X	X	Yes
TRIZ: Theory of Inventive Problem Solving	X	X	X	X	No
Taking Time to Think	X	X	X	–	Yes

described in the Chapter 2 so that you can more creatively and innovatively address IPOs. Table 3.1 lists twenty whole-brain methods described in this text. The items in this cognitive toolkit will stimulate you and, more powerfully, your group to think more deeply and widely. Your group might focus on a project, planning, design, research, experimental, marketing, or another area. Your group's goal is to generate more ideas, analyze them, explore many and varied optional courses of action, select from among them, and implement the best choice.

Do you or your team miss the satisfaction of creating and innovating? Maybe you're not in your right mind—or more precisely, not in your right mind *enough*. This book's methods, as introduced in Table 3.1, will get you there. This text's methods support the idea that "a problem well-stated is a problem half-solved," as stated by engineer and inventor Kettering. "If we really understand the problem, the answer will come out of it," according to Indian philosopher Krishnamurti, "because the answer is not separate from the problem." As shown by the second column in

Table 3.1, essentially all of the twenty methods can help you define an IPO. The second and third columns indicate that most of the methods are applicable in both defining an IPO and for resolving it. Columns four and five reveal that most of the methods can be used by an individual or group. Finally, half of the methods are highly visual, as noted in the last column.

The methods in this text's toolbox stimulate more right-brain activity to supplement your left-brain activity and, as a result, yield more creativity and innovation. Rather than relying only on what Gerard Nierenberg, author of *The Art of Creative Thinking* (1982), calls "accidental creativity," these methods facilitate intentional creativity and innovation by engaging both hemispheres, the conscious and unconscious minds, and the synergism among all of them.

We cannot will ourselves to be more creative and innovative. Instead, we need stimulating techniques to steer us away from conventional thinking (Michalko 2001). The Russian inventor Altshuller (1996), while acknowledging that trial and error works, argues for a more systematic approach, such as his Theory of Inventive Problem Solving, one of this book's methods (Section 7.9). Creative and innovative work will always require some trial and error, but why not minimize it?

Having made a case for a more systematic and intentional approach, I will note that there seems to be a tendency to believe that creativity and innovation are more accidental than intentional, more the result of inspiration than perspiration, and like magic and limited to very few of us. A 2013 survey (Kluger 2013) asked 2,040 consumers this question: "Does it take a lot of time thinking about a problem to produce creative ideas, or are they usually sparked by sudden inspiration?" About 60 percent of the respondents selected "sudden inspiration." The accident-inspiration-magic approach will produce some creativity and innovation, but much less than if we proactively pursue it.

Creative and innovative ideas lie within most of us, but we need mechanisms to release them. "We know where most of the creativity, the innovation, the stuff that drives productivity lies," according to former GE Chairman Welch, "in the minds of those closest to the work." We need methods to engage those minds and synergistically release that creativity. Good news: You and your team and organization are loaded with creative and innovative ideas; you and those you work with are a gold mine of creativity and innovation. You need only to mine the gold using whole-brain methods.

3.2.2 Just Tools

I sometimes refer to the whole-brain methods we are about to discuss as *tools*. In doing so, I am suggesting that we should avoid fancy-sounding euphemisms, such as associative thinking methodologies, creativity/innovation stimulation devices, or neuro-optimization techniques. I choose to suggest that the methods in this text—like the tools you have in your shop, at your desk, in your laboratory, or on your computer—should be viewed by you as readily available aids that you select and apply as needed.

Some methods can be explained and then applied somewhat methodically—that is, in step-by-step manner—such as Brainstorming, Fishbone Diagramming, Mind Mapping, Strength-Weaknesses-Opportunities-Threats (SWOT), and Process Diagramming. Other methods are more of a way of thinking about an IPO, a manner used to approach a challenge, an attitude taken when faced with a complex situation, or an environment in which good things happen—for example, Borrowing Brilliance, Medici Effect, Taking a Break, What If?, Freehand Drawing, Supportive Culture and Physical Environment, and Taking Time to Think. I mention this spectrum of methods, ranging from methodical to attitudinal in how they are described, to prepare you for the discussions in Chapters 4 and 7.

Although the features of each method are important, equally important is your or your group's ability, acquired through experience, to select the most appropriate tools for a given situation and use them effectively and efficiently. You may be able to drive a nail with the handle of a screwdriver, but a hammer produces better results—and while both ball-peen and claw hammers can drive nails, the latter can also remove them.

3.2.3 Breaking Barriers

Application of the Medici Effect, which means assembling and then energizing a highly diverse group, is discussed in Section 4.6. Various kinds of diversity are available and desirable, including people with markedly different organizational power. Individuals such as presidents, department heads, mayors, and other highly placed individuals accustomed to being on top of things and always in control may be reluctant to wholeheartedly participate in open discussions seeking creative and innovative resolution of IPOs. Nevertheless, they can be valuable sources of knowledge and experience (Brenner 2014). Because of their structure and full-participation expectation, whole-brain methods can relax such constraints and engage individuals who tend to be reserved and guarded in normal interactions within highly diverse groups. This assumes that the initial "ice" has been broken, as discussed in Section 3.8.4.

3.2.4 Free to Be Foolish

Asimov, biochemistry professor and prolific author of popular science books, suggests that the creative and innovative process can be embarrassing. "For every good idea you have, there are a hundred . . . foolish ones, which you naturally do not care to display." The path to creatively and innovatively resolving the current IPO requires the freedom to be foolish, daring, unreasonable, unconventional, and eccentric, and, to use Asimov's words, to "fly in the face of reason, authority, and common sense." He notes that initially suggesting that the earth was round instead of flat or that it moved around the sun seemed very unreasonable (Asimov 2014).

You or I, when working and thinking alone, may be able to free ourselves to be at least temporarily foolish, but we may have difficulty doing so when interacting with our teams. We are naturally likely to be inhibited and fearful of embarrassment, and want to act "professional." One way to enable temporary foolish, daring, unreasonable, unconventional, and eccentric thinking and behavior is to use the methods described in this text, especially when working in a group setting. A given method can be viewed as a game we agree to play as we divert attention from personal concerns and foolishly generate lot of ideas, out of which comes an amazing solution. That solution often will seem obvious after the fact and cause us to wonder how anyone could have initially labeled it as foolish. For example, why did we put a person on the moon before we put wheels on luggage?

3.2.5 Using Multiple Methods

As will become more apparent, many whole-brain methods are available, with each intended for one or more circumstances or purposes. Just as you might use a series of software tools to complete a class assignment or tools available on your workbench to work on your car or complete a home project, so too you can use a series of creativity and innovation methods to conduct a project.

Figure 3.2
A team might use a series of methods to define and then solve a problem.

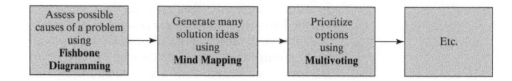

For example, assume your team wants to solve a problem. As shown in Figure 3.2, your group might use Fishbone Diagramming to thoroughly explore the possible causes of the problem. After selecting the most likely causes and building on that broad understanding, Mind Mapping might be used to generate many potential solutions, which could then be prioritized using Multivoting, which is presented in Section 4.4.2 as a supplemental tool. After identifying the highest-priority solution, the team might discuss how to implement it and, in doing so, use one or more additional methods.

As an individual, you might use the Ohno Circle to observe and define a problem (Figure 3.3). Then, you could engage an interested group in Brainstorming to generate many solution ideas, and then thoroughly analyze the options using Six Thinking Caps. You and/or the team might then use other methods to explore ways to implement the selected solution.

3.3 A TWO-CHAPTER APPROACH

The twenty whole-brain methods offered in this book are presented in Chapters 4 and 7. This two-chapter format is intended to help you appreciate the diversity of the described methods as reflected by factors such as the effort required to understand and apply them, their use by individuals and teams, how they draw on brain basics, the many functions they perform, their positive and negative features, and the kinds of results they produce.

Accordingly, Chapter 4 includes eleven methods, which differ in important ways, and that can be quickly learned and applied to yield useful results. For example, traditional Brainstorming is quickly understood and generates many ideas in the form of a list. In contrast, Mind Mapping—which may be viewed as a highly visual and nonlinear form of brainstorming—typically produces more ideas. As indicated in Table 3.1, very few of these methods only address IPO definition or IPO resolution; most are applicable to both functions. Most of the Chapter 4 methods can be used by an individual or by a team. Chapter 4 alone offers a powerful toolbox that you and/or your group can readily use.

For those who want an even larger toolbox, Chapter 7 offers nine additional, more advanced methods (Table 3.1). Almost all of these methods apply to IPO definition and resolution, and most can be applied by an individual or a group. These advanced methods typically take more time to understand and effectively apply, and that effort might be rewarded by even better results. For example, Six Thinking Caps, a team procedure, requires special props, a detailed explanation, and an effective facilitator. However, in return, this method can fully engage participants by expecting all team members to serially focus on specific aspects of an

Figure 3.3
An individual might apply one method to define a problem and then engage a team using more methods to resolve it.

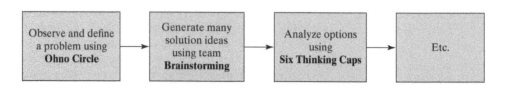

IPO, such as facts, emotion, risks, hope, creativity and innovation, and organization and control.

A first-year, introductory, *exploring engineering* type of course that uses this book may readily achieve its creativity and innovation learning objectives by using Chapter 4. The Chapter 7 methods are available for students to use in subsequent undergraduate or graduate courses and in professional practice.

3.4 AVOIDING THE EINSTELLUNG EFFECT TRAP

Another way to view the methods in Chapters 4 and 7 is to recognize the need to set aside, at least temporarily, old ideas and processes, even though they have worked and can work. As noted by change thinker Maxwell (2003), "The difficulty lays not so much in developing new ideas as in escaping from the old ones." The methods described and illustrated in this text can help you and your team escape from doing what you have always done, or at least supplement or parallel your traditional approaches with potentially powerful new thinking methods.

More specifically, this text's methods can help you complement the traditional approach called the Einstellung Effect (Brooks 2011). The German word *einstellung* means approach, mind set, or attitude. The Einstellung Effect means trying to resolve an IPO only by using approaches, mind sets, or attitudes that have worked in similar situations, rather than looking at each new situation on its own terms. This dogged tendency "sometimes blinds people to more efficient or appropriate solutions than the ones they already know" (Bilalic and McLeod 2014).

Another term for this creativity/innovation barrier is *design fixation*, defined as an "unintentional adherence to set of ideas or concepts limiting the output of the conceptual design" (Genco, Holtta-Otto, and Seepersad 2012). The ominous word in that sentence is *unintentional*; it reminds us that we may unknowingly or habitually rule out a fresh perspective. We may welcome a new challenge and be committed to resolving it but be unwittingly locked into the past. This predisposition to familiarity may prevent consideration of much better approaches.

Engineering professor McCuen (2012) explains the Einstellung Effect by putting it in the context of the following four-step process:

1. **Observation:** "Facts are collected and observations are made on the system."
2. **Recollection:** "Past experience is reviewed and solutions to similar problems in the past are identified."
3. **Reasoning:** "The pros and cons of the possible decisions are identified and the implication of each alternative stated."
4. **Decision:** "The best alternative is selected."

This traditional, time-proven engineering approach is sound. It's resulted in untold numbers of successful engineered structures, facilities, systems, products, and processes. So why the concern? Why question it and mess with success?

Looking at McCuen's crisp, four-step description of the standard operating procedure (SOP), I'm most concerned about Step 2, which only focuses on similar past problems and their solutions. Shouldn't we try to do more than rehash old solutions—successful as they may have been? Might we find great value in also exploring fundamentally new approaches? How can we resist the Einstellung Effect?

The first part of the answer to the last question is to be aware of the effect, and that's the major reason I present it in this text. We can't fix something if we don't know it exists. Couple being aware of the Einstellung Effect with using this text's combination of relevant neuroscience and whole-brain methods. Consider the tried-and-true approach to address a given IPO while paralleling it with a fresh perspective, a whole-brain approach. The French philosopher Bergson in effect warned us about the Einstellung Effect trap when he said that our eyes see only what our mind is inclined to comprehend. We should prepare our minds to comprehend more than what we have done in the past.

VIEWS OF OTHERS: THINK FRESH

Consider reflections on the *same old, same old* approach from a variety of individuals. "Given that most engineers are exposed to a plethora of existing engineered products or systems, the prevalence of design fixation is a significant concern because it indicates that engineers may find it difficult to generate original or creative solutions" (Genco, Holtta-Otto, and Seepersad 2012). "Business [people] go down with their businesses because they like the old way so well they cannot bring themselves to change," according to Ford, who led the development of the automobile assembly line. He went on to say that they are people "who do not know that yesterday is past and who woke up this morning with their last year's idea" (Brinkley 2003). If his sentiment was true over a century ago, think how much more applicable it is in today's dynamic global and technical environment. Commenting on our reaction to reflecting on someone else's creative experience, author May (1976) asks, "Why were we so stupid as to not have seen it earlier?" He goes on to provide the answer: "We were not psychologically ready to see it"; in other words, we habitually fall into the same old approach. We are stung by Einstellung.

3.5 HOW DO WE KNOW THE METHODS WORK?

I am confident you will benefit significantly from the whole-brain methods described in Chapters 4 and 7, based on the following three types of evidence:

1. **Personal experience:** I have successfully used some of the methods in my engineering, management, teaching, and facilitation work.
2. **Observation of students and practitioners:** I consistently see and hear animated conversation and enthusiasm and then observe results when students in a classroom or practitioners in a conference room are invited to form small groups and use whole-brain methods to creatively/innovatively address hypothetical or real IPOs. Overwhelmingly positive post-event evaluations by participants reinforce my observations.
3. **Neuroscience findings:** Scientists tell us that we can't use more of our brain, because our whole brain is working all the time, but we can make our brain work more productively. The following three brain-oriented strategies are available to those of us who want to be more creative and innovative:
   - The first is to *focus, to stay on task*: "By concentrating, your brain can master the neural tools it needs to tackle a complex problem" (Gordon 2012). Research reveals that "our performance deteriorates drastically when we attempt to focus on more than one task at a time" (Strayer and Watson 2012). Therefore, a group's use of a whole-brain method to define and resolve an IPO is one way to focus for a prescribed time period. The methods provide "social glue" (Cain 2012) to bind diverse individuals, for at least a short

period of time, in a fruitful collaborative process. As Einstein said, "It's not that I'm so smart; it's just that I stay with problems longer."

- The second brain-oriented strategy is to *escape established ways of thinking*—that is, seek a wider variety of possible answers by "looking beyond your personal biases and blind spots to consider [even more] possible solutions" (Gordon 2012). Methods help us to escape from or to complement the previously-discussed Einstellung Effect or design fixation. "Recent studies show promise for techniques that break down people's established ways of viewing the world" (Chrysikou 2012). Most of the methods described in Chapters 4 and 7 enable individuals and groups to take a much wider view of possibilities than they would without the methods.

- Finally, studies reveal great promise for thinking methods that *encourage subconscious thought processes* (Chrysikou 2012; Dijksterhuis and Meurs 2006). For example, based on experiments by Dijksterhuis and Meurs, they "concluded that whereas conscious thought may be focused and convergent, unconscious thought may be more associative and divergent." Some of the whole-brain methods presented in Chapters 4 and 7 explicitly engage the subconscious mind, such as Stream of Consciousness Writing and Taking a Break. However, all the methods can leverage the subconscious minds of participants if the process is used intermittently. That is, apply a method as an individual or as a group, put it aside for a day or so, and then resume and expect fresh insights.

3.6 HOPING FOR FORTUITOUS ERRORS AND ACCIDENTS

While applying whole-brain methods, expect—better yet, hope for—errors and accidents. They can be the stuff of creativity and innovation. I don't want you and/or your team's errors or accidents to cause physical harm to you or others or to result in great economic loss or other problems. However, some embarrassment or ego deflation is acceptable and, as suggested by the following five examples, can be very fruitful.

3.6.1 Cardiac Pacemaker

While a student at Cornell in 1951, electrical engineer Greatbatch learned from surgeons about the danger of irregular heartbeats. Five years later, while teaching electrical engineering in Buffalo, New York, and perhaps guided subconsciously by the danger of irregular heartbeats, he helped a physician by developing an oscillator that could record human heartbeats using silicon transistors, which at the time were replacing vacuum tubes.

While working with the device, he inserted the wrong resistor into the oscillator. Because of that error, the device simulated heartbeats rather than recording them, which in turn stimulated Greatbatch and the physician, Chardack, to develop the cardiac pacemaker. Two years after the error, a cardiac pacemaker was successfully implanted in a dog's heart. By 1960, pacemakers were functioning within ten human hearts, and pacemakers have now lengthened the lives of millions of people around the world. Besides illustrating a fruitful accident, this story points to the role of engineering in medicine (Beakley, Evans, and Keats 1986; Johnson 2010).

3.6.2 Vulcanization

Think of some of the uses of rubber: balls, boots, erasers, floor mats, gloves, rubber bands, and tires. We owe these products to the worker, dreamer, self-taught scientist-engineer, and entrepreneur Goodyear (Kumar and Nijasure 1997; Mann 2011;

Somma 2014). His obsessive venture that eventually led to commercialization of rubber began in New Haven, Connecticut, in the mid-1800s. At that time, milky sap bled from trees in Brazil became a crude form of rubber when it hardened. This rudimentary rubber held promise because it could be molded into various forms and was impervious to water. However, on the negative side, this early rubber cracked in the winter cold and melted in the summer heat. The rubber industry was in need of a temperature-stable version.

Goodyear devoted five years to experimenting with various rubber and chemical mixes, sometimes in his kitchen. In 1839, after suffering financial, health, family, and other setbacks, he accidentally spilled a portion of rubber, sulfur, and other ingredients on a hot stove. The rubber did not melt, and its interior retained its shape and elasticity at high temperature. The persistent Goodyear had discovered a way to produce temperature-stable rubber. He worked for several more years and received a US patent in 1844 (ten years after taking on the challenge) for the process called vulcanization, after Vulcan, the Roman fire god.

Somehow, a sample of Goodyear's practical rubber was obtained and studied by the English engineer Hancock. He claimed the vulcanization process as his and also obtained a patent from the British government in 1844. Although both Goodyear and Hancock knew how to cause vulcanization, neither understood the chemistry behind why it worked, that sulfide bridges connect rubber polymer chains.

In 1860, Charles Goodyear died in debt, having never been able to overcome his financial circumstances and the health and family price he paid. We may be reminded of his persistent creativity and innovation when we use a rubber product, see the Goodyear blimp, or think of the Goodyear Tire and Rubber Company, which was named in Goodyear's honor but had no direct connection to him.

3.6.3 Photosynthesis

Scientist and clergyman Priestly put a mint plant in a sealed jar in about 1773 and expected it to die, like similarly placed spiders and mice. He was wrong: The plant thrived and did so even when he burned the oxygen from the jar. Priestly discovered, contrary to his erroneous hypothesis, that plants produced oxygen via photosynthesis. Oh, that we could make such a productive mistake! As a child, Priestly trapped spiders in glass jars and watched and wondered why they died. Perhaps his subconscious mind had been pondering the mysteries of sealed glass jars for decades (Johnson 2010).

3.6.4 Microwave Oven

In 1946, self-taught electrical engineer Spencer was working at Raytheon on a team that was building a magnetron—that is, an electron tube used to generate alternating currents at microwave frequencies and used in radar. During an experiment with electromagnetic radiation, he noticed that a candy bar in his pocket melted. This little accident led to the big invention of a way to cook with high-frequency radio waves: the microwave oven, which early on was called the radar range (Johnson 2010; Murray 1958). Would you like to have an accident like that?

3.6.5 Penicillin

In 1928, Scottish biologist Alexander Fleming, while conducting research on antibacterial substances, inadvertently contaminated one of his slides with the mold *Penicillium notatum*. Later, he noticed a circle around the mold that was free of bacteria. Maybe the mold came through an open window or from a crumb of moldy bread. Regardless, this accident led to the discovery of penicillin, as named by

Fleming, which destroys bacteria that cause many types of infections and inspired scientists to develop other antibacterial drugs (Johnson 2010; Van Doren 1991).

3.6.6 Errors and Accidents: Learning Opportunities

When accidents or errors occur, see them as opportunities to learn what not to do and gain insight about what to do next. Take comfort in British economist Jevons' observation that "in all probability the errors of the great mind exceed in number those of the less vigorous one" (Johnson 2010). You and/or your team may be in good company, and that last accident or error may be the door to a creative or innovative result.

Of course, we all like to be right and to avoid errors and accidents, but try to put that aside as you seek creative and innovative approaches to IPOs. Recognize that "being right keeps you in place. Being wrong forces you to explore" (Johnson 2010). Finally, consider the advice of Bonasso (2005), engineer, inventor, and entrepreneur: "Success is when we predict something will happen and it happens. Failure is when we predict something will happen and something else happens." Remember that failure provides new information. Success isn't final, and failure isn't fatal.

3.7 CAVEATS

Before I begin to describe and, in most cases, illustrate the use of whole-brain methods, consider some caveats. I already mentioned one: Successful use of the methods depends on your and/or your group's prudent selection and wise use of one or more of them. Here are some other factors to consider when selecting and using the whole-brain methods described in Chapters 4 and 7:

- **Individual versus team use:** As indicated in Table 3.1, only a few of the methods are intended for use only by an individual and a few others only by a team or group. However, importantly, almost all methods can be used by an individual *or* by a team or group.
- **Inconsistent names:** The methods are named, by and large, using their formal or most common names. Accordingly, the names come from many and varied sources and are not in a consistent style. Furthermore, some names are descriptive and/or familiar (e.g., Brainstorming and Freehand Drawing), whereas others are not very informative (e.g., Mind Mapping and Six Thinking Caps). Because many of the names are not descriptive, if a particular one attracts your attention for whatever reason, simply go directly to its description to quickly determine the tool's essence. With one exception (Taking Time to Think), the methods are arranged alphabetically in each part of Table 3.1 and in Chapters 4 and 7 for quick access.
- **Not mutually exclusive:** The methods are not mutually exclusive; some overlap with others. For example, Brainstorming and Mind Mapping have common elements. However, the latter is more visual and less likely to be viewed as a linear, one-idea-follows-another, left-brain listing process.
- **Define challenges and then address them:** As shown in Table 3.1, a few methods facilitate only IPO definition, and one supports only resolving an IPO. For example, Fishbone Diagramming is effective for exploring possible causes of a problem or determining the likely facets of a challenge. In contrast, Biomimicry focuses on finding the "best" solution to a problem. As appropriate, these strengths are noted when the individual methods are discussed.
- **Individual and group use of multiple methods:** Creatively or innovatively addressing an issue, solving a problem, or pursuing an opportunity is likely to

engage several to many methods. Furthermore, during that process, some methods will be used by a team or group and others by individual members of the team or group.

- **Wide applicability:** Please remember that although I am an engineer writing to students of engineering and other scientific and technical professions, essentially all of the whole-brain methods are applicable in both technical and nontechnical areas. That is, although the methods can be applied to planning, design, research, experimentation, IT, and other technical areas, they can also be used to address marketing, finance, project management, human resources, strategic planning, and other nontechnical areas or processes.

  Besides being applicable to widely varying functions, creativity and innovation would seem to be important in all professions, thus further expanding the potential uses of these methods. Finally, the methods described in this chapter are readily used outside of the education and work spheres—that is, in your community, family, and personal lives.

Soon, you will have access to and understanding of a large set of highly varied, whole-brain tools. Their use builds on the foundation of the brain basics described in Chapter 2. Most of the methods can be used by an individual or by a team or group. The methods are not mutually exclusive. Some help define a challenge, some assist in resolving it, and most do both. Multiple methods are likely to be used by individuals and by a team in addressing an issue, solving a problem, or pursuing an opportunity. Finally, the toolbox can be used for technical and nontechnical challenges—both within engineering and in other professions and beyond.

3.8 FACILITATION

We turn now to facilitation, a process you are likely to benefit from and hopefully lead. After describing the need for facilitation, I describe the work of the facilitator before, during, and after a facilitated session.

3.8.1 What Is Facilitation?

Section 3.2.1 noted that almost all of the twenty whole-brain methods presented in this text can be used productively by teams or groups. Most team or group discussions of any IPO can be enhanced and often greatly improved, as indicated by the value of the outcomes, through the efforts of a facilitator, who strives to enable all members to do their best thinking and to effectively share the resulting thoughts so that the group benefits from the synergism. One indication of a facilitator's success is that an IPO is resolved and all participants know that they have contributed.

Facilitation is introduced now in this text because Chapters 4 and 7 describe and illustrate many whole-brain methods. When your team or group applies these tools, facilitation will enhance your effectiveness; by definition, such methods are intended to stimulate thinking in new directions. New-direction thinking is hard for some of us and will need nudging, which is one of a facilitator's roles.

You may already have benefitted as an engineering student or practitioner from the efforts of a facilitator, or maybe you have been a facilitator. Be assured that as you go forward in your career you will participate in many more facilitated sessions and have opportunities, which I urge you to accept, to serve as the facilitator. While preparing for and performing facilitation, you will grow and you will contribute to your team's or group's efforts. Traditional group discussions that are not facilitated are far more commonly encountered, but you and others in your group should at least experiment with the much more productive facilitation approach the next time you take on an IPO.

One way to consider the merits of facilitation is to review the tendencies listed in Table 3.2. The left column lists tendencies, not certainties, associated with traditional group discussions that are not assisted by a facilitator. The right column presents the much more positive and productive tendencies associated with facilitated discussions.

Table 3.2   Traditional versus facilitated team or group discussions tend to exhibit very different interaction environments and, as a result, produce very different outcomes, with the facilitated discussions being much more productive.

In traditional group discussions, the tendency is for. . .	In facilitated group discussions, the tendency is for. . .
. . .a few aggressive/articulate individuals to dominate the discussion and to overly influence the results.	. . .everyone to participate because they are expected to and because, if they don't, the facilitator will engage them.
. . .participants to frequently interrupt, as in "If I don't state my view now, I may not get the chance."	. . .participants to allow others to express themselves because everyone is expected to contribute and have opportunities to do so. "I'll listen to your idea because I know I will get a turn to share mine."
. . .participants to listen for what they want to hear or to not listen, because they feel compelled to push their agenda right now, lest things get out of hand. They do not want to hear contrary views, which must then be disputed in a combative manner.	. . .participants to listen to others, even those with very contrary views, because they know they will be able to question them and be able to offer their views.
. . .different views to be seen as problems or potential conflicts that must be ignored, challenged, or quickly resolved.	. . .different views to be taken as positive inputs and as having the potential to ultimately help resolve the issue, problem, or opportunity at hand.
. . .probing questions to be viewed as challenges, or even threats, to be dealt with in a protective or defensive manner.	. . .probing questions to be viewed as desirable means to understand the views of others and the breadth and depth of the challenge faced by the group.
. . .deep disagreements to be ill-defined or denied and then carried outside of the group and shared with others, most of whom are not in a position to resolve the matter.	. . .deep disagreements to be acknowledged, discussed, understood, and resolved within the group.
. . .the real discussions and the real decisions to be made outside of the group discussions, because the members lack a common vision or goal and mistrust prevails. "The three of us know what's best; the others don't know how things work around here. Let's go through the motions with the team and then get together and make it happen our way."	. . .the real discussions and the real decisions to be made within the group. What you see is what you get in that all significant business is conducted in the groups. "That's a different idea. Let's take it to the team and see if it flies."
. . .an IPO to be considered resolved when the fastest, most aggressive "thinkers" announce the course of action. Others are expected to go along.	. . .an IPO to be considered resolved when essentially all participants involved in the decision making and all stakeholders affected by the selected course of action understand the reasoning, and most support what has been decided.

Source: Adapted, in part, from Kaner et al. 1996.

3.8.2 Who Is the Facilitator?

Sometimes, the chair or leader of a committee, project team, or other group has the knowledge, skills, and attitudes to serve as the facilitator when certain topics are discussed. If the chair or leader is not an effective facilitator or is unable to take a neutral stance in a particular situation, then he or she could ask someone else within the group to serve as facilitator. A third option is to arrange for an outside facilitator, someone who is not a member of the group. This third option can be the best choice when a potentially contentious IPO must be addressed and/or when special subject experience and knowledge are needed.

Let's further explore facilitation by seeing the process from the facilitator's perspective, or maybe from your perspective as a potential facilitator. More specifically, consider how the facilitator might prepare for, conduct, and follow up on a facilitated discussion. I've drawn on my facilitation and meeting experiences (Walesh 2012) and on ideas offered by others (Kaner el al. 1996; McCuen 2014). Review the many suggestions and select those most suited to your facilitation situation.

3.8.3 How Does the Facilitator Prepare to Facilitate?

The sound advice to *plan your work and work your plan* (PYWAWYP) certainly applies for the facilitator. He or she should consider the following while preparing for the facilitation:

- Understand the IPO to be addressed by the group. If it is not already articulated and documented in writing, make that happen, and then frequently refer to it and sometimes quote it. Groups of smart and energetic people can easily go off on a tangent, and it's your job, beginning with planning the first session, to keep the group on target.
- Influence the diversity of the group, to the extent you can. For an in-depth discussion of the meaning and value of diversity, refer to Section 4.6, "Medici Effect."
- If you can, affect the size of the group. Somewhere in the range of five to ten members will provide enough individuals to assure diversity and not so many as to become unwieldy.
- Select the methods that you believe will be most effective with the group and for the IPO. Candidates include many of the methods described in Chapters 4 and 7.

PERSONAL: METHODS USED IN FACILITATION

As part of my work, I have facilitated sessions using some of this book's methods. For example, SWOT, Freehand Drawing, and Six Thinking Caps helped groups define challenging situations. In other cases, Brainstorming and Mind Mapping generated many and varied options for teams. In one case, a combination of What If? and Mind Mapping enabled a group to more fully explore the possible implications of two viable and very different courses of action. Using methods like these always seems to produce better results than if the facilitation had proceeded without them. The tools are effective because they are highly visual, they focus the participants, and they encourage whole-brain thinking.

- Arrange the on-site logistics. Select an attractive, well-lit room. Have a large table with comfortable chairs for participants on three sides and, if you care to sit, for you on the fourth side, so that participants can see each other and you and you can see all of them. Avoid classroom-style seating, which impedes face-to-face communication among participants. Regardless of the methods you plan to use, you are likely to need a newsprint pad on a tripod, a whiteboard, or another means to record progress in real time during the session. Consider arranging for someone else to assist with recording results. Prepare handouts and arrange for special equipment, props, or other items that may be needed. The devil is in the details.
- Ask some members of the team or group to do specific tasks in preparation for the upcoming meeting. For example, be prepared to brief the participants on some aspect of the challenge, arrange for special equipment, host a new member or visitor, or bring refreshments. Asking people to do "jobs" engages them in the overall effort, causes them to think about the upcoming session, and spreads the workload.
- Send materials to the group to help them prepare, such as an agenda, the description of the IPO be addressed by the group, a statement of the hoped-for outcome (without presuming too much), and maybe some background documents.

3.8.4 What Does the Facilitator Do During the Session?

Everyone has arrived and is ready to go to work. Here are some things the facilitator may want to do and can tailor to the particular situation:

- Make sure that everyone knows something about everyone else. Brief self-introductions work well.
- Discuss the IPO to be addressed by the group; get everyone on the same page. Perhaps write and post a summary, in a highly visible manner, so that the challenge is figuratively and literally in front of the group throughout the session.
- Consider discussing and agreeing on the definitions of key words or expressions and documenting those definitions. Failure to do so can lead to later unnecessary disagreement or even conflict.
- Review the agenda and include an explanation of the tool or tools to be used.
- Suggest protocol such as everyone is expected to contribute, participants are urged to frankly share their views, turn off cell phones, honor action items, and not exceed ninety minutes.
- Launch into the process; get the discussion going. Try to engage everyone while not allowing anyone to dominate the conversation. Draw people out by using what you know about their position or their experience. Assume an unbiased, neutral, encouraging, nonjudgmental, and helpful position. Paraphrase some ideas offered by participants to reassure them that their ideas have value and to clarify the ideas.
- Offer a prepared and thought-provoking concept, idea, or suggestion if there is a lull in the conversation. For example, apply the What If? method (Section 4.12), as in, "How would we solve this problem if funds were unlimited?" or "What would Superman do?" or "How would we build this thing if we had to do it in a week?" (See the Taco Bell restaurant story in Section 4.12.2.) Do something to stimulate the group to think wider and deeper.
- Discourage premature closure during the divergent thinking phase, which was discussed near the beginning of this chapter. Some groups want to move quickly to closure—to defining the IPO or identifying options for resolving it—so that

they can move on to other concerns or tasks. In doing so, they may miss the opportunity to fully define the IPO or find truly creative and innovative alternatives. Similarly, a team may want to rush convergent thinking and, as a result, not fully consider all the implications of the available options.

- Recap the principal points and the action items.
- Set a schedule, with emphasis on the date, time, place, and focus of the next session.
- Take photos of the visuals that were prepared by the group for possible use when documenting the session.

3.8.5 What Does the Facilitator Do After the Session?

The just-concluded facilitated session is likely to have generated many ideas and posed many new questions. The facilitator should maintain the thinking process and synergy momentum by promptly performing tasks such as the following:

- Within a day or two of the session, document ideas generated, questions posed, action items agreed to, the go-forward schedule, and various inevitable loose ends.
- Complete whatever action items were taken on by the facilitator; he or she should set an example.
- Begin planning the next session if that was one of the outcomes of the first session.
- Do whatever is needed (reminding, pushing, pulling, encouraging, stretching, and cajoling) to continue the process or bring it to closure. Get a return on the investment of the facilitator's and team members' time and, more important, their thinking.

Facilitation is not needed for all meetings. However, its absence sometimes means that the team or group and the organization of which it is a part is failing to use fully their most valuable resources: the motivated, experience-laden, and creative/ innovative brains of their personnel. As a student or practitioner, you can help avoid that waste by using facilitation to bring readily available resources to bear on any IPO.

3.9 FORMAT USED TO PRESENT EACH METHOD

A similar format is used for presenting each whole-brain method so that you can easily move from studying one method to studying another one. Each description begins with a short overview to provide context and initial insight into the value of the method. Then it is described, sometimes as noted earlier in a step-wise manner, usually with the use of one or more actual or hypothetical examples. The neuroscience basis for the method follows, to link the method to your growing understanding of the human brain, as discussed in Chapter 2. This stresses the scientific basis for each method. Finally, positive and negative features of the method are noted.

For some methods, one or more Personal, Historic Note, and Views of Others textboxes supplement the description. Exercises at the end of Chapters 4 and 7 provide at least one opportunity to apply each of the twenty whole-brain tools included in this text.

3.10 SUMMARY

Building on the case for more creativity and innovation presented in Chapter 1 and the brain primer offered in Chapter 2, this chapter prepares you to learn about and apply eleven easy-to-learn and -use whole-brain tools in Chapter 4 and nine more-advanced methods in Chapter 7. The key points presented in this chapter are as follows:

- The more ideas, the better
- The methods are just tools; their value lies in your selection and use
- Avoid using only the stifling Einstellung Effect
- Science and experience indicate that the methods work
- Hope for fortuitous errors and accidents
- Recognize common-sense caveats
- Consider facilitation to optimize the knowledge and experience of team members

Now, onto the thinking tools in Chapter 4—your way to start working smarter and being more creative and innovative.

Nothing is impossible; there are ways that lead to everything,
and if we have sufficient will, we should always have sufficient means.
—*Francois de La Rochefoucauld, French writer*

CITED SOURCES

Altshuller, G. 1996. *And Suddenly the Inventor Appeared: TRIZ, the Theory of Inventive Problem Solving.* Translated by Lev Shulyak from the original 1984 Russian version. Worcester, MA: Technical Innovation Center, Inc.

Asimov, I. 2014. "On Creativity." *MIT Technology Review*, October 20. http://www.technologyreview.com/view/531911/isaac-asimov-asks-how-do-people-get-new-ideas/.

Beakley, G. C., D. L. Evans, and J. B. Keats. 1986. *Engineering: An Introduction to a Creative Profession.* New York: Macmillan Publishing Company.

Bilalic, M., and P. McLeod. 2014. "Why Good Thoughts Block Better Ones." *Scientific American* 310 (3): 72–79.

Bonasso, S. 2005. "Creativity and Leadership." Presented at the College of Business and Economics, West Virginia University, Morgantown, WV, November 11.

Brenner, R. 2014. "Rationalizing Creativity at Work: Part 1." *Point Lookout* email newsletter, October 29. http://www.chacocanyon.com/pointlookout/archive.shtml.

Brinkley, D. 2003. *Wheels for the World: Henry Ford, His Company, and a Century of Progress:* 1903–2003. New York: Viking.

Brooks, D. 2011. "Tools for Thinking." *The New York Times*, April 1.

Cain, S. 2012. *Quiet: The Power of Introverts in a World That Can't Stop Talking.* New York: Crown Publishers.

Chrysikou, E. G. 2012. "Your Creative Brain at Work." *Scientific American Mind*, July/August: 24–31.

Dijksterhuis, A., and T. Meurs. 2006. "Where Creativity Resides: The Generative Power of Unconscious Thought." *Consciousness and Cognition* 15 (1): 135–146.

Genco, N., K. Holtta-Otto, and C. C. Seepersad. 2012. "An Experimental Investigation of the Innovative Capabilities of Undergraduate Engineering Students." *Journal of Engineering Education*, ASEE, 101 (1): 60–81.

Gordon, B. 2012. "Ask the Brains." *Scientific American Mind*, March/April: 70.

Johnson, S. 2010. *Where Good Ideas Come From: The Natural History of Innovation.* New York: Riverhead Books.

Kaner, S., L. Lind, C. Toldi, S. Fisk, and D. Berger. 1996. *Facilitator's Guide to Participatory Decision-Making.* Gabriola Island, British Columbia: New Science Publishers.

Kluger, J. 2013. "Assessing the Creative Spark: What Americans Think About Creativity." *Time*, May 20.

Kumar, C. S. S. R., and A. M. Nijasure. 1997. "Vulcanization of Rubber: How to Alter Molecular Structure and Influence Physical Properties." *Resonance* 2 (4): 55–59.

Mann, C. C. 2011. "Black Gold." In *1493: Uncovering the New World Columbus Created*, 238–278. New York: Random House.

Maxwell, J. C. 2003. *Thinking for a Change: 11 Ways Highly Successful People Approach Life and Work,* New York: Warner Books.

May, R. 1976. *Courage to Create.* New York: Bantam Books.

McCuen, R. H. 2012. "Creativity: An Important Problem-Solving Tool for Water Resources in 2050." In *Toward a Sustainable Water Future: Visions for 2050*, edited by W. M. Grayman, D. P. Loucks, and L. Saito, 313–321. Reston, VA: American Society of Civil Engineers.

McCuen, R. H. 2014. Professor and Ben Dyer chair in civil engineering, University of Maryland, College Park, MD, pers. comm., August 22 and September 1.

Michalko, M. 2001. *Cracking Creativity: The Secrets of Creative Genius.* Berkeley, CA: Ten Speed Press.

Murray, D. 1958. "Percy Spencer and His Itch to Know." *Readers Digest*, August.

Nierenberg, G. I. 1982. *The Art of Creative Thinking.* New York: Barnes & Noble Books.

Somma, A. M. 2014. "Charles Goodyear and the Vulcanization of Rubber." ConnecticutHistory.org. Accessed October 7, 2014. http://connecticuthistory.org/charles-goodyear-and-the-vulcanization-of-rubber/.

Strayer, D. L., and J. M. Watson. 2012. "Supertaskers and the Multitasking Brain." *Scientific American Mind*, March/April: 22–29.

Van Doren, C. 1991. *A History of Knowledge.* New York: Ballantine Books.

Walesh, S. G. 2012. "Communicating to Make Things Happen." In *Engineering Your Future: The Professional Practice of Engineering*, 3rd ed. Hoboken, NJ: John Wiley & Sons.

EXERCISES

Notes:

1. The goal of the exercises is to provide students, usually working alone, the opportunity to think about and use the ideas, principles, and information offered in the chapter.

2. However, many circumstances and corresponding teaching-learning opportunities may arise. For example, a stated situation may be altered to meet specific concerns or needs. Rather than work with the largely hypothetical situation described in a particular exercise, an individual or team may wish to take on an actual issue, problem, or opportunity facing the team or one or more of its members. These and similar variations are encouraged, subject to the concurrence or direction of the instructor.

3.1 **RECOGNIZING THE EINSTELLUNG EFFECT TRAP:** How did you choose your current career or course of study? Did you make the decision yourself or were you influenced by others? Were you guided only by the Einstellung Effect? If not, describe how you escaped the trap. If yes, describe the decision you originally made, and if it was controlled by the Einstellung Effect, and indicate one or more creative or innovative alternative actions that you could have taken; and perhaps you still can. Rethink creative actions that you can take now to redirect your career or studies.

3.2 **FORTUITOUS ERROR OR ACCIDENT (BY OTHERS):** This exercise, which is intended for individuals, further illustrates the possible positive role of errors and accidents in the creative and innovative process. That process is inherently risky because it delves into the unknown, and therefore some errors and accidents are likely to occur.

Find another example similar to the cardiac pacemaker, vulcanization, photosynthesis, microwave oven, and penicillin incidents described in Section 3.6 in which a lucky error or accident stimulated a creative or innovative result. Describe that result and the events leading to it. Cite all of your sources.

3.3 **FORTUITOUS ERROR OR ACCIDENT (BY YOU):** Recall an incident in which you made a major error or experienced an accident that caused you to gain great insight, learn a valuable lesson, or be creative or innovative. Describe the incident and the resulting insight, lesson, or creative/innovative outcome.

3.4 **YOUR TURN TO FACILITATE:** Have you ever tried to facilitate a meeting or negotiation and felt shy or uncomfortable doing it? If your facilitation was successful, identify all that you had done (as per Section 3.8 or maybe outside it) that enabled you to succeed. If you were not successful, identify all the mistakes that you had committed.

Then, assume that you could redo the meeting and that you would be the outside facilitator. Drawing at least initially on the ideas and suggestions presented in Section 3.8, what would you do to encourage the group to make progress and perhaps even be creative and innovative? Does this exercise get rid of your shyness or discomfort?

3.5 **HOW DO WE KNOW WHEN TO BE CREATIVE/INNOVATIVE?:** Do we need to be creative/innovative all the time and in all contexts? The class should divide itself up into teams of 2. Each team assumes they are a particular company, like Pixar, Nokia, The Bill and Melinda Gates Foundation, the International Labour Organisation, a small company making steel pipes, a student organization and so on. There should be diverse types of organizations. Let the class do some background study, then imagine under what personal and organizational situations they would be motivated to be creative/innovative.

4 Basic Whole-Brain Methods

Half a brain is better than none.
A whole brain would be better.
—Betty Edwards, artist and author

Objectives:

After studying this chapter, you will be able to:

- Illustrate the universality of divergent-convergent thinking
- Summarize how whole-brain methods enable intentional creativity/innovation
- Discuss the importance of method selection
- Show the value of using a series of multiple methods on a project

- Demonstrate understanding of the wide applicability of whole-brain methods
- Explain eleven basic, quickly learned, and rapidly applied whole-brain methods
- Cite the positive and negative features of each method
- Report the neuroscience basis of each whole-brain method

4.1 INTRODUCTION

The more ideas, the better is one theme in the preceding chapter. When faced with a carefully defined issue, problem, or opportunity (IPO), the quality of our ultimate decisions is likely to be better when we have more ideas—more options. We want the divergent thinking effort to be rich and varied. Most of the eleven whole-brain methods presented in this chapter will help you or you and your teams generate many and varied ideas—more than you would without them. In addition, most of the tools can also be used to complete what should be the first order of business: thoroughly defining the IPO.

4.2 ASK-ASK-ASK

In keeping with the principle that an IPO well-defined is half resolved, *Ask-Ask-Ask* is a great place to start. We ask questions to fully define an IPO so that we can eventually resolve it and not just treat symptoms. Putting a bucket under a leaking ceiling is a quick fix but, in the long run you should find the source of the leak (Fogler, LeBlanc, and Rizzo 2014). Once an IPO is defined, we ask questions to help generate ideas for resolving it. "Ask" is in the name of this method three times to emphasize that the tool goes well beyond superficial, innocuous, and obvious questions. Instead, drill, probe, and *onionize* (Fox 2000)—that is, get to the heart of the matter by peeling away layer after layer.

Your initial thought may be that the need to ask questions is obvious, so why devote time to it, why call it out as a whole-brain method? There are two reasons. First, question asking may seem obvious, but my experience indicates that many engineers (and probably many members of some other professions) are reluctant to go beyond superficial questions. Therefore, we engineers should be aware of our possible question-asking reluctance so that we can overcome it. Second, if you agree with the importance of asking questions, you may want to know about some question-asking techniques.

To fully explore Ask-Ask-Ask, we consider three reasons you may be reluctant to ask probing questions, outline five powers of questions, and describe four question-asking techniques that you may find useful. Anecdotes and examples illustrate the role of Ask-Ask-Ask in creativity and innovation.

4.2.1 Reluctance to Ask Questions: Three Reasons

As a student or a young practitioner, you may be reluctant to embrace Ask-Ask-Ask for one or more of the following three common reasons:

- **Questioning authority:** Recognize that most of us are authorities, just on different things. The person you interact with, such as a professor, your supervisor, or a potential client or customer, is an authority on one or more things. Similarly, you as a professional or aspiring professional are an authority on other things. By asking questions, you are not questioning the authority of the other person. Instead, you are revealing your own and doing it for another's potential benefit.
- **Appearing uninformed/poorly prepared:** Some people foolishly think that if they ask questions they will be viewed as uniformed or poorly prepared, that as experts they should know everything, or pretend they do. To illustrate the fallacy of that line of thought, consider this scenario: You awake with pain in your chest and are rushed to the emergency room. The doctor asks: "What's wrong?" and you answer, "Chest pain." The doctor says, "I am immediately performing triple bypass heart surgery." The pain aside, how would you feel? Might you want the doctor to ask more questions as part of a careful diagnosis of your problem before deciding how to solve the problem? Maybe the pain is caused by something you ate!

  Asking questions does not indicate that you are uninformed or poorly prepared; it should mean just the opposite. If you are well informed, you know what to ask. The type and number of questions you ask reveal your expertise.
- **Considered rude:** Someone said, "I don't care how much you know until I know how much you care." You demonstrate care, not rudeness, by preparing and asking thoughtful, probing questions in a polite, sensitive manner.

Do one or more of the preceding obstacles apply to you? If so, revisit your obstacles and try to address them. Failure to do so could hamper your creativity and innovation. Why? Because we need to first define an IPO in order to resolve it, and question asking is an important part of the definition process. Ask-Ask-Ask is a powerful whole-brain tool that challenges you to more fully use your brain and does the same for those you are conversing with.

VIEWS OF OTHERS: VALUE OF QUESTIONS

Consider some thoughts about asking questions from members of diverse professions and specialties. Management guru Peter Drucker said, "My greatest strength as a consultant is to be ignorant and ask a few questions." According to Charles P. Steinmetz, the electrical engineer who led the development of alternating current, "No man really becomes a fool until he stops asking questions." Robert Half, founder of a staffing firm, said, "Asking the right questions takes as much skill as giving the right answers." Finally, a comment from physician Jonas Salk, discoverer of the polio vaccine, directly relates to creativity and innovation: "What we think of as a moment of discovery is really discovery of the right question." (For additional thoughts about asking questions, see Views of Others: Value of Questions, in Section 5.10.)

4.2.2 Five Powers of Questions

The use of "power" in the title of this subsection is intended to suggest the benefits of asking probing questions; it does not suggest manipulating, misrepresenting, or pressuring. The overarching benefit of Ask-Ask-Ask is that it helps you define what someone or some entity wants and needs so that you, and perhaps your team, can creatively and innovatively fulfill those needs.

With that caveat in mind, five powers of questions (adapted from Leeds 2000) are as follows:

1. **Create an obligation to respond:** Remember a time in class when a teacher or professor asked you a question and then was silent? Most people's natural inclination is to fill that silence—that *vacuum*—with something, and so we do our best to answer the question. Silence is uncomfortable when a question is asked. This is what I mean by saying that asking a question creates an obligation to respond. I am not suggesting that we overtly try to cause discomfort, but am simply noting a natural tendency and recognizing its value if carefully used.
2. **Stimulate thinking of the asker and answerer:** Preparing and asking questions causes you to think more deeply and broadly about the other person or persons and their situation. Similarly, their thinking is enhanced as they respond to your questions.
3. **Provide valuable data/information/knowledge:** Recognize that although question asking reveals your expertise and your concern for another person and another's wants and needs, answers to your questions also provide data, information, and knowledge needed to resolve the challenge at hand.
4. **Put the asker in the driver's seat:** You can use questions to gently direct a conversation to topics that could be potentially useful to you and those you hope to assist. Furthermore, if you tend toward introversion, asking questions enables

you to start a conversation and then steer it in a potentially productive direction. Most people will respond to thoughtful, positive questions and appreciate the attention (Walesh 2004).

5. **Enable people to persuade themselves:** Thoughtful questions and the thinking they stimulate help to define IPOs and move all parties toward an IPO's resolution. The question-asking and -answering process tends to go beyond symptoms to causes, define constraints, reveal assumptions, distinguish between wants and needs, and suggest some ways to resolve the IPO.

To benefit from the five powers of questions, we need to listen. Go beyond just hearing, which is one of the six senses (Section 2.4.1) and requires little effort; it comes naturally. Move into listening, which is a skill and demands effort. Listen attentively for facts and listen empathetically, aided by sense of sight, for feelings. Facts and feelings define an individual's wants and needs and what the individual is inclined to do about them.

4.2.3 Four Question-Asking Techniques

Ask-Ask-Ask can yield many benefits and, if the situation warrants, prepare you to take a creative and innovative approach. With those benefits in mind, consider the following four question-asking techniques:

1. **Mix closed-ended and open-ended questions:** Use some closed-ended questions—that is, questions that can be answered with yes, no, or statements of fact. They typically begin with or include "how many," "how much," "when," or "who" (Parkinson 2009). For example, "How much is budgeted for designing the cable under the bay?" We engineers and other technical professionals tend to ask closed-ended questions. We want the facts. This is good, but not sufficient.

   Also ask open-ended questions, which often begin with or include "why," "how," or "what" (Parkinson 2009). For example, "Why are you considering designing and installing a completely new manufacturing line instead of modifying an existing one?" An open-ended question like that is intended to give others the opportunity to reflect, elaborate, and fill in the blanks. Closed-ended questions tend to end a conversation, at least temporarily. In contrast, open-ended questions are less likely to do so (Rhein 2009). Mixing closed and open-ended questions is likely to generate a very enlightening conversation.

2. **Use the Five Whys to drill down:** The *Five Whys* is a persistent questioning tactic that enables you to drill down—to get to the bottom of things—to move past symptoms and get to causes (Liker 2004). Assume you are an engineer meeting with a potential new client, the director of public works for a large municipality. She wants to solve a basement flooding problem caused by the backup of a mixture of storm water and wastewater from the combined sewer system. Based on your experience, you know that there are many possible causes of basement flooding in combined sewer systems and numerous ways—some very creative or innovative—to solve such problems, but your first priority is to begin to define the cause, so you apply the Five Whys as follows:

   • Why are the basements flooding? *Answer:* Because the combined sewer system surcharges when rainfall exceeds about 0.2 inches per hour. You could stop here, but you don't.

   • Why do the sewers surcharge during such rainfalls? *Answer:* Because the receiving stream rises above the level of most basement floors during those rainfall events. Again, you could stop the drill down questioning, but don't.

- Why does the receiving stream rise during those rainfalls? *Answer:* Possibly because the city's dam is downstream of the combined sewer system outfall.
- Why might the dam be relevant? *Answer:* Because it has a very short weir.
- Why does the dam have a short weir? *Answer:* Maybe because it was constructed over a century ago, before this small watershed was urbanized.

Notice how the Five Whys technique is likely to lead you and others to the cause of a problem, not just the symptoms, and the forces driving an issue and/or the benefits inherent in an opportunity.

In order to emphasize the importance of repeatedly asking why—of drilling down—I began each of the five example questions with *why*. Although the intent is to ask a series of probing questions, avoid lapsing into a mechanical, if not rude, *why-why-why-why-why* pattern. Instead, finesse the questions. For example, maybe the third question could be softened to "I'd really like to get an even better understanding of your flooding problem. Do you have any ideas about why the receiving stream rises during those rainfalls?"

3. **Apply the echo technique to help others expand their thoughts:** This technique (Johnson 2010) is an asking-listening aid. It helps the answerer further explain his or her want or need and helps you better understand that want or need. For example, the person you want to help says: "We've been dealing with this type of equipment failure for over three years." You repeat or echo the last few words in the form of a question—"Over three years?"—then be still and listen as the other person elaborates and gives you added insight into the problem he or she is trying to solve.
4. **Consider Kipling's six:** In saying "I had six honest serving men; they taught me all I knew. Their names were Where and What and When and Why and How and Who," English writer Kipling offers another method for effective questioning. It's hard to imagine a challenging IPO that does not have Kipling's six elements. In a variety of situations, recall Kipling's "six" and use them to guide your questions.

For additional question-asking concepts and tools, refer to Chapter 3 of *Strategies for Creative Problem Solving* (Fogler, LeBlanc, and Rizzo 2014).

4.2.4 Examples from Marketing of Professional Services

Marketing may be defined as "creating the climate that will bring in future business" (Smallowitz and Molyneux 1987), with the ultimate aim being "to make selling superfluous" (Kolter and Fox 1985). I've been fortunate to have had many diverse, good and bad, experiences in marketing professional engineering and related services and learned useful lessons as a result. You too will have opportunities to assist with marketing efforts, especially if you work in the private sector. As you may suspect, the first and most useful lesson I've learned is to use Ask-Ask-Ask right from the start. Once you or your organization identifies a desirable client or customer, ask a lot of questions before doing anything else.

Consider some examples of ideas and information I acquired and feelings I sensed over many years by asking questions of clients and potential clients (Walesh 2014). Essentially none of these items—the payoff of the questioning process—appeared in formal requests for proposals or qualifications or in other documents provided by clients or potential clients that I talked with. They were learned as a result of Ask-Ask-Ask. The kinds of ideas, information, and feelings described ahead provided valuable insight into how to proactively, creatively, and innovatively secure contracts and deliver on them.

- Wants a readily accessible project manager who is technically competent and can *communicate with all types of audiences.*
- *Hates surprises:* As an engineering firm representative, I was told I could have "one minute" with the director of public works of a community for which our firm was pursuing a large storm water planning project. Accordingly, as soon as I met him, I asked, "What do you like least about consultants?" His quick answer: "Hate surprises." He went on to say he preferred face-to-face meetings. Although our meeting was short, it did exceed one minute. More importantly, our subsequent proposal stressed communication and included many face-to-face meetings and the cost of those meetings. Our firm was selected for the project. Were we selected partly because of the question asked during the "one-minute" meeting? Maybe.
- Project team *must have local knowledge* and access to experts with national experience. Notice the contrast between this and the next unwritten criterion stated by another potential client.
- Project team must have technical expertise but no local history, presence, or interest in order to provide complete objectivity. The *no local history, presence, and/or interest* criteria described the firm I worked for, and we were selected for the project and follow-up projects.
- Wants *no more public involvement* other than what is absolutely necessary.
- Wants proactive, *high-profile public involvement* from day one. Note the contrast between this and the previous requirement, which stresses the extreme differences in (often unwritten) client and customer expectations and which you need to know if you want to earn the right to serve certain clients.
- We want our project to *gain national attention* through presentations and papers co-authored by us and our consultant.
- During the course of this project, we want one of our engineers to learn how you *operate the computer models.*
- This project is really all about money. *How are we going to fund* whatever solutions you recommend?

To reiterate, when Ask-Ask-Ask is applied during the marketing phase of a potential project, it yields supplemental and often crucial ideas, information, and feelings. They can be used to proactively, creatively, and innovatively secure contracts and then, in similar fashion, deliver on them.

4.2.5 Additional Thoughts about Asking Questions

If we essentially only use one type of question and/or we accept superficial or shallow answers, we risk making unnecessary assumptions or creating a false sense of getting adequate information (Rhein 2009). We may see just the tip of the iceberg, mistake it for the whole iceberg, and then inadvertently fix a symptom rather than resolve the IPO, or our questions may fail to cause the kind of thinking that generates creative and innovative ideas.

Electrical engineer Fruechte (2014), former director of a research and development laboratory, shares a story that illustrates the importance of asking stimulating and insightful questions. He says that personnel were asked to offer new ideas for future automobiles, and the results were vague and unimaginative. However, when asked for ideas to develop a "car that never crashed," the response was amazing. Electrical and electronic specialists had ideas for putting varied devices into cars to sense other vehicles and other objects around them. Mechanical engineers were excited by the possibility of designing structures that "did not need to withstand a crash since it never would occur." Thoughtful and focused questions are likely to generate thoughtful and focused answers.

Engineering professor Eris studied the effect of what is referred to here as Ask-Ask-Ask on the quality of team solutions to challenges. He sought to determine the role of questioning in encouraging imagination and in arriving at effective results. Eris concluded that "the most effective teams asked the most questions and the questions they asked were evenly balanced between generative [divergent] and convergent" (Goldberg and Somerville 2014).

I encourage you to ask many and varied probing questions, but I also urge you to be prepared. For example, assume a professor in your department connected with a local manufacturing firm offers to have a student team tackle one of the firm's technical problems within the senior project program. As a representative of your senior project team, you're scheduled to meet with an engineer at the company. Clearly, you want to prepare for the meeting by gathering basic information about the company; don't go in cold—do your homework. Then, ask probing questions informed by that basic background information.

Finally, specific question-asking methods aside, I urge you to talk to strangers in various settings. The strangers might be students, faculty, staff, other employees, or people on the street. This advice is likely to be contrary to the "don't talk to strangers" advice you received as a child. However, that was then, and this is now. In her book *How to Work a Room*, consultant Roane (1988) challenges readers to "work the world." She urges us to adopt the philosophy that we are surrounded by opportunities to ask questions, learn, and expand our networks, but we often have to take the initiative, whether we are at the university, at work, running personal errands, sitting in an airport between flights, or attending a conference.

Will talking to strangers always provide useful information or a new contact? Certainly not. However, Roane says: "That's not the point. The point is to extend yourself to people, be open to whatever comes your way, and have a good time in the process . . . The rewards go to the risk-takers, those who are willing to put their egos on the line and reach out—to other people and to richer and fuller lives for themselves."

PERSONAL: INTROVERTS MAKE GOOD ASKERS

As an example of talking to strangers, I obtained a rewarding, multiyear consulting arrangement because I approached a speaker after his presentation at a conference. I complimented him on his presentation, mentioned that we seemed to share technical interests, exchanged business cards, and, as they say, "one thing led to another."

I tend toward introversion, as do the majority of engineers. Partly because of my introversion, I've made an effort to approach strangers in a variety of business, professional, and other settings and ask lots of questions. Rather than talk about me, unless others indicate interest, I ask questions and give others opportunities to talk, including talking about themselves, which some seem to enjoy doing. TV commentator Rooney suggests, "In a conversation, keep in mind that you're more interested in what you have to say than anyone else." This question-asking approach has provided many positive results. Like hockey great Gretsky said, "You miss 100 percent of the shots you never take." Asking questions is like taking shots; you have little to lose and much to gain.

Maybe persistent question asking, whether closed- or open-ended, using the Five Whys, the echo technique, or Kipling's six, just doesn't seem to be your forte in academic or professional matters. In that case, experiment by asking more questions in low-risk situations. For example, say to the cashier at a restaurant, "I like the new menu. Why did you make the changes?" Then, ask a follow-up question. Or the next time you attend a concert, approach one of the performers during an intermission or after the event, and ask a question or two. My experience with this type of low-risk question asking is that the other person typically responds favorably to my interest and I learn. It can be win-win for you and others, and in the process you will become more adept at Ask-Ask-Ask and increasingly use it in your student and practitioner roles.

4.2.6 Neuroscience Basis

Ask-Ask-Ask fully engages the left hemisphere, in that broad and deep thought is needed to prepare and then articulate meaningful questions, listen carefully to the responses, and then ask productive follow-up questions. In addition to hearing the facts, the empathetic listener engages his or her right hemisphere to "hear" and "see" the emotions accompanying the answers. On hearing the answers and then going on to other activities, the questioner's subconscious mind is very likely to work on the answers and then share some additional insights with the questioner.

4.2.7 Positive and Negative Features

The most powerful aspect of Ask-Ask-Ask is that it is, by far, the best way to define an IPO prior to resolving it. This method seeks to engage those who are most interested in resolving an issue, resolving a problem, or pursuing an opportunity by probing their minds for relevant concepts, ideas, facts, and feelings. As noted in Section 6.2.2, we engineers are ultimately in the people business, serving engineering, so let's focus on those people who may have engineering needs we can fill. On the negative side, some student and practicing engineers will not fully embrace Ask-Ask-Ask. Fear of questioning authority, appearing unprepared, and seeming rude will deter them. To those people, I repeat my earlier suggestion to at least experiment in nonthreatening situations with probing questions.

4.3 BORROWING BRILLIANCE

Engineer, entrepreneur, and author Murray (2009) argues, in his book *Borrowing Brilliance*, that the most effective path to creativity and innovation mixes and matches the concepts of others, especially when the others are in disparate fields. He repeatedly suggests, hopefully tongue-in-cheek, that his approach is a game bordering on stealing. For example, he says, "My personal approach to creative thinking was pretty much hack, I just stole or borrowed ideas from other places." He also says, "Since ideas are born of other ideas, this creates a fine line between theft and originality."

Murray may have some fun with "borrowing brilliance" and suggest that it's stealing, but any of us who conduct scholarly research and participate in other professional endeavors know that we build on the work of and stand on the shoulders of others. "If I have seen farther than others," said British scientist Newton, "it is because I was standing on the shoulders of giants." We also recognize that scholars cite their sources and, as appropriate, obtain permission to use the intellectual products of others.

4.3.1 Six Steps

Murray's Borrowing Brilliance consists of six steps for constructing a creative and innovative idea. I suspect that many student engineers interested in creativity and innovation will be attracted to a six-step or similar approach. In fact, except for some of the terminology, Murray's six steps as described here may be viewed as an enlightened version of the engineering design process. The six steps are as follows:

1. **Defining:** Let's define the problem we are trying to solve and, I must add, the issue to be resolved or the opportunity to be pursued. This broader perspective is important because engineers and similar scientific-technical professionals, starting from their time as students, are very adept at solving problems, but they also have the potential to prevent problems from occurring, to identify and pursue opportunities, and to address broader issues.
2. **Borrowing:** Look for ways to borrow ideas from situations having similar problems.
3. **Combining:** Combine and connect the borrowed ideas.
4. **Incubating:** Temporarily step away from the problem-solving process, enabling the combinations and connections to incubate and provide one or more solutions; that is, provide time for the subconscious mind to work.
5. **Judging:** Evaluate each potential solution's strengths and weaknesses.
6. **Enhancing:** Seek to remove the negatives and enhance the positives of potential solutions, and then select the best one.

4.3.2 Examples of Borrowing Brilliance

Murray offers informative examples of creative and innovative efforts that built on the work of others—that borrowed brilliance—including the following:

- **Reusable type printing press:** As explained in Section 1.3.2, Guttenberg borrowed woodblock printing from the Chinese, weapon and coin forging from the Romans, and the screw press from the winemakers and olive oil producers to innovatively design the reusable type printing press (Boorstin 1985; Murray 2009).
- **Theory of evolution:** To create his evolution theory and publish *On the Origin of the Species* in 1859, Darwin borrowed from biologists who cataloged species. However, biologists cataloged differences in species, whereas Darwin cataloged similarities during his five-year voyage as naturalist on the HMS Beagle. Darwin also borrowed from geologists, particularly the English geologist Lyell, who published *Principles of Geology* in 1830. Lyell's book argued that geological features represented the cumulative effects of various processes, such as wind, water, and precipitation occurring over long periods of time. This stimulated Darwin to think about the effect of long periods of time on biology (Boorstin 1985; Murray 2009).
- **Automobile assembly line:** The Ford Motor Company borrowed from meat-packing companies when developing the moving assembly line between 1908 and 1915. Ford workers visited the Swift meat-packing plant in Chicago and saw how it "used a moving hook and conveyor system [and workers fixed in place] to disassemble a cow" (Murray 2009). One Ford person who visited a Chicago slaughterhouse said, "If they can kill pigs and cows that way, we can build cars that way" (Brinkley 2003).

    Ford borrowed the disassembling carcass system, reversed it, and in 1913 produced a more efficient process for assembling cars. The company created the first version of today's very sophisticated process for manufacturing cars and numerous other products. Cars—being assembled, not disassembled—move

Figure 4.1
Ford borrowed the means for efficient disassembly of carcasses from the meat-packing industry to create the means for efficient assembly of automobiles.

(Beata Kulasik/Fotolia; Gjeerawut/Fotolia)

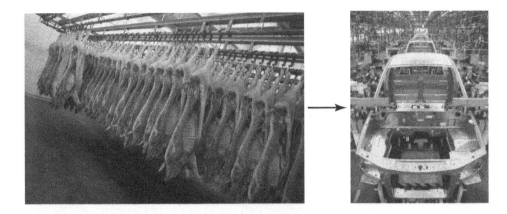

past fixed stations where workers and robots add value to each car. In summary, the Ford Motor Company borrowed a fundamental idea from the meat-packing industry to create the automobile assembly line (Figure 4.1; Brinkley 2003; Murray 2009).

What IPO do you face that might be resolved by borrowing an approach or process from a very different discipline or specialty?

4.3.3 Ten Supporting Principles

Murray (2009) offers ten principles to support his six-step Borrowing Brilliance process. Even if you are not explicitly using Borrowing Brilliance, one or more of the following principles may enhance your creativity and innovation effort:

1. **Get out of our silo:** Look close by, but also far and wide. Murray states: "The further away from your subject you borrow materials from, the more creative your solution becomes." Recall Guttenberg the printer borrowing from wine makers, Darwin the biologist borrowing from a geologist, and Ford the automobile manufacturer borrowing from slaughterhouses. In Section 6.3.3, we will learn about Philo Farnsworth, the inventor and electronics expert, who borrowed from farming to invent television, and Section 6.6.3 tells the story of a Japanese engineering team that borrowed from birding to redesign the lead unit on a high-speed train.

2. **Recognize patterns and inconsistencies within them:** Observation of patterns and their distribution or dispersion is an important part of creating. For example, in the 1660s, Newton noted that although many apples fell from a tree, the moon did not fall from the sky, which led him to develop the theory of universal or mutual gravitation. He didn't know what gravity was, but by noticing inconsistencies, he determined how it behaved (Boorstin 1985; Van Doren 1991).

3. **Master the metaphor:** According to Murray, "Great creative thinkers master the metaphor. Unfortunately your English teacher may have ruined the concept for you by relegating it to a simple writing technique." Creative individuals strive to think of their subjects—issues, problems, or opportunities—in terms of a different subject. For example, Newton viewed an apple as a metaphor for the moon, Disney used a movie metaphor (storyboards, set, props, and cast members) to create Disneyland, Gates and Microsoft saw a desktop as a metaphor for software, and Zuckerberg used the college yearbook as a metaphor to develop Facebook. We also need to know when to cast out metaphors. For example, early automobile designers used horse-drawn carriages as metaphors for the first horseless carriages and as a result placed passengers in dangerous upfront positions.

4. **Hope for parapraxes:** Be aware of parapraxes, or misunderstandings, because they may enable the subconscious mind to speak to the conscious mind in a productive manner. Murray describes three types of parapraxes. The first is the familiar Freudian *slip of the tongue;* we say something we didn't mean to say, but whatever we said might turn out to be a subconscious-driven insight or good idea. The second parapraxis is the *slip of the ear,* when we hear something incorrectly, but what we thought we heard could have value. Finally, we have the *slip of the eye;* we read or see something incorrectly, and although we erred, what we thought we saw might be useful.

For example, consider Bell's invention of the telephone, which was partly due to a visual parapraxis. Bell tried to read the book *On the Sensation of Tone,* written by the German scientist von Helmholtz and published in German. Because Bell could not read German well, he misread a passage. The passage stated that vowel sounds could be reproduced with electric tuning forks. Bell misread it as saying that vowel sounds could be reproduced using electric wires—and then he went on to make it so.

If you realize you just said something you didn't mean to say, misunderstood something you heard, or misread some text, reflect on the circumstances. Perhaps your subconscious mind has been working on something that your conscious mind told it was important, and now your subconscious mind is trying to tell you something that may be insightful and useful.

HISTORIC NOTE: THE REAL FIRST TELEPHONE?

Telephone means a device to hear the sound of speech (*phone*) from far or from a distance (*tele*). With that broad definition in mind, we should more specifically credit Bell with inventing the electric telephone and look earlier for the invention of more fundamental telephones.

For example, about 1,200 to 1,400 years ago, someone in the Chimu Empire (in what is now northern Peru) invented a telephone. Now in the collection of the US National Museum of the American Indian, this early telephone is a gourd-and-twine device. Two resin-coated gourd speakers/receivers, each 3.5 inches long, are connected by seventy-five feet of cotton twine. If, with one person at each end, the line was pulled taut and someone spoke into the gourd at one end, the person at the other end would clearly hear what was said. As a child, perhaps you connected two tin cans with string and conversed with a friend. Anthropologists and archaeologists theorize that this early telephone was used by a Chimu "executive" to give instructions to assistants in other rooms (Baldwin 2013).

Discovery of the Chimu telephone reminds us that creativity and innovation are an essential and timeless feature of humanity. For example, because of my interest in water engineering, I once researched the origin of some of the water-related methods and tools we use today. As you may suspect, I learned that many can be traced back decades and centuries and to places around the globe (Walesh 1990).

5. **Embrace multiple hypotheses:** Work at developing the multiple working hypotheses ability; be able to simultaneously weigh various viewpoints as to the cause of a challenge or how you are going to resolve it. Accept temporary

ambiguity while recognizing its potential value. "The test of a first-rate intelligence," according to novelist Fitzgerald, "is the ability to hold two opposed ideas in mind at the same time."

6. **Take a break:** Consistent with the Taking a Break tool described later in Section 4.11, Murray says that what he refers to as the *pause in thinking about your issue* "allows the subconscious to speak and the conscious to listen." What we call *sleeping on it* has the same effect.

7. **Recognize that you may accidentally fix or create something else:** Be open to the possibility that in searching for a way to resolve an issue, solve a problem, or exploit an opportunity, you may find a way to fortuitously resolve another issue, solve a different problem, or exploit some other opportunity. See Section 4.3.4 for two examples.

8. **Focus:** When a creation or innovation appears, keep it as simple as possible. Discard useless or marginal features. Follow Albert Einstein's advice: "Make everything as simple as possible, but not simpler."

9. **Welcome critiques:** Welcome and offer sincere and specific criticism. Murray (2009) says: "Without exception, all of the creative people who have been profiled in [*Borrowing Brilliance*] were critics. They criticized the ideas of others, criticized their own ideas, and criticized themselves."

10. **Love creating, not the creation:** According to Murray, this advice recognizes the danger of an individual or team holding onto the first stage of what could be an evolving creation or innovation and thus never realizing its full potential. As he suggests, love the journey, not the destination—or what appears to be the destination.

In my view, the key to the approach described in Murray's book is to recognize the possibility of borrowing ideas, patterns, forms, and processes from other widely varying fields, subjects, or topics, as exemplified by Guttenberg, Darwin, and Ford. In the process, we may benefit from the unexpected, such as recognizing pattern inconsistencies, experiencing parapraxes, and accidentally fixing something else. Most of Murray's book is devoted to examples of the six-step process.

4.3.4 Examples of "Accidental" Creativity

Principle 7 suggests that when we focus on an IPO and persist, we may fortuitously resolve another issue, solve a different problem, or exploit some other opportunity. I place "accidental" in quotes to emphasize that the two examples presented here did not just come out of the blue with minimal effort. Each of the described creations was part of a concentrated effort. Before considering the following two examples of "accidental" creativity, recall the related Section 3.6 discussion of fortuitous errors and accidents.

Phonograph
Murray (2009) relates Thomas Edison's experience when searching for a way to automate telegraph messages as they were relayed down the line, rather than having operators read incoming dots and dashes and then reenter them. While experimenting with a prototype, he noticed that dots and dashes, when played at a high speed, sounded like human voices. This led him to invent the phonograph. Edison's search for a solution to the telegraph problem led him to the phonograph opportunity.

Suspension Bridge
For another example of "accidentally" fixing something else, consider the creation of the world's first major suspension bridge. The story begins two centuries ago in

Figure 4.2
The 150-foot-span Craigellachie Bridge in Scotland exemplifies the iron bridges designed and built in Britain in the late 1700s and early 1800s.

(Jasperimage/Shutterstock)

Wales. Scottish civil engineer Telford designed elegant iron (wrought and cast iron) bridges all over Britain in the late 1700s and early 1800s. One example is the graceful Craigellachie Bridge, shown in Figure 4.2, which was completed in 1814 in northern Scotland. The 150-foot-span bridge is constructed of cast iron and, after some modifications in 1965, is still used today (Billington 1996). These and many of his other iron bridges were innovative—but that's another story.

The Menai Strait is a waterway separating the Wales island of Anglesey from the Wales mainland. A goal was to construct a road from Holyhead on the Irish Sea in northwestern Wales to London. Crossing of the 500-plus-foot-wide Menai Strait was one of the challenges, and another was to cross the Snowdonia Mountains. In 1810, Telford considered crossing the straits with his specialty: an iron bridge. His "proposal included a construction plan to support the arch temporarily with rods that go above the bridge over temporary towers and then down to anchors at the abutments" (Billington 1996). This proposal for a temporary construction step was not implemented.

However, the point of this example is that the innovative idea of a suspension bridge was created—that is, a bridge deck supported by cables supported by towers. While Telford was looking for a temporary way to support the construction of another iron bridge, he conceived of a completely new way to permanently construct a major bridge. Think of the temporary measures we might use during construction and manufacturing. Might some of these contain ideas for use in permanent construction and manufacturing?

Sixteen years later, Telford's suspension idea became a reality. He designed a 580-foot suspension bridge across the Menai Straits, as shown in Figure 4.3. It was the world's first major suspension bridge, and it used four parallel wrought-iron chain-link cables. The original four wrought iron cables were replaced in 1941 (135 years after the original construction) with two steel cables (Billington 1996; Sandstrom 1970).

Figure 4.3
Scottish civil engineer Telford designed the 580-foot Menai Straits bridge in Wales—the world's first major suspension bridge.

(Violetstar/Fotolia)

PERSONAL: AN ACCOMPLISHED AND REVERED ENGINEER

In the summer of 2012, my wife and I were on a bus tour of northwestern Wales. We saw the beautiful Menai Straits suspension bridge and a mountain portion of Telford's Holyhead to London road. Several times, the tour guide lauded Telford's work; he's considered a hero in Scotland and beyond. Besides designing bridges, roads, canals, harbors, and tunnels, Telford had other creative and innovative accomplishments to his name. For example, he was a founder of and served as the first president of the British Institution of Civil Engineers, he published poems, he was elected a member of the Royal Swedish Academy of Sciences, and Ediburgh's Telford College—one of Scotland's largest colleges—is named in his honor (Sandstrom 1970; Smiles 1997).

The suspension bridge creativity and innovation story goes on. Telford's studies, tests, and designs stimulated more fundamental efforts by Gilbert, a Wales road commissioner who eventually became president of the British Royal Society. He developed and published a mathematical theory for suspension bridges (Billington 1996). Capturing the essence of a structure or process with a theory and mathematics is creative and innovative and enables others to benefit from the originating project. One creative endeavor led to another, which is a common occurrence. We are fortunate in most of our design work to have theory precede design—not follow it. As I mentioned in Section 3.7, creativity and innovation are applicable in all of our professional functions and beyond, including research and development.

4.3.5 A Hypothetical Example

Contemplate another example of how a team might use Borrowing Brilliance—especially the *get out of our silo* and *master the metaphor* aspects. Imagine you are part of a team or group twenty years from now that is organizing or reorganizing your national engineering consulting firm. You want to structure it in the most effective

Figure 4.4
This wagon wheel is a metaphor for the initial idea of how to structure a growing organization.

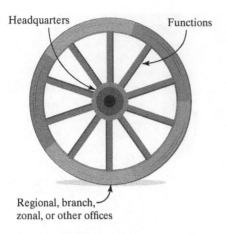

manner and anticipate growth. To generate options, you look over the top of your silo and begin to think of metaphors you can borrow from the world all around you. How about a wagon wheel? As shown in Figure 4.4, the hub could represent the organization's headquarters; spokes could represent corporate functions; and the rim represents regional, branch, zonal, or other offices.

As soon as group members begin to see this potential organizational structure, which is displayed in front of them on a whiteboard, questions arise that tend to push the wheel metaphor further. One question is, "So what do the offices on the rim do?" Answering that query leads to this possibility: The rim offices use the internal services (e.g., accounting, human resources, marketing) and deliver external services (e.g., design) that are produced in the corporate office.

However, the team is not satisfied with that approach and arrives at the modified structure shown in Figure 4.5. Although the spokes still represent corporate functions, all functions are not necessarily conducted only in the corporate office. Now, some of the other offices also perform one or more of the same functions. That is, each rim entity specializes in one or more corporate functions.

On seeing Figure 4.5, someone asks, "Why do we need a corporate office?" and suggests that corporate internal and external functions be spread over various

Figure 4.5
The initial organizational idea changes to put increased emphasis on the rim entities.

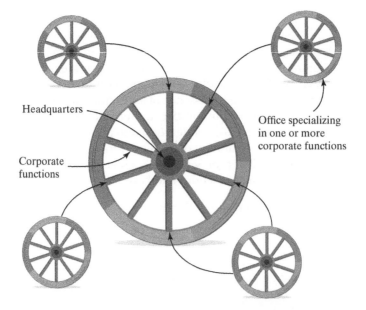

Figure 4.6
The final structure eliminates the corporate office and distributes functions across the organization based on personnel capabilities and local client/customer needs.

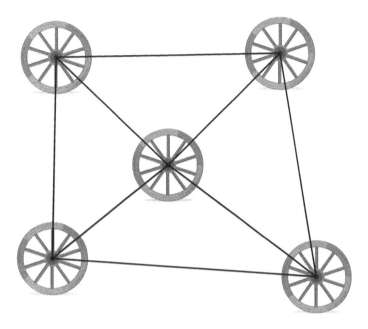

offices, as shown in Figure 4.6, based on personnel capabilities and local client/customer needs. With this approach, regardless of where a function originates, it could be delivered to or through any office. This hypothetical example illustrates how the evolving wheel metaphor could stimulate creative and innovative thinking about how to organize an evolving organization.

PERSONAL: TWO EXAMPLES

Although the wheel metaphor example is hypothetical, it reflects two personal experiences. The first is a conversation I had with one of the owners of an engineering firm of which I was an employee. The firm was thinking of expanding via acquisitions of other firms into other parts of the United States. The owner used the wagon wheel metaphor to explain to me how the expanded company could be organized. Each region would be a wagon wheel, and the company would be a collection of interconnected wagon wheels.

The second personal experience is from working as a consultant for an engineering firm. The firm is organized similarly to the structure shown in Figure 4.6; it has evolved to have no corporate office. Most of the time, the president is in one office and the vice presidents and other top executives are in other offices. The system appears to work seamlessly.

4.3.6 Neuroscience Basis

Consider some ways in which Borrowing Brilliance reflects our growing knowledge of neuroscience. For example, this method recognizes the mind's ability to make new connections if adequately stimulated, such as the Ford Motor Company connecting carcass disassembly to automobile assembly. Using the Medici Effect (a tool discussed later in this chapter) to form a team greatly increases the likelihood of success with Borrowing Brilliance because of the varied backgrounds of team members.

This method also makes explicit use of the subconscious mind in that Murray (2009) urges us to hope for parapraxes because they enable the subconscious mind to speak to the conscious mind. He also suggests taking a break because doing so "allows the subconscious to speak and the conscious to listen."

4.3.7 Positive and Negative Features

The most positive feature of Borrowing Brilliance is that at its core it invites ideas from everywhere, thus offering great creative and innovative possibilities. For example, at the divergent stage of searching for ways to resolve a challenging IPO, a diverse Borrowing Brilliance team can look far and wide for ideas. Other positive features of this method include that it can be applied to both defining and resolving an IPO and that it can be applied by an individual or group.

A negative aspect of this method is that such uninhibited lateral thinking is so contrary to traditional or left-brain oriented thought processes that it may not occur. Just suggesting it may invoke the negativity biases (Section 2.12) of some group members and place the team under the influence of the Einstellung Effect (Section 3.4). Such negative tendencies can be offset by an effective facilitator (Section 3.8).

4.4 BRAINSTORMING

Most people have heard of *Brainstorming*. Sometimes, the word is used as a verb, as in "let's brainstorm solutions to our problem"; in other situations, Brainstorming is a noun, the name of a method that we use individually or with a group. The word is commonly used, but I suspect that this seemingly simple method is rarely applied effectively.

HISTORIC NOTE: OSBORN'S FAITH IN CREATIVITY

The development of Brainstorming is credited to advertising executive Osborn, who described the idea-generation method in his 1953 book *Applied Imagination: Principles and Procedures of Creative Problem-Solving*. From 1952 to 1964, he also published three other books offering advice on how to be more creative. Consistent with this text, the widely acknowledged father of Brainstorming said that he wanted his readers to "become more conscious of the creative power within [their] reach" (Koberg and Bagnall 1991; Wheeler 2014).

4.4.1 Seven Steps of Brainstorming

Assume you are responsible for a functional area in your organization that is faced with a well-defined technical problem and that you decide to use Brainstorming to generate ideas for possible solutions. The suggested Brainstorming process is as follows:

1. In the spirit of the Medici Effect, invite a wide variety of participants, not necessarily a large number. For example, if this is a malfunctioning manufacturing process, invite an engineer who designs products and an engineer who designs manufacturing processes, a marketing person who understands customer expectations, a technician or technologist who operates and maintains manufacturing processes, a line worker who is closest to how the processes actually work, and an administrative person who is familiar with peripheral activities.

2. Create a nonthreatening environment so that all participants feel free to say what they think. This can be challenging in those organizational cultures in which individuals who are low down in the administrative structure are not encouraged to share ideas and information with individuals who are high up in the hierarchy. Avoid having a boss, a high-level executive, or another authority figure facilitate the Brainstorming session or even be present because some participants may be intimidated or otherwise reluctant to offer their views.

3. Pose the problem and explain the history (how we got here), and describe the desired result, such as fewer breakdowns, more production, and/or improved quality.

4. Invite—in fact, expect—everyone to offer ideas. Doing this from the get-go and keeping it going typically requires a skilled facilitator.

5. Be careful not to evaluate any ideas during the Brainstorming session. Again, a skilled facilitator is usually needed because many of us, especially engineers, want to analyze. Discourage any form of disapproval, including body language such as eye rolling, heavy sighing, shrugging, spinning a document on the table or desk, laughing at (not with) a contributor, and emailing or texting (Brenner 2007). Sometimes, individuals don't realize that they create these distractions. Distractions aside, at this stage, many and varied ideas typically begin to appear because
   - participants have brought and begin to share and reflect widely varying knowledge, skills, and attitudes;
   - some participants are very close to the problem at hand—but no one has ever asked for their views before; and
   - contributed ideas stimulate piggyback thinking and generation of more ideas by others.

6. Go for quantity of ideas, not quality (Byrne 2005).

7. Record all of the ideas as they are offered and do so in some manner, such as on a whiteboard or on newsprint, in which all participants can see the evolving list, which will serve as a stimulant.

If feasible, consider temporarily stopping the Brainstorming after Step 7 and resuming it for a short period in a day or two. This approach will stimulate cognitive processing in the subconscious minds of all or most participants. Accordingly, when the group reconvenes, new ideas are certain to appear. Conclude the Brainstorming process and then, and only then, begin to think about how you or others will evaluate and prioritize the many and varied solutions that have been generated.

4.4.2 Multivoting

Brainstorming and other idea-generation tools, such as Mind Mapping and Ohno Circle, typically yield many potential options, which then present the challenge of evaluating and prioritizing them. Multivoting, as illustrated in Figure 4.7, offers a systematic, democratic, and effective means by which a team can collectively prioritize ideas.

Figure 4.7
Multivoting provides a systematic, democratic, and effective way to prioritize a large number of ideas.

- Invite *a cross section* of participants

- Review the problem and *available ideas*

- *Distribute a predetermined number of votes* to each person

- *Vote*

- *Develop* top choices

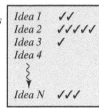

Begin by convening the group, which might be the original Brainstorming group or a new heterogeneous group. Set the scene by listing the available ideas in a highly visible fashion, such as on a whiteboard or sheet of newsprint. If this is a new group, then some background explanation will be required.

Give each person multiple votes. As a guideline for determining the number of votes per person, divide the number of ideas by about five. Ask participants to anonymously cast their allotted votes any way they wish, such as dedicating all of their votes to one idea or distributing their votes over two or more ideas. Participants will use their votes in accordance to the relative values they assign to options that interest them. Rank the results and then discuss one or more high-priority ideas and develop an action plan.

4.4.3 Electronic Brainstorming

Brainstorming can be conducted electronically, generally following the steps outlined previously. Cain (2012) reports that "Groups brainstorming electronically, when properly managed, not only do better than individuals; research shows, the larger the group, the better it performs." Using Figure 4.8, consider how electronic brainstorming might work.

Assume that a facilitator invites four diverse individuals to participate—and all four accept. Of course, we could have essentially any number of participants. Using email, the facilitator explains the process, describes the IPO, and invites each participant to share ideas by emailing them to the facilitator within a prescribed period, such as one day.

The first set of ideas arrives and is used by the facilitator to start an idea list. The list is immediately shared with all participants and they are asked, with their conscious and subconscious minds being stimulated by the list, to offer more ideas within one day while not sharing evaluations of the existing ideas. The process of generating ideas, adding them to an evolving list, and sending the list to participants with a request for more ideas could go on for several cycles until the process yields diminishing returns. As with conventional Brainstorming, the list could then be analyzed and prioritized and an action plan developed. Brainstorming software is readily available online. You may want to experiment with one or more software options after trying manual Brainstorming.

4.4.4 Neuroscience Basis

The modest visual aspect of Brainstorming in the form of the simple, real-time, readily seen list of ideas tends to stimulate both hemispheres of participants. If

Figure 4.8
Brainstorming can be conducted electronically.

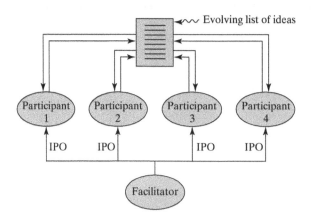

Brainstorming, a largely conscious mind process, is temporarily stopped, then useful cognitive processing will occur unnoticed in the subconscious minds of all or most participants. Therefore, when the process resumes, more ideas will appear.

4.4.5 Positive and Negative Features

The positive aspect of Brainstorming is that, with facilitation, it provides a means by which a diverse team can quickly generate many ideas. It can be used in the divergent mode to produce a list of possible causes of an IPO or a list of possible solutions to an already well-defined IPO. Other than for the facilitator, little or no preparation is required by the participants. Although you will produce more ideas if you ask invited participants to think about the topic ahead of time, thus engaging their conscious and subconscious minds, you also will generate many ideas without such preparation.

On the negative side, a study (Cain 2012) conducted by a psychologist concluded that group Brainstorming is less effective than individual Brainstorming. That is, under certain conditions individuals produced more and better ideas when they brainstormed alone versus in groups. The potential advantage of individual Brainstorming assumes that individuals will brainstorm on their own, in contrast to the more likely occurrence of effective Brainstorming if people are brought together in a focused, facilitated group (Section 3.8). Reasons given for the failure of group Brainstorming (Cain 2012) include the following:

- **Social loafing:** Some participants sit back and let others work.
- **Production blocking:** Only one person can talk or produce at a time, frustrating some others.
- **Evaluation apprehension:** People may fear appearing uninformed or even stupid.

Of course, these possible causes of group Brainstorming failure can be addressed at least in part by the facilitator, as a group works through the seven-step process described earlier. Furthermore, electronic Brainstorming can offset some of the previously mentioned reasons for failure of face-to-face Brainstorming. For example, during electronic Brainstorming, each participant will enjoy periods of solitude during which he or she can contemplate the issue and then offer thoughts, thus offsetting social loafing, production blocking, and evaluation apprehension. Finally, another way to offset social loafing and evaluation apprehension is to ask each participant to prepare a few initial ideas and bring them to the Brainstorming session.

4.5 FISHBONE DIAGRAMMING

Fishbone Diagramming, which is also called *cause-and-effect diagramming* or *Ishikawa Analysis* (Dhillon 2006; Hensey 1993), provides a systematic means for identifying widely varying possible causes of a problem. It's a diagnostic tool that can be used by an individual or a group to enhance the breadth and depth of the search for possible causes of or motivations for an IPO. The strongest argument for using Fishbone Diagramming is this principle: an IPO well-defined is half-resolved.

4.5.1 Description and an Example

Let's explain the Fishbone Diagramming process with an example based on one of my consulting experiences. Assume that you and your very diverse team (e.g., engineers, technologists, technicians, maintenance personnel, construction personnel) are studying a recently constructed storm water retention facility that seemingly failed to protect downstream properties during a large rainfall event.

Figure 4.9
Fishbone Diagramming provides a systematic means for identifying widely varying possible causes of a problem such as suspected failure of a storm water retention facility.

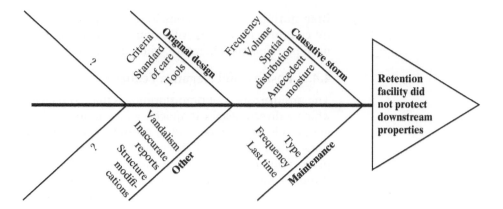

A storm water retention facility is typically designed and constructed to serve multiple purposes in an urban area. It normally contains some water for aesthetic and recreation purposes. However, its configuration and outlet works allow the facility to temporarily store additional water (storm water runoff) for later slow release to avoid downstream flooding.

Your group wants to determine the probable cause or causes of the apparent failure. Begin by drawing the "head" of the fish, as shown in Figure 4.9, on a whiteboard or sheet of newsprint so all can see it. Write "Retention facility did not protect downstream properties" in the head.

Next, collaboratively identify "bones," as shown in Figure 4.9—that is, categories of possible causes of failure, such as the causative storm, maintenance, the original design, and others. Detail each bone, make judgments as to the likely cause or causes of failure, and develop an action plan to further investigate the most likely causes. The process of having an individual or team carefully identify each bone and then detail each one encourages breadth and depth of up-front thinking and reduces the likelihood of jumping to incorrect conclusions.

PERSONAL: THE IMPORTANCE OF DOCUMENTATION

The Fishbone Diagramming example is based on one of my consulting assignments. I was retained by a city as an objective outside consultant to investigate the cause or causes of flooding that occurred immediately downstream of a recently designed and constructed storm water retention facility. My conclusion: The retention facility "failed" because the causative storm was more severe than the design storm, the severity of which had been selected by the municipality that retained the design consultant. Prior to my analysis, some local citizens and officials were quick to blame the flooding on faulty design and/or construction. On the contrary, the retention facility performed as expected.

My experience on this and other projects indicates that no matter what is being designed by engineers, they and those they serve need to fully understand and agree on the design criteria. Furthermore, the criteria and their implications should be carefully documented.

Consider another example. An engineering firm designed an improved system of storm sewers for a community, and shortly after it was constructed a major rainstorm resulted in extensive flood damage. The community started a legal action against the engineering firm, alleging negligence and breach of contract. I was retained as a consultant by the engineering company's law firm to determine what had happened. I concluded that the causative storm exceeded the conditions for which the piped system was designed.

However, the engineering firm had failed to document the meeting at which it and the community had agreed on the design criteria. That documentation lapse resulted in unnecessary postflooding actions, during which the engineering firm incurred large consulting, legal, downtime, and settlement costs. Within engineering practice, not documenting meetings is usually penny-wise and pound-foolish—no, ton-foolish.

4.5.2 Neuroscience Basis

Fishbone Diagramming is effective because its highly visual nature stimulates right-hemisphere processing to supplement that of the left hemisphere. The process is open-ended and stimulates whole-brain thinking because the evolving fishbone can have an unlimited number of bones and each bone can have an unlimited number of features. If this method is conducted as a series of events, ongoing stimulation of the subconscious mind will result in additional bones and/or elements of bones.

4.5.3 Positive and Negative Features

One positive feature of Fishbone Diagramming is its highly visual aspect: The fish skeleton is drawn in real time in response to suggestions offered by participants. Seeing each new bone appear stimulates individuals to think of possible additional bones. Similarly, adding a detail to any given bone challenges participants to think of additional details appropriate for other bones. Another positive feature of this method is that it can be used by an individual or a group.

The only negative aspect of Fishbone Diagramming is the possibility of giving insufficient attention to identifying all possible bones and their elements. This could result in missing a key aspect of an IPO. One way to avoid this omission problem is to work on the fishbone diagram, stop, and then resume on another day, thus giving each participant's subconscious mind an opportunity to weigh in.

4.6 MEDICI EFFECT

You will increasingly be able to influence the makeup of teams charged with meeting a challenge. Use the *Medici Effect* to select highly diverse team members. This section describes diversity, mentions the sometimes surprising novice effect, explains the four steps of successful team development, and provides examples of the creative and innovative work of diverse teams.

4.6.1 Back to the Renaissance

Assume that you are part of or leading a group that is about to tackle a challenging IPO. Recognize that success of the creativity and innovation methods presented in this chapter and in Chapter 7 usually depend in part on assembling and then energizing a highly diverse group. One way of describing the Medici Effect is to think of gathering a whole-brain team—a team composed of individuals with highly varied left- and right-brain capabilities (Leonard and Straus 1997). As someone said, "None of us is as smart as all of us." Sutton, an engineering professor, characterizes the Medici Effect as bringing together "people who know too much and people who know too little" (Wolff 2012).

What does he mean by "people who know too much?" I don't think we can know too much. However, when someone knows a great deal about a particular topic, maybe the approach to moving forward in that topic depends too much on how it has been approached in the past. That is, the Einstellung Effect (Section 3.4) rules the thinking process. Having some team members who know "too little" about the subject at hand can offset the downside of those team members who know "too much." We'll return to this later when we discuss the novice effect.

A related aspect of team diversity is to engage one or more individuals who are knowledgeable about, and maybe even experts in, creative and innovative processes such as the principles and tools presented in this book. Their process expertise can synergistically combine the relevant subject matter expertise of some participants and the varied inputs of the other team members.

HISTORIC NOTE: THE RENAISSANCE

In advocating the practice of assembling and then energizing a truly diverse group, we are in effect using a miniversion of the Medici Effect, which formed the foundation for the Renaissance. As explained by consultant and author Johansson (2006), in the fifteenth century the wealthy Medici banking family of Florence, Italy, became a strong supporter of the arts and sciences. More specifically, the Medicis and a few others brought into Florence and generously supported "sculptors, scientists, poets, philosophers, financiers, painters, and architects," which led to "a remarkable burst of creativity."

Today, we may view establishing a diverse community as simple because of the Internet, but Arciszewski (2009) notes that the process once "was a rare occurrence [because] the Dark Ages was a time when interactions between individuals of different disciplines were not the norm." The interaction of highly varied individuals living in comfortable and interactive physical proximity in Florence gave birth to the Renaissance. You can use the six-century-old Medici Effect to establish a Renaissance-like atmosphere in your organization.

The Medici Effect can be used in your team efforts, beginning as a student, to stimulate creative and innovative means of resolving and solving problems and pursuing opportunities. Doing so requires assembling a diverse group and then diplomatically choreographing its efforts so that the group appreciates and draws on its diversity.

4.6.2 Types of Diversity

Consider the following kinds of diversity you might seek, depending on the IPO, when forming a team charged with thinking collectively in a creative and innovative manner (based in part on Johansson 2006):

- **Disciplines:** For example, engineering, accounting, planning, law, technology, surveying, architecture, or medicine.
- **Specialties:** For example, robotics, tall structures, private development, nanotechnology, precision agriculture, finance, or thermal imaging.

- **Positions:** For example, project architect, vice president, project manager, technical specialist, human resources manager, research and development director, president, resident project representative, marketing manager, administrative assistant, chief surveyor, chief executive officer, technologist, mayor, or engineer intern.
- **Attitudes:** That is, how various individuals think and feel in response to a fact or situation, such as optimistic or pessimistic and proactive or reactive, and degrees of commitment, sensitivity, and thoughtfulness (American Society of Civil Engineers 2008).
- **Ethnicity:** For example, racial, religious, linguistic, historic, or physical characteristics.
- **Geography:** Familiarity with different physical geographies may have implications for some IPOs.
- **Age:** Members of generation Y and generation X, baby boomers, and traditionalists offer highly varied experiences, knowledge, and skills.
- **Gender:** For example, as noted in Section 2.14.6, females are generally considered better communicators.
- **Personality profiles:** For example, leader, task person, people person, or free spirit.
- **Novices:** That is, individuals whose experience and expertise are not related to the IPO at hand and its possible resolution. Examples include a new employee, a first-year engineering student or a nonengineering student, a colleague who is employed elsewhere, your former professor, or a co-op student who just started working in an engineering office.

The last two of diversity characteristics—personality profiles and novices—are discussed in more detail in the next sections.

4.6.3 Personality Profiles

Informed by experience, we know that we collectively represent widely varying personalities. "Personality is generally agreed to be a group of behavioral characteristics typically exhibited by an individual. . . . Personality can be seen as a bundle of habitual responses." Your personality is determined by genetics and learned behavior (Carter 2009).

As suggested by the preceding list of diversity types, diverse personality profiles are desired when creating teams for creative/innovative work. Many personality-profiling systems are available, such as the Myers-Briggs Type Indicator (Culp and Smith 2001; Wankat and Oreovicz 1993), Whole-Brain Model (Herrmann 1996), Personal Profile System (Carlson Learning Company 1994), Behavioral Types (Alessandra 2015), and People Mapping (Lillibridge 1998). Although delving into an array of these profiling techniques is beyond the scope of this book, a brief look at one system—People Mapping—can help you see the potential value of personality profiling.

With People Mapping, after completing a questionnaire, each participating person is placed into one of the following four personality types as their primary tendency:

- **Leader:** Will want to know about long-term impacts of an idea
- **Task person:** Will want to know how an idea would be implemented
- **People person:** Will want to know how an idea would impact others
- **Free spirit:** Will want to know what is unique/exciting about an idea

Although most of us can relate to and appreciate each of the four personality traits, People Mapping's premise is that most of us have a dominant trait. Having each of the four dominant traits represented on a team enhances the Medici Effect and strengthens the team. The Medici Effect aside, understanding your personality profile will give you a better understanding of you! Recognizing the personality profiles of others helps you work more effectively with them.

4.6.4 The Novice Effect

Why are novices included in the list of desirable types of diversity? Because we want to stimulate the novice effect. This is the sometimes surprising and powerful result of giving a task normally done by an "expert" to an "amateur" (Gross 1991). The amateur, unencumbered by much relevant expertise, may have a creative/innovative idea for addressing your IPO. The novice, unlike an expert, does not know what can't be done and what won't work. Many of the creativity/innovation examples presented in this text illustrate the novice effect, such as the creation of Velcro by an electrical engineer (Section 1.3.2), the weed eater by a dance instructor (Section 6.6.1), and masking tape by a sandpaper salesperson (Section 6.6.2).

PERSONAL: NOVICE EFFECT IN ACTION

Shortly after starting work as an engineering dean many years ago, I noticed that department chairpersons in the engineering college invested a large amount of time each semester scheduling engineering faculty, students, and classrooms for the next semester and I understood this to be an important and complex process. On asking one of the chairpersons how his group carried out the task, he pointed to his head and said "it's all up here."

In the spirit of helping, I suggested that the chairpersons' efforts might be reduced if they involved my administrative assistant. Prior to my hiring her, she had scheduled work in a production line at a local manufacturing plant. Furthermore, she was a computer whiz and welcomed challenges. The department chairperson didn't think the administrative assistant could be helpful because, among other things, she wasn't even a college graduate. However, he reluctantly agreed to let her sit in on the meetings at which the chairpersons did the scheduling.

Within a year, she had most of the scheduling process on a spreadsheet and from then on saved several personnel a lot of time every semester. She didn't know what she couldn't do—the novice effect in action.

4.6.5 Four Steps for Successful Team Development

Assume that, as the leader of a team of students, you just pulled a highly diverse group together (in keeping with the Medici Effect) and asked the group to address an issue, solve a problem, or pursue an opportunity. Some group members know some other members, but the individuals have not worked closely together. Or, assume you are a new member of such a new team. The team plans to meet face-to-face and via conference calls.

The challenging IPO aside, the immediate priority is to enable the group to work together. You plan to use some of the whole-brain tools described in this chapter and in Chapter 7 partly to break down barriers as discussed in Section 3.2.3, but first you have to get the team acquainted and moving forward. This may be difficult because the group is by design composed of very diverse individuals who are not well acquainted and have not functioned as a team.

Figure 4.10
Diverse teams often must work through a four-step development process.

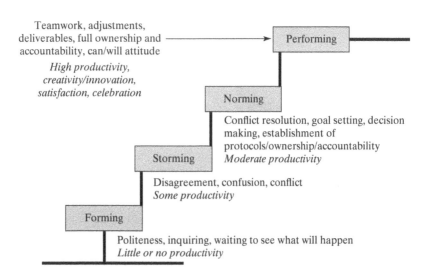

Teamwork, adjustments, deliverables, full ownership and accountability, can/will attitude

High productivity, creativity/innovation, satisfaction, celebration

Performing

Norming

Conflict resolution, goal setting, decision making, establishment of protocols/ownership/accountability
Moderate productivity

Storming

Disagreement, confusion, conflict
Some productivity

Forming

Politeness, inquiring, waiting to see what will happen
Little or no productivity

Forming

As shown in Figure 4.10, the first step is Forming. At this stage, team members start to become acquainted (some have never met), and the group begins to become organized. This is usually a polite and pleasant interlude, with little or no productivity, while team members wait to see what will happen.

Storming

However, when the group tries to do some work and make some decisions, the second step, Storming, often occurs, as suggested by Figure 4.11. Storming is fueled partly by the group's diverse design. Factions form and disagreements, confusion, and/or conflicts occur. Some individuals knock heads. Team members may have very different understandings of the group's purpose and/or ways to address it. Nevertheless, some productivity may occur. More importantly, Storming can hamper, if not destroy, the effectiveness of a truly diverse team.

Consider some ways to minimize the turmoil of the second step and mitigate Storming:

- **Arrange an early face-to-face meeting:** Increasingly, because of geographic separation coupled with more communication options, we form or join virtual teams.

Figure 4.11
Resolving the potential storming step is one of the challenges in implementing the Medici Effect.

(DragonImages/Fotolia)

Typically, members are geographically separated and often are employees of different organizations. Many have never met most of the others. I urge a very early face-to-face meeting of a new virtual team, even if the monetary costs are high, because the teams may be virtual, but their relationships should be real (King 2007). We want to avoid Team In Name Only (TINO; Brenner 2008). Most of us are much more likely to communicate and collaborate electronically once we've met face-to-face. We want another person to be more than an email address. The desired team creativity/innovation ultimately comes from connectivity, not proximity. The early-on, upfront, face-to-face meeting can be the foundation of that connectivity.

- **Provide context:** By context, I mean, how did we get here? Looking forward, where do we want to go? Who cares about the results and why?
- **Agree on terminology:** I find that terminology is often a major stumbling block. For example, I served on a committee with the charge of "entering the professional practice of civil engineering." Defining this deceptively simple-looking expression took a major effort but proved valuable and enabled the committee to move forward. Agree on terminology and put it in writing. Maybe start a glossary, especially if one team deliverable is a report.
- **Encourage sharing:** Encourage everyone to speak up. Recall why we assembled all these different people in the first place. Leverage the diversity. One way to draw on diversity, especially if you are the group's leader or facilitator (Section 3.8), is to go beyond the golden rule. Rise up to the platinum rule: Instead of treating team members as you would like to be treated, strive to communicate with them as you perceive they would like to be approached based on what you are learning about their personality profiles and other characteristics.
- **Respect:** Roles often follow from diversity. Assume someone volunteers to edit the team's report because of his or her writing knowledge and skill. Try to defer to that person on routine editing decisions.
- **Establish meeting protocol:** For example, prepare agendas and minutes, mute cell phones, expect everyone to participate, never exceed one hour, and honor action items. You could also consider somewhat higher-level protocols, such as 1) transparency—issues are discussed here, involving the entire committee, team, or group, and decisions are made here; and 2) no repercussions—honest views are expected and those who express them will not be penalized (Tompkins 1998). One of my clients went so far as to adopt *rules of the road* for the management group, frame them, bring them to meetings, and set them in the middle of the conference table for all to see.

Norming, Performing, and Maybe Mourning

Step 3, as shown in Figure 4.10, is Norming, which begins when most group members see diversity as a source of energy and synergy, as the fount of creativity and innovation. The interpersonal difficulties of the Storming step fade away. The team starts to produce by applying some of this text's whole-brain tools. Step 4, Performing, is the ultimate step. This is where the real work gets done.

Sometimes, team members experience a fifth step, Mourning. That is, the joint effort was so uplifting, satisfying, and productive that members miss the group when the creative/innovative effort is completed.

4.6.6 Avoiding the Cloning/Sameness Approach

When an individual gathers a group to address an issue, solve a problem, or pursue an opportunity, one tendency (perhaps subconscious) is to clone oneself—or if not that extreme, to gather very similar individuals, as in, "Let's get the usual gang together, all of whom are mostly like us, to kick this around." Although this natural cloning or sameness inclination is likely to provide comfort, it is not likely to promote creative or innovative thinking. Homogeneity of participants stifles creativity and innovation, whereas heterogeneity stimulates them.

The tendency towards sameness also occurs when groups or teams self-organize. That is, when members of a large group are asked to form small groups or teams, the natural inclination is to gravitate toward similar individuals: similar in appearance, education, background, philosophy, and other features. Psychologists call this the similar attraction effect, and "it can have a devastating impact on our efforts to create diverse teams," according to consultant Johansson (2006).

Herrmann (1996), who conducted extensive left- and right-brain investigations, also studied the effect of team composition on the resulting degree of creativity/innovation. He concluded:

- *Homogenous teams* will tend to experience high communication effectiveness; require little time to make decisions, such as how to address an issue, solve a problem, or pursue an opportunity; and arrive at results that are *low in creativity/innovation.*
- *Heterogeneous teams* will tend to experience low communication effectiveness (at least initially, as explained in the discussion of the four steps of effective team development), take a long time to make decisions, and arrive at *highly creative/innovative results.*

If you want a group to function creatively and innovatively, don't let cloning and sameness considerations drive team formation. To reiterate, diversity means diversity; it does not mean homogeneity, nor does it mean exclusivity, as in the idea the only high-ranking individuals in the organization should be engaged in addressing challenging IPOs.

PERSONAL: EVERYONE CAN CONTRIBUTE

I recall drafting a proposal to conduct a creativity and innovation workshop for an engineering firm. The proposal advocated including technicians and administrative assistants in a group of engineers that would participate in the workshop. A proposal reviewer said, "It is not clear to me how the laboratory technician or the administrative assistant would necessarily help." Perhaps that is a common response to the kind of diversity I am advocating. Frankly, a laboratory technician and an administrative assistant are likely to hear, see, and think about things relevant to the IPO at hand that others will not.

If anyone wants to learn what is really going on and should be going on within the office of an engineering organization, ask an administrative assistant who has survived several bosses and many employees and has been around for a long time. If you want to learn more ways in which designers in offices could produce more useful plans and specifications, ask a technician who works in the field observing or directing manufacturing or construction in accordance with those plans and specifications.

4.6.7 Examples

Despite having heard the argument for the Medici Effect and the effectiveness of teams composed on the basis of highly varied diversity, some of us may still view creativity and innovation as being primarily the result of individual effort—personal genius in action. For example, William Shakespeare, Thomas Edison, and Steve Jobs come to mind as solo, heroic creators and innovators. But were they? Probably not:

- "Some scholars are now saying that the plays we attribute to Shakespeare, among the greatest works of genius in all civilization, were probably created by a team" (Cooper 2006).
- Edison's Menlo Park, New Jersey, laboratory "was filled with highly-talented innovators" even though Edison "took most of the credit for his breakthroughs" (Cooper 2006).
- The late Steve Jobs, who led Apple, may not have been the highly individualistic creator he was commonly viewed to be. For example, he was known for giving unique, casual, conversational, and passionate presentations when releasing new products. Did he create these presentations by himself? No, noted communication writer Reynolds (2008), who said that Steve Jobs "and his team prepare and practice like mad to make sure it looks easy."

During World War II, the German navy quickly assembled groups of submarines, called *wolf packs*, to attack and sink allied ships. Any German submarine that observed an allied ship or a convoy of them would use a coded message to call in other submarines, and then the wolf pack would converge and destroy the ship. They were effective: For a year or two, the Germans sank an average of fifty ships per month, with total casualties of over fifty thousand (Johansson 2006). The allies had to break the code called Enigma so that they could warn and protect their ships and take other military offensive and defensive actions.

Accordingly, the British intelligence unit gathered a diverse group of potential code breakers, in Medici Effect style, who worked in a Victorian mansion northeast of London. The group included linguists, mathematicians, chess grand masters, scientists, crossword puzzle experts, and individuals from many countries all committed, for various reasons, to breaking Enigma. Their achievement was described as the greatest intelligence triumph of World War II or any war because the allies could now read Germany's highly secret messages (Johansson 2006; Macintyre 2012).

4.6.8 Neuroscience Basis

The Medici Effect connects to our expanding neuroscience knowledge in two ways. First, it recognizes that although our brains may look similar, each of us has a unique knowledge-skills-attitudes set and personality profile, which, among other implications, means that each person can make one-of-a-kind contributions to any team's creative/innovative effort. Second, and as explained by the novice effect, sometimes what we do not know about a particular IPO enables us to make fresh and powerful contributions, given the ability of our brains to see connections among areas of expertise.

4.6.9 Positive and Negative Features

On the positive side, research and experience indicate that diverse groups typically resolve IPOs in a creative or innovative manner. A possible negative feature of the Medici Effect is the challenge of working with a highly diverse group, especially guiding it through the possible Storming stage. Another potential negative for some users is that to be effective, the Medici Effect should be used with one or more other methods described in this chapter or in Chapter 7; this may cause some confusion. The suggested approach is to use the Medici Effect when forming a team that will be charged with taking on a challenging IPO and doing so in a creative and innovative fashion. Then, suggest one or more other methods from this chapter or Chapter 7 that the group could use to get started.

4.7 MIND MAPPING

Mind Mapping (Arciszewski 2009, Gross 1991), also known as *clustering* (Rico 2000), is a highly visual method that helps an individual or team address an issue, solve a problem, or pursue an opportunity. It is effective in initially defining the IPO and then, by applying Mind Mapping again, in identifying potential ways to resolve it.

HISTORIC NOTE: ORIGINALLY A NOTE-TAKING METHOD

Mind Mapping was advanced in the 1980s by Buzan, a British psychologist, educator, and author of books about the human brain (1983, 1984, 1991). Early on, he suggested that Mind Mapping was an effective tool for note taking, which may have been inspired by Leonardo da Vinci's method of note taking (Gelb 2004). More specifically, Buzan suggested the following when taking notes (Buzan 1983): "Rather than starting from the top and working down in sentences or lists, one should start from the center of the main idea and branch out as dictated by the individual ideas and form of the central theme."

Therefore, Mind Mapping was originally used by an individual to organize ideas he or she hears from others. However, as stressed in this chapter, Mind Mapping evolved to also be used by a team to define an IPO and to be applied prospectively to prepare a presentation, construct a project plan, identify options, and for other forward-looking, creative/innovative efforts. Stressing the whole-brain aspect of mind mapping when used in a prospective manner, Gelb (2004) says, "Mind mapping frees you from the tyranny of premature organization, which stifles your generation of ideas."

4.7.1 A Team Mind Map in Action

As a means of describing the Mind Mapping process, consider Figure 4.12, a mind map developed by a group of four. They were addressing a problematic pond in a residential area. A twenty-five-minute Mind Mapping session was used to define the problem. For the purpose of sharing the result, the subject of the mind map is not important, other than to say that the topic being addressed was poorly defined at the outset, in that the four individuals had different perceptions of the problem. The important aspects are the resulting format and the process used to create it.

To get started, state and show the topic in a manner visible to everyone, such as on a whiteboard or newsprint (in this case, as indicated in Figure 4.12, the topic was a pond problem). Ask each participant, "What does this make you think of?" or "What comes to mind?" Whatever pops into anyone's mind and is shared is added to the mind map in ovals connected by arrows. This tool "radiates visual and spatial cues from a central idea" (Miles 1997).

Anything goes; if someone thinks his or her idea is connected in some way to what is already shown on the mind map, then it is. As with brainstorming, don't judge any of the suggestions other than to ask for clarification. Also as with brainstorming, one or more participants may want to go into an analysis mode. The facilitator must nip this in the bud. My experience in using Mind Mapping is that once

Figure 4.12
Preparing this mind map enabled a group to quickly define a problem and then focus on solving it.

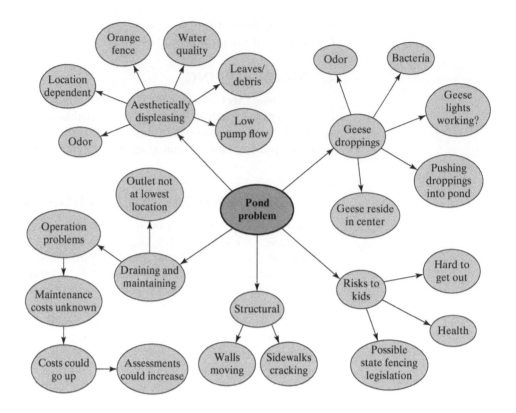

a group gets started, a flood of ideas quickly appears. Very soon, a large mind map or cluster appears. To reiterate, while Mind Mapping, do not be judgmental of any suggestions. If someone suggests it, then it's mapped.

As shown in Figure 4.12, Mind Mapping identified five problem areas (aesthetics, geese, safety, structural, and draining/maintaining) and elaborated on each of them. As soon as the mind map was finished, the group turned to a discussion of possible solutions, one of which was implemented. The essence of this Mind Mapping example is that a problem well-defined is half-solved, and group Mind Mapping is an excellent problem-definition tool.

Mind Mapping software is available (e.g., see Prestpin 2011), but I suggest that you draw by hand, at least in your initial uses of this tool, so that you fully appreciate the method's potential. Hand drawing is uninhibited, enhances spontaneity, and more fully engages the right hemisphere of your brain (Arciszewski 2009). I have yet to see the need for Mind Mapping software for group use of Mind Mapping and am concerned with adding anything that detracts from the ability of the facilitator to read the audience, engage all members, and capitalize on the usual spontaneity of the process. However, you may want to experiment with software after initial manual efforts.

4.7.2 An Individual's Mind Map in Action

Several years ago, I wanted to create text and visuals for a presentation about cold calls as a marketing technique. Within engineering, making a cold call means that an engineer meets with a potential client or customer that does not know much about the engineer or his or her organization. The engineer's goal is to have the other person's organization eventually become a client or customer.

Figure 4.13
This mind map was used as the basis for creation of a cold calls presentation.

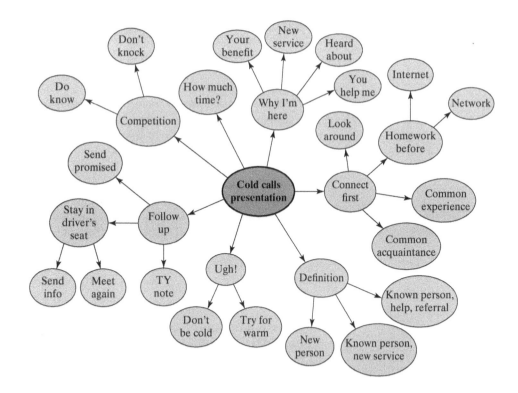

I needed to create an in-depth presentation about a topic that was somewhat new to me. Therefore, to get started, I prepared a mind map over a four-day period, devoting no more than a total of fifteen minutes to the effort. I subsequently took the hand-drawn version of the mind map and used it to make a neater version, which is shown in Figure 4.13. Remember, this mind map was created in only fifteen minutes over four days.

To get started, I wrote "Cold calls presentation" in the center of a piece of paper and then added whatever occurred to me in ovals. For example, my first thought was "Ugh!"—as in, "Who wants to make cold calls?" This led to the idea that maybe the calls didn't really have to be "cold" and instead could be somewhat "warm." Then I moved to defining who an engineer might be calling on and under what circumstances. After that, the mind map rapidly expanded and provided more than I needed to prepare my presentation.

Note that I prepared the mind map in spurts over a four-day period. If you do this, your conscious mind will prime your subconscious mind with the task at hand. Each time you return briefly to the Mind Mapping process, you are likely to discover new ideas and information to add to the map. Your subconscious mind will have been working behind the scenes for you.

I frequently use Mind Mapping in my work, either on an individual basis, as in the preceding example, or as a facilitator for a group. This tool has helped me and/or teams get started on reports, courses, proposals, presentations, and other tasks.

4.7.3 More Examples

As suggested by the two Mind Mapping examples, this tool can be used by an individual or a team in a variety of situations. As a consultant for a city utility studying whether or not to continue fluoridation of the public water supply, I facilitated two Mind Mapping exercises to help the city's Fluoride Commission imagine the many and varied possible consequences of whatever they decided to do. One session assumed that they would recommend terminating fluoridation, and the other session assumed they would continue fluoridation. Both sessions quickly generated many ideas that proved useful in making their final recommendation, which was to continue fluoridation and revisit the issue in five years (Fluoride Commission 2014).

As additional examples, a team of graduate students used Mind Mapping to identify fourteen potential uses for highway median barriers, in addition to safety. Exercises 4.4 and 4.9 at the end of this chapter challenge you to do better. Another student team used Mind Mapping to list structural and nonstructural ways to quickly and temporarily flood-proof a highly vulnerable manufacturing plant that was threatened with flooding because of melting, unusually heavy watershed snow cover (Walesh 2011). That project is the basis for Exercise 4.12.

Former professor Arciszewski (2009) prepared a mind map showing ways to create the ambience needed for a successful engineering department at a university. The use of Mind Mapping in marketing is described with specific examples by Prestpin (2011). Gelb (2004) also offers Mind Mapping advice and presents examples of mind maps, including some using simple images instead of words.

4.7.4 Why Is Mind Mapping Effective?

Whether used individually or by a team, Mind Mapping is an effective means for generating ideas and information for the following reasons:

- Other than for the efforts of a possible facilitator, no preparation is required beyond choosing the topic and selecting participants, who should be very diverse, in keeping with the Medici Effect. This is not to say that participants could not be primed ahead of time to think about the IPO that they will address.
- Mind Mapping can be done quickly in real time (a half-hour to an hour per session for a group) by simply drawing on an individual's knowledge and experience or, better yet, on the combined knowledge and experiences of team members.
- Once the process starts, ideas and information flow, and each contribution, which is readily seen by all participants, tends to stimulate more contributions. Like Brainstorming, the process is all about generating unevaluated content for later consideration, but Mind Mapping is more visually stimulating.
- This process is nonlinear. It does not require one item to logically follow another in left-brain, step-by-step fashion. At any point, the mind map can grow up or down, left or right. Therefore, this tool also engages the right brain and many highly varied ideas are generated as a result. Stated differently, Mind Mapping supplements valuable left-brain abilities with equally valuable right-brain abilities.
- If Mind Mapping is conducted as a series of short episodes, the subconscious mind of one or more individuals will contribute additional information and ideas.

4.7.5 Uses of a Completed Mind Map

What do you do with the completed mind map—that is, the display of many connected, somewhat organized ideas and information? Consider the following possibilities, which are not necessarily in a preferred order, and mix and match them as appropriate:

- **Combine and distill:** Group ideas into categories and remove repetitious topics. When you do the former tempered by the latter, you will begin to sense that which is important to your group while revealing some completely new concepts, ideas, and directions.

- **Cherry-pick:** Select some ideas and pieces of information, recognizing that you may not be able to address all of them, and then prioritize and develop an action plan for the most viable ones.
- **Prepare and share an outline version:** Convert the mind map, or at least most of it, into a more organized outline. Send the outline to others, including the team that conducted the Mind Mapping, and ask for their thoughts. The outlined ideas and information will stimulate additional insights.
- **Conduct research:** Research selected topics and summarize the results.
- **Draft a document:** Use the Mind Mapping results to prepare and distribute a memorandum, report, or other document as needed, with supporting figures and tables. Request input.
- **Reconvene the original group:** Bring the Mind Mapping group back together, review post-Mind Mapping documents and activities (such as the aforementioned outline), discuss further, and decide on a course of action and implement it.
- **Develop more mind maps:** For example, the first mind map may have defined an engineering challenge, the second one could explore options to address it, and the third consider ways to implement the selected option.

4.7.6 Neuroscience Basis

Mind Mapping is informed by neuroscience partly because when this method is applied, the subconscious mind, or minds, are directed by the conscious mind or minds, become engaged, and begin to contribute ideas and information, especially if a follow-up session occurs.

Furthermore, this method's strong visual feature in the form of an expanding, highly visible cluster of ovals or other shapes stimulates activity in both hemispheres of participants.

4.7.7 Positive and Negative Features

The most positive aspect of Mind Mapping is its highly visual nature, which engages both of the brain's hemispheres, whether it is being applied by an individual or a team. The addition of an oval as a result of one person's suggestion stimulates others to think of more ovals. This is an especially important benefit for engineers, who tend to rely on left-brain thinking. Another benefit is that no preparation is required other than that of a possible facilitator. Considering the small amount of time required to apply it, Mind Mapping typically generates numerous and varied content.

The only significant negative feature of Mind Mapping is that optimum effectiveness when used by a group requires gathering a diverse group of individuals, consistent with the Medici Effect, and facilitating their interactions and contributions. Assembling such a group may be difficult, especially in hierarchical organizations in which important functions like decision making and long-range thinking have traditionally been reserved for a homogeneous set of individuals high in the organizational structure.

4.8 OHNO CIRCLE

Named after engineer Taiichi Ohno, an early innovator of the Toyota Production System, this method is "used to make deep observations of a process or scene with the goal of improving what you see" (Wilson 2011). The *Ohno Circle* differs from most of the other methods in that it is used only by an individual, not a group or team. However, it may be used to enhance group or team performance, as discussed later in this section. Therefore, I include it in the set of methods intended to help you and your groups more creatively and innovatively address issues, solve problems, and pursue opportunities.

4.8.1 Description

"The story is that Mr. Ohno would have his engineers and managers who were new to a manufacturing facility draw a circle about two feet in diameter on the floor at a visually advantageous location in a factory. Then he would ask them to stand in the circle and observe what was going on for up to eight hours at a time" (Wilson 2011). They would share what they learned and any improvement ideas they may have. As suggested by Figure 4.14, one can imagine that the novice effect (Section 4.6.4) would naturally occur as novice engineers or managers ponder largely new processes and activities. Engaging the novice effect could lead to creative and innovative ideas.

We might argue that standing in a circle for many hours and observing is a waste of time. Instead, why not look at hard operations data—which assumes we have such data. However, "To Ohno, the big difference was that data was one step removed from the process, merely 'indicators' of what was going on," according to Liker (2004), a professor of industrial and operations engineering, who goes on to say, "What you want to do is verify the on-the-scene facts of the situation." Liker says that Ohno taught "the power of deep observation." This aligns with what is taught by Freehand Drawing, a whole-brain tool described in Section 7.4.

I realize you are not going to draw a circle on the floor and stand in it for eight hours or ask someone else to do so. However, how about taking thirty minutes, finding a quiet, unobtrusive place in one of your classes, laboratories, meetings, offices, or manufacturing plants, or at a construction site, and simply observing? Look and listen carefully, searching for wasteful or otherwise undesirable situations in categories such as the following (adapted from Wilson 2011):

- **Underutilized resources:** Capital, equipment, or personnel that are not being fully deployed or utilized
- **Excess motion:** Unnecessary movements of personnel, equipment, raw materials, and products that waste time and energy
- **Defects:** Production that repeatedly fails to meet standards and requires fixing

Figure 4.14
Ohno asked new personnel to stand in a circle, observe, and then share what they learned.

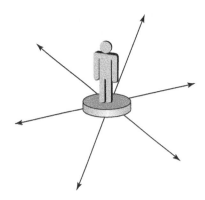

- **Excess inventory:** Retention and storage of parts, raw materials, and/or production not needed now
- **Non-value-added processing:** Performing work for which clients/owners/customers aren't willing to pay
- **Waiting:** Not having the materials, information, or resources at the right place or time
- **Safety and health hazards:** Objects to trip over, lack of eye protection, and similar risky situations

Search for ways to remove the deficiencies and make improvements in areas in which some of your suggested changes are likely to be creative and/or innovative. Document the improvement ideas and act on them.

Members of a team also could use the Ohno Circle. For example, assume that a diverse group of individuals has been formed and charged with finding ways to improve output from a production line in a manufacturing plant. An explanation of the Ohno Circle is part of the agenda at the team's first meeting. Prior to the second meeting, each person is asked to visit the production line alone and conduct a thirty- to sixty-minute Ohno Circle session. Observations are shared in writing and discussed at the group's second meeting and provide an informed basis for subsequent deliberations, some of which might include other methods described in this chapter and in Chapter 7.

4.8.2 Examples

While teaching one week of a graduate management-leadership course for civil engineers in Spain (Walesh 2011), I asked each student to select a situation, apply a modest thirty-minute version of the Ohno circle, and give me a written summary. Although students were limited by time and travel constraints, they selected a variety of everyday situations, observed them, and arrived at many and varied improvement suggestions. Examples of situations they observed and offered improvements on included team projects to be completed in class, passenger movement at a bus station, being productive in an engineering office, vehicle and pedestrian movement at an intersection, passenger movement on and off urban trains, and receiving service at a campus administrative office. These individual efforts generated some fresh and potentially useful ideas and illustrated the value of a modified version of Ohno's method.

Procter and Gamble's invention of the Swiffer floor cleaner includes Ohno Circle elements. In the 1980s, the company was looking for some new floor products and focusing on stronger detergents for use with cloth mops. After realizing the stronger detergents were not the answer, because they could damage the very floors they were trying to clean, the company's researchers decided, Ohno Circle style, to watch people clean floors.

They did this for several months, and one conclusion was that people devoted more time to cleaning mops than to cleaning floors. They also observed a cleaning person remove some spilled coffee grounds from the floor by using a moistened towel. These and other observations led to the conclusion that the long-reigning mop must be upgraded—and it was, by Swiffer, a floor-cleaning device with a disposable wet or dry cleaning surface (Lehrer 2012).

Innovation may seem obvious in retrospect, which is often the case. However, we don't create and innovate in retrospect. We need to start were we are, use tools such as the Ohno Circle, and move forward. What structure, facility, system, product, or process might you or your team be able to improve if you simply took the time to really observe it?

4.8.3 Neuroscience Basis

Use of the Ohno Circle resonates with the research-based advice shared in Section 3.5: Our brains are much more productive when we focus—that is, stay on task for a meaningful period. The Ohno Circle capitalizes on vision, the most dominant of the six senses (Section 2.4.2). Applying this method also tends to cause conscious mind–subconscious mind interaction. That is, once problems have been identified by applying the Ohno Circle, the desire to solve them will be planted in the subconscious mind, the subsequent working of which could lead to breakthroughs.

4.8.4 Positive and Negative Features

The most positive feature of the Ohno Circle is the ease with which anyone can unilaterally apply it. Another plus is the ability to use the Ohno Circle as a prelude to productive work by a team charged with addressing a challenging IPO. That is, each team member could be asked to personally apply the Ohno Circle to some aspect of the team's charge and share his or her observations with the team. The only possibly negative aspect of the method is the potentially unpleasant experience of staying in one place for an extended period while diligently seeing, listening, and thinking—but on second thought, isn't that what smart people ought to do, at least every now and then?

4.9 STREAM OF CONSCIOUSNESS WRITING

This method, like the Ohno Circle, is intended primarily for personal use, although members of a group could each do it for a predetermined question or topic and then share key aspects of their results. A group version exists and will be discussed shortly. Innovator Gelb (2004) describes *Stream of Consciousness Writing* as a "marvelous tool for plumbing the depths of your questions" and, I would add, any topic that interests or challenges you. He suggests that this tool can lead to insights and creative/innovative ideas because it overrides the "habitual, superficial aspects of your thought processes."

4.9.1 Individual Application

Stream of Consciousness Writing, which is also called *Brain Writing* (Fogler, LeBlanc, and Rizzo 2014), is the simplest method in this chapter and takes the least amount of time to apply. The following description of individual application is based on suggestions offered by Gelb (2004).

Select an issue that you want to address, a problem you need to solve, an opportunity you are considering, a question you are trying to answer, or a topic that you want to learn more about. Find a location where you will not be interrupted. With pen or pencil and paper or at your computer, write without stopping—without lifting your pen or pencil from the paper or your fingers off the keyboard—for ten minutes. Write whatever enters your mind and do not edit. Yes, some of what you write will be foolishness, but every now and then a fresh idea will emerge as you write; even as you continue to write, you may ask yourself, "Where did that come from?" Arciszewski (2009), a former engineering professor, had this to say about his teaching experience with this method: "The results of this exercise are usually amazing since it forces the student to think with both hemispheres of his/her brain."

When you are finished, read out loud what you have written and highlight words and ideas that seem insightful, creative and/or innovative, and potentially useful. Follow up with investigation and other actions as appropriate.

PERSONAL: AWKWARD AND REWARDING

During my first use of Stream of Consciousness Writing, which I tried because I was considering including the method in this book, I selected a business question that had been on my mind for some time. As soon as I started, I felt awkward, partly because I typically try to think widely and deeply when I write, which involves stopping, contemplating, occasionally walking around, and sometimes taking a break. However, I was quickly able to put aside my usual practices, disengage my internal editor, and simply write whatever popped into my mind. Some of it was foolishness placed on the paper so that I could dutifully keep writing. However, after the ten minutes of writing, I reviewed what I had written. Amid the debris, I found some fresh insights. Try Stream of Consciousness Writing: Your cost and risks are low, and the probability of benefits is high.

4.9.2 Group Application

Stream of Consciousness Writing can also be applied in a mostly silent mode by a group or team assisted by a facilitator as follows (Dhillon 2006):

1. Ask participants to sit around a table and give each person one sheet of paper.
2. Describe the issue to be resolved, the problem to be solved, or the opportunity to be pursued and a particular aspect of it, such as defining the issue or proposing solutions to the problem. Once the IPO is understood, request silence while participants work.
3. Encourage each person to write whatever comes to mind for one to several minutes—this is the time to be very freewheeling and not practical.
4. Ask each participant to pass their sheet of paper to the person next to them, or to encourage anonymity, mix the sheets up in the center of the table and have each person take one sheet, but not his or her own.
5. Repeat Steps 3 and 4 until written ideas diminish.
6. Gather all of the pages, post or summarize them, and engage the previously silent participants in evaluating the results. If group Stream of Consciousness Writing was used to define an IPO, it could be used again, now or later, to enable subconscious thinking and to generate resolution options. Multivoting (Section 4.4.2) might be used to rank the resulting options.

4.9.3 Neuroscience Basis

As noted by Arciszewski (2009), Stream of Consciousness Writing seems to draw on both sides of the brain. Perhaps this is because we are compelled to write for ten minutes when the method is applied individually (or for less time with the group process) no matter what happens. This encourages us to draw on all of our cognitive resources. According to Gelb (2004), if you persevere for the required period of continuous writing, "you'll eventually open a window through which your intuitive intelligence will shine." *Intuitive* means that you will engage your right hemisphere to supplement the left one. If the focused writing, whether in the individual mode or the group mode, is intentionally interrupted, then new ideas are likely to be generated when the effort resumes.

Recall the Section 2.12 discussion of your brain's negativity bias. As explained there, because of evolution, we are still subject to our ancestors' need to see danger or potential danger in a variety of common daily circumstances and to act defensively. The pressure attendant to Stream of Consciousness Writing may help you temporarily set aside the limiting thinking characteristic of negativity bias and reveal some heretofore unseen possibilities in your student life, professional practice, or personal life.

4.9.4 Positive and Negative Features

Clearly, the most positive aspect of Stream of Consciousness Writing is the ease with which you can try it. When used individually, less than a minute of your time is required to understand the individual version of the method, ten minutes to use it initially, and five minutes to review and think about the results. The return on that small time investment will probably be some fresh insights and maybe some creative/innovative ideas. Other than possible temporary discomfort while performing the writing, there are no negatives. The group approach might produce many ideas because it combines the effect of each participant thinking deeply and broadly about the topic, as in the individual version, with the stimulation of seeing the ideas of others.

4.10 STRENGTHS-WEAKNESSES-OPPORTUNITIES-THREATS

Although this method can be used by an individual, it's much more effective when applied by a group. *Strengths-Weaknesses-Opportunities-Threats* (SWOT) enables a group to thoroughly define and analyze essentially all aspects of an issue to be resolved, a problem to be solved, or an opportunity to be pursued.

4.10.1 Description

As is often the case with the use of the whole-brain methods described in this book, SWOT begins by having a facilitator assemble a heterogeneous group. Provide background information and pose the IPO that is to be thoroughly defined and analyzed prior to exploring resolution options.

Assume the IPO is a problem: a poorly performing service line in an engineering consulting firm. Within the engineering environment, the problem could also be a poorly performing research and development department, academic department at a university, design team, or manufacturing line. Create a readily seen matrix, like the one in Figure 4.15, in which the first column contains various elements or aspects of the problem. The remaining four columns represent the strengths, weaknesses, opportunities, and threats associated with each of those elements.

Start with the first row (Our personnel). In the Strength column, a group member suggests writing "Bill is an expert"; for the Weaknesses column, someone offers, "Bill does not listen to clients or colleagues." The Opportunities column entry might be "Maria contacted us concerning possible employment, and she is known to have great client communication skills." A Threats column entry might be "We will lose even more clients if our personnel continue to miscommunicate, mostly because of Bill." Stimulated by all of this, more short statements are likely to be suggested for the Our personnel row.

Then, the group moves on to the other rows. By the time the table is completed, at least in a first pass, many highly varied aspects of the poorly performing service line issue are now displayed, representing the collective view (at least the

Figure 4.15
The SWOT method generates a thorough understanding of a challenging issue, problem, or opportunity.

Element	S	W	O	T
Our personnel				
Our tools				
Existing clients				
Potential clients				
Regulatory environment				
Financing available				
	Internal		External	

initial collective view) of many diverse individuals. If the group temporarily adjourns and then gathers again in several days or so to resume the SWOT, be assured that many more contributions will be offered because of the workings of subconscious minds during the interval. Based on what is collectively learned as a result of the SWOT analysis, use other tools to generate ideas for how to solve the now well-defined problem, select a course of action, and develop an action plan.

As a student, you could readily imagine a group using SWOT to analyze why your senior project team is not productive, why the student chapter of your engineering professional society is struggling, or why your Greek organization has a poor reputation on campus. SWOT would also be useful, applied individually, for analyzing the first session of your multi-session co-op program or the first part of your job or graduate school search.

4.10.2 Examples

In the process of serving my clients, I have often used SWOT to assess situations and generate improvement ideas. In one case, office staff at a city's water utility participated in SWOT with the goal of improving their effectiveness and efficiency. We identified the following topics and determined strengths, weaknesses, opportunities, and threats for each: working space/layout, customer service, computer support, working with other units, communication, and personal recognition/reward. The result was a current and comprehensive snapshot of the office's operations, which led to many ideas for improvement.

I facilitated SWOT sessions with technical staff at the aforementioned water utility, with leaders of a wastewater district, and with managers of public festival grounds. The results were always the same: active participation by essentially everyone, a broader and deeper understanding of the situation, and generation of ideas for improvement, some of which were creative/innovative.

As suggested by the preceding examples, SWOT can be used in a variety of ways. For example, Milosevic (2010) describes using SWOT to determine how investors and contractors view a particular construction project. You can use SWOT as part of group efforts to improve your sorority or fraternity, campus organization, or senior project team. Later, you will find applications in engineering practice, some within your organization, and some involving your clients or customers. SWOT enables a group to quickly obtain a snapshot of its situation and use it as the basis for beginning to generate ideas, using other tools for making improvements.

4.10.3 Neuroscience Basis

SWOT connects to our growing neuroscience knowledge in four ways. First, the highly visual nature of the evolving matrix will stimulate both hemispheres of participants. Second, if a group applies SWOT to the same IPO in two or more sessions, the analysis will benefit from the conscious–subconscious mind interactions of each of the participants. Third, some group members may begin the SWOT effort with a narrow view of the IPO, possibly because of their strong left-brain orientations. However, their views will change and become more informed as they consider the input of others, as manifested by the many items in the first column of the rapidly developing table and the four aspects of each in the other four columns. Fourth and finally, the need to address both positives and negatives (Section 4.10.4) stimulates thinking, including emotional aspects, which tends to further engage the right hemisphere.

4.10.4 Positive and Negative Features

One positive aspect of SWOT is that it cannot degenerate into a complaining or whining session, which sometimes happens when troublesome issues or problems are discussed. While weaknesses and threats are unpleasant or negative, strengths and opportunities are uplifting and therefore positive. Furthermore, with respect to the group's potential to act and as shown at the bottom of Figure 4.15, although opportunities and threats are external and largely out of the group's control, strengths and weaknesses are internal and can be addressed by the group.

A possible negative aspect of SWOT is its seemingly somewhat restrictive structure. Once the participants begin the process, some may be inhibited or frustrated by the well-defined matrix. This potential obstacle can be easily offset by encouraging the group to be open to adding rows (elements or aspects of the IPO) to the matrix and to be willing to revisit any area within the matrix to add or modify content.

4.11 TAKING A BREAK

As a student, whether working individually or within a group, you're sometimes bogged down when intensely studying, researching, experimenting, analyzing, designing, writing, or engaging in some other challenging endeavor. You hit a wall, draw a blank, or experience writer's block. Similar frustrating experiences occur in professional practice. When this happens, whether you are a student or practitioner, take a break!

4.11.1 Description

Most of us welcome the invitation to take a break or the personal inclination to do so. However, we may also feel some guilt because walking away from the task at hand may conjure up thoughts of procrastination or laziness. Don't go there! Why? Because *Taking a Break*—that is, changing from one type of activity to another—stimulates creativity and innovation. This is especially true when transitioning from intense work to leisure, exercise, or a hobby.

Professor May (1976) tells the story of Einstein asking a friend, "Why is it I get my best ideas in the morning while shaving?" The friend's answer was, "Often the mind needs the relaxation of inner controls—needs to be freed in reverie or daydreaming—for the unaccustomed ideas to emerge." More specifically, according to Restak (2009), studies indicate that eureka moments tend to involve a shift in brain activity from the left to the right hemisphere. That shift tends to occur when we *power-down*, to use his term—that is, when we take a break or sleep.

PERSONAL: CHANGING GEARS TO MOVE AHEAD

One day, first thing in the morning, I began work on a book proposal for submission to a publisher. After about two hours, I had a good start, including an outline and some text. However, I began to bog down and also get hungry. I biked to a nearby restaurant and, while enjoying a light breakfast, three proposal-related ideas popped into my head. I wrote about them on the backside of a paper placemat, folded it, and tucked it into my pocket. I then began a ten-mile bike ride, during which I stopped three times to briefly jot down more ideas that appeared out of the blue. These specific situations are typical of many similar creative experiences I've enjoyed over the years that were stimulated by intensely working on a project and then changing gears. By the way, the proposal was accepted, and the book was published (Walesh 2000a).

May (1976) recognizes that what he refers to as "the insight [that] comes at a moment of transition between work and relaxation" is common. However, and this is critical to optimizing Taking a Break, he strongly suggests that these vivid breakthroughs of the subconscious mind to the conscious mind are preceded by "intense, conscious work." Think about an instance when an idea suddenly appeared to you out of the blue, perhaps during relaxation or exercise. Although the idea appeared to come from nowhere at the time, personal reflection is likely to reveal that it was preceded by one or more sessions of focused effort.

As illustrated in Figure 4.16, your conscious mind must make an intense effort before resting and (hopefully) allowing your subconscious mind to share creative and innovative ideas. Gelb (2004) says this about conscious mind–subconscious mind interplay: "Without periods of intense, focused work, there is nothing to be incubated." We cannot relax our way into creativity and innovation. As noted by engineering professor Cross (1952), "Hard work has a surprising way of paying unexpected dividends through later inspirations." However, we need to know when to stop and take a break.

Consider one specific way to leverage that hard work. Recall (as explained in Sections 2.9.2 and 2.9.3) that your conscious mind ceases operations while you are sleeping. In contrast, your 24-7 subconscious mind continues to function. Therefore, before retiring, summarize in writing the challenge you are facing and the hard work you have done to meet that challenge. Then, apply Taking a Break—that is, sleep. You may wake with some fresh ideas as a result of the work done by your subconscious mind while you slept.

Figure 4.16
Creative/innovative breakthroughs from the subconscious mind are preceded by intense conscious effort.

(Doble.d/Fotolia; Haveseen/ Fotolia)

4.11.2 Example: Bar Code

Reflecting on beaches, breakthroughs, and the work that precedes breakthroughs, consider the bar code story. In 1948, while an electrical engineering graduate student at Drexel Institute of Technology, Bernard Silver learned that a food store chain wanted to speed up the checkout process at its stores. He partnered with Norman Woodland, a friend and fellow graduate student, and they started to work on a system. Their first working model used fluorescent ink, but it faded and was expensive. This was the beginning of what would prove to be persistent effort with a breakthrough ending.

Eventually, mechanical engineer Woodland moved to Florida, near the beach, and continued to work on the project, now inspired by Morse code, which he had learned as a Boy Scout. He began to think about dots and dashes. One day at the beach during the winter of 1948–1949, while lying back in a beach chair, he stretched out a hand, put it in the sand, and pulled it back. He looked at his finger marks in the sand, saw lines of varying width, and this led to the bar code concept.

Silver and Woodland received a patent in 1952 for a "Classifying Apparatus and Method." The patent included the printing patterns and the mechanical and electronic systems needed to read the code. Philco bought the patent from Silver and Woodland for $15,000 in 1952, then RCA purchased it in the 1960s, a decade after the patent was issued. The missing element was the laser, which eventually enabled effective reading of bar codes.

On June 26, 1974, a ten-pack of Wrigley's Juicy Fruit gum was scanned with a device made by the National Cash Register Company (now NCR) at Marsh's Supermarket in Troy, Ohio. That package of gum is on display at the Smithsonian Institution's National Museum of American History. The first use of the bar code occurred twenty-six years after the day in 1948 when Silver conceived of it.

Astounding success followed: By 1980, 8,000 stores per year were converting to bar codes. Benefits to stores included a 1 to 2 percent decrease in operating costs and a 10 to 12 percent increase in sales that never dropped off. Of course, now we see bar codes all over (Adams 2014; Boehler 2012; Fox 2012).

Let's reflect on the Taking a Break tool in light of the bar code story. The bar code inspiration occurred while Woodland was relaxing at the beach and applying what we are calling Taking a Break from his roughly one-year effort to speed up the checkout process at stores. That insight was followed by an approximately twenty-five-year implementation period.

4.11.3 Example: Student Work

As a student, do you sometimes encounter a proverbial brick wall when trying to solve a difficult assigned exercise, understand a textbook's description of a topic, or make progress on your research project? Instead of trying to break through the wall macho style, apply Taking a Break and benefit from the productive interplay between your conscious and subconscious minds, between explicitly thinking about your mental challenge and letting it incubate in your other mind. For example, consciously and intensely work on the exercise, text, or research for about fifteen to thirty minutes, then set it aside and focus on something else.

Be confident that your subconscious mind will take over the task and provide you with new insights, either as an out-of-the-blue "aha!" moment or as a revelation when you consciously resume work on completing the exercise, understanding the text, or moving forward on your research. Engineering professor Oakley refers to student use of the conscious mind–subconscious mind interaction as the focused mode–diffused mode process (Oakley 2014).

4.11.4 Neuroscience Basis

Taking a Break is successful because it combines consciously focusing on a topic for a constructive period of time (one way to more productively use our brains, as explained in Section 3.5) with giving the subconscious mind an opportunity to function (as discussed in Section 2.9). The focused conscious effort primes the subconscious mind by giving it an increasingly well-defined task to work on. We may consciously try to engage both our left and right brains and do it with some success, but our subconscious minds enable us to draw on all of our cognitive resources.

4.11.5 Positive and Negative Features

One positive feature of Taking a Break is that its use is natural, at least in a rough way. When faced with a challenging IPO whose resolution is important to us, we naturally work intensely at it, while taking breaks to do other work-related tasks or to enjoy other activities. However, effective use of Taking a Break requires knowing when to back off—to temporarily walk away from the intense effort—and then having the confidence that your subconscious mind will eventually make one or more major contributions to helping resolve the IPO. Another positive aspect of this method is that, like most of the methods in this book, it can be used by an individual and by a team.

A possible negative feature of Taking a Break is that the conscious thinking efforts, whether done individually or by a team, will lack intensity. This denies the subconscious mind the breadth and depth of concepts, ideas, and information needed to perform its cognitive functions. Another negative is that an impatient person may not stick with the process long enough to effectively engage his or her subconscious mind. Consider Albert Einstein's view: "It's not that I'm so smart, it's just that I stay with problems longer." I might add that extra time allows the whole brain—left and right, conscious and subconscious—to contribute.

4.12 WHAT IF?

When faced with a challenging IPO, consider asking *"What if?"* in a way that temporarily and radically changes your point of view (Nierenberg 1982; Tice 2011). As a way of fully engaging both hemispheres, briefly view the challenge from totally different vantage points; for the time being, remove conventional constraints. As a result, you may literally or metaphorically see new realistic possibilities.

4.12.1 Description

Let's say you and your team are focused on an especially challenging IPO. Maybe it's a complex design, diagnosing a failed facility, dealing with a troublesome manufacturing line, or a vexing personnel problem. Up to now, you have adopted an up-close, frontal perspective. This is the time to ask, "What if?":

- What if, as illustrated in Figure 4.17, we were to metaphorically take a bird's-eye view? Look at it from just above, a worm's-eye view? Look at the challenge from the bottom? Or from a thirty thousand-foot view? Look at it from way above to see the bigger picture—the wider context?

Figure 4.17
What if we looked at our challenge with a new point of view, such as from just above, from below, or from way above?

(Erni/Fotolia; Fotomaster/Fotolia; Arturas kerdokas/Fotolia)

- What if funds were unlimited? They never are, but our thinking is sometimes unnecessarily constrained by limited financial resources.
- What if we had to build a bicycle out of cardboard?
- What if all subsurface conditions at a proposed construction site were known?
- What if, although we always perform some process as a series of steps (as shown at the top of Figure 4.18), we changed the order, performed some steps in parallel, and/or omitted low or no value steps?
- What if we just learned that a well-known consulting firm will enter our regional marketing area in three months?
- What if we had to install the new manufacturing line in one week? Yes, that is impossible, but what might trying to do it make us think of that would never have entered our minds?

What If mind sets, as foolish as most may be, enable you or members of your group to temporarily think beyond constraints and obstacles and maybe see new possibilities and find creative/innovative ways to overcome those impediments. An initial outlandish What If might be a stepping stone to a more reasonable What If.

For example, a Netherland city had a problem with out-of-control refuse because people were not using trash cans. An initial thought was to wonder, what if

Figure 4.18
What if we changed the order of steps in a process, performed some steps in parallel, and/or omitted low or no value steps?

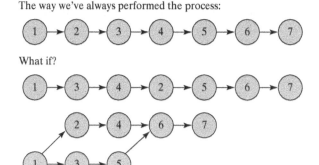

the city installed electronic sensing devices in trash containers that would use a coin mechanism to pay people when they put trash in the container? That unusual idea might solve the refuse problem but could bankrupt the city because of the cost of installing and maintaining the system, including keeping the containers stocked with cash. The flawed idea lead to further consideration of providing rewards for using trash containers. Researchers asked, what if we rewarded people for using trash containers by developing a sensor that would sense when refuse was added and activated an audio system that would play a joke, with the jokes being frequently changed? It worked (von Oech 1990)!

As another example of how an initial What If can be a stepping zone to a better one, consider a dog food company for which researchers explored the idea of putting nondigestible flower seeds and fertilizer in dog food. The dogs would be the means by which flowers would be planted and fertilized around a neighborhood. That What If was rejected, but it lead to the idea of putting grass seed in cattle feed as a means of reseeding range lands, which worked (von Oech 1990).

4.12.2 Example: Taco Bell Restaurant

Recall one of the preceding What If statements: "What if we had to install the new manufacturing line in one week?" The Taco Bell restaurant company provides an example of the benefits of looking at a similar seemingly extreme What If statement. The six-day disastrous August 1965 riots in the Watts area of Los Angeles, California, resulted in thirty-four deaths, over one thousand injuries, four thousand arrests, and forty million dollars in property damage, which included one Taco Bell restaurant (Civil Rights Digital Library 2014).

The Taco Bell company vowed a Watts comeback, and to emphasize its commitment, the firm announced that it would rebuild the restaurant over a forty-eight-hour period: This is the Taco Bell What If. After careful design and planning, the restaurant was prepared to rebuild as promised. Taco Bell placed a concrete slab; marshaled personnel, materials, and equipment on the site; and simultaneously started construction and a large on-site clock. The next forty-eight hours of carefully planned construction were recorded on video (Taco Bell, n.d.). Within just under forty-eight hours, the new restaurant started serving tacos. The company's application of What If yielded two benefits:

- Taco Bell earned positive publicity.
- The restaurant learned how to reduce construction time, which back then was fifty to seventy-five days. Building future restaurants in forty-eight hours would not be economically feasible, but the business learned enough about materials, personnel, and process as a result of the forty-eight-hour challenge to reduce the cost of more conventional construction by 20 to 50 percent. At the time, Taco Bell was building three hundred stores per year, which translated into major, ongoing cost savings for the company.

4.12.3 Example: Street Storage of Storm Water

In the 1980s, the 8.6 square mile community of Skokie, Illinois, a suburb north of and contiguous with Chicago, faced increasingly frequent and widespread basement flooding caused by backup of combined sewers during rainfall events. At the time, sewer separation was a common solution, but applying this approach in Skokie would mean converting the existing combined sewers to sanitary sewers and constructing new storm sewers at a cost of $203 million, in 1999 dollars. That level of funding was not available; a much less costly approach was needed.

Accordingly, engineers collectively and innovatively applied What If. More specifically, they asked, "What if we were to design and construct a system that would temporarily store much of the storm water on the streets throughout the entire community and then slowly release it into the combined sewers so that they would not surcharge?" This would solve the basement flooding problem.

Although unusual, this new idea of community-wide use of short-term street storage was attractive for three reasons: First, it might cost much less than traditional approaches. Second, it could counter the limited availability of off-street surface storage sites given the dense urban development. Third, temporary storage of storm water before it mixed with sewage addressed the cause of the problem—that is, out-of-control storm water. The concept of temporarily storing storm water on streets in a controlled manner to mitigate uncontrolled basement and surface flooding is illustrated in Figure 4.19.

The project began in 1982 and moved through discussion, public education and involvement, research, establishment of design criteria, preliminary design, hydrologic/hydraulic modeling, pilot testing, and final design. The system was built in phases from 1983 to 1999. The street storage system required constructing or installing 871 street berms like those shown in Figure 4.20, twenty-nine hundred flow regulators in catch basins as shown in Figure 4.21, ten off-street surface storage facilities, eighty-three subsurface storage facilities, sixty-four thousand feet of storm sewer, and twenty-nine thousand feet of combined sewer.

Much of the storm water storage and conveyance occurred on the streets in a controlled manner, as suggested by Figure 4.22, with supplemental storage provided off-street and beneath streets. The cost of the project was $78 million in 1999, or 38 percent of the cost of sewer separation (Walesh 2000b; Walesh and Carr 1999).

Figure 4.19
The street storage approach uses temporary ponding of storm water to mitigate uncontrolled basement and surface flooding.

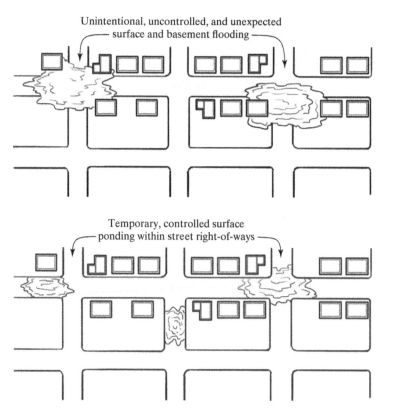

Figure 4.20
Mild berms constructed across streets and intersections help to temporarily store storm water on the streets.

(Stuart Walesh)

Figure 4.21
A flow regulator in a catch basin and a berm function as the outlet works of a temporary street storage facility.

Source: Adapted from Walesh 2000b.

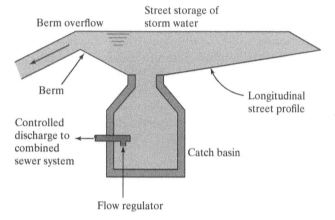

Berm overflow

Street storage of storm water

Berm

Longitudinal street profile

Controlled discharge to combined sewer system

Catch basin

Flow regulator

Note: Not to scale and great vertical exaggeration

Figure 4.22
Controlled temporary flooding of streets prevents uncontrolled basement flooding.

(Wckiw/Fotolia)

Because the project was innovative, the US Environmental Protection Agency commissioned a post-project study (Walesh 2000b). This investigation addressed a range of technical and nontechnical factors and concluded that the innovative system

- greatly reduced flooding;
- helped to raise the community's credit rating, adding $40 thousand to the average value of houses;
- avoided large increases in property taxes because of the phasing;
- resulted in only two claims and no litigation;
- increased system operation and maintenance, which was expected; and
- caused minimal pavement icing and left no evidence of pavement deterioration, both of which had been early concerns.

4.12.4 Example: Combining Features while Retaining Functions

Another application of What If is to look at one or more useful devices and ask, "What if we simplify them by combining features without compromising desired functions?" Benefits could include improved function and reduced cost. Reusing a proven design as a part of a new structure, facility, system, product, or process can significantly reduce design, manufacturing, construction, and other costs. Sometimes, repurposing is better than creating something new (Pisasale 2014).

Micropiles

After WWII, buildings and monuments across Europe were damaged. In response during the 1950s, the Italian civil engineer Fernando Lizzi invented micropiles as a means of underpinning war-damaged structures and monuments. These ingenious devices "develop their axial capacity primarily through the bond between the grout and soil or rock in the bonded zone of the pile." Advantages of these innovative underpinning devices include the following (Bennett 2010):

- Appropriate in low-headroom situations
- Low vibration and thus suitable for work close to existing structures
- "Can be installed in soil and rock conditions where the use of other conventional deep foundation systems is not a reasonable alternative, such as Karst topography or where modest subsurface obstructions or boulders are present"
- Applicable below the water table where other foundation systems are prohibited because of caving

Of relevance to this section on combining features is the observation that the drill used to form the hole within which the micropile will be formed becomes the means of inserting grout and then becomes the piling (Bennett 2010; Bennett and Hothem 2010).

Other Combining Examples

Some fast food restaurants provide customers with a spork, a plastic utensil that is a combination of a spoon and a fork (Figure 4.23). On my car, the usual gas filler access door and the gas filler screw-on cap are combined into one easier-to-use and presumably less costly unit (Figure 4.24). The creation of the integrated circuit, which is described in Section 6.3.3, nicely illustrates combining features in that now all circuit components can be made of a single material and interconnected to form a complete circuit. Another combining functions example is the Gratefish, a storm water system grate in the shape of a fish that replaces the conventional grate and the signage warning that the storm water system discharges into local surface waters (Neumeier 2014).

Figure 4.23
This utensil combines a plastic spoon and a plastic fork.

(Stuart Walesh)

Think about objects you use; that structure, facility, system, product, or process building you are designing; and the tasks you routinely and frequently perform. Ask yourself, "What if I could retain desired functions while combining features, simplifying, and reducing costs?"

4.12.5 Example: The Panama Canal

In the late nineteenth century, the French tried but failed to construct a sea-level, interoceanic canal across the Isthmus of Panama. They were defeated by a combination of yellow fever, malaria, other deadly tropical diseases, and the challenge of having to excavate an unprecedented amount of earth and rock.

The United States purchased the assets of the French canal company and started work on a sea-level canal in 1903. The sea-level approach was soon abandoned in favor of building a dam on the Chagres River to create a lake, now called Gatun Lake, on the isthmus. As shown in Figure 4.25, the lake would be connected to the

Figure 4.24
The usual gas filler access door and the usual gas filler cap are combined into one unit.

(Stuart Walesh)

Figure 4.25
The original sea-level method for constructing the Panama Canal was replaced with this lake and locks approach.

(Peter Hermes Furian/Fotolia)

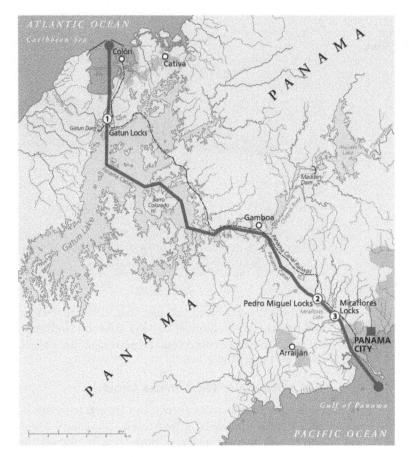

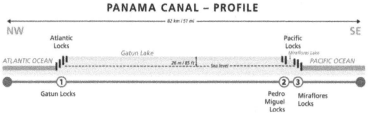

Pacific Ocean by one series of descending locks and to the Caribbean Sea by another series of descending locks. Gatun Lake would provide water by gravity to operate the locks. This approach to the fifty-one-mile project greatly reduced the amount of material to be excavated and hauled away (Brown 2014).

The Panama Canal project was facing many challenges when engineer Stevens took over its leadership in 1905, bringing with him many engineering achievements, especially in railroading. "The question was whether the entire American venture in Panama could be rescued from humiliating defeat" and lead away from failure such as the French experienced. The lock system approach was finalized early in Stevens' tenure, and then he addressed many challenges (McCullough 1977).

One challenge, as already noted, was figuring out how to excavate and haul rock and earth. Stevens' French and American predecessors saw the project as an excavation project, but he took a What If approach and viewed it as a railroad project. He saw the cut workers were excavating across part of the isthmus as a "gigantic railroad pass" (Fredrich 1989). Although excavating was a challenge, hauling the excavated rock and earth to either coast or to wherever fill was needed, such as the site of the dam that would form the lake, was a much bigger challenge. Stevens instituted what was known as the Railroad Era, during which his objective was "to create a system of dirt trains that would function like a colossal conveyor belt, rolling endlessly beside steam shovels working at several levels at once" (McCullough 1977).

"The ultimate goal of the excavation operations was to keep an empty muck car next to the steam shovel every second of every work shift" (Rogers 2014), as shown in Figure 4.26. Doing this required the creation of a track-mounted machine that could quickly pick up and move a section of rail with ties attached so that rail cars could always be close to the excavating machines. "Building the Panama Canal was, among other things, one of the greatest of all triumphs in American railroad engineering." The construction of the canal continued under the leadership of a series of engineers, with the canal opening quietly in 1914 (McCullough 1977).

In relating this story of engineering creativity and innovation, I am not saying that Stevens explicitly applied What If shortly after his arrival in the isthmus.

Figure 4.26
A steam shovel loads excavated material onto railroad cars as part of the railroad approach to constructing the Panama Canal.

(Everett Historical/Shutterstock)

However, his radical and successful change in focus from an excavation project to a railroad project and the attendant developments and actions exemplifies What If. A lesson learned from Stevens is that when we find ourselves in the position of having to clean up, fix, or finish someone else's project (and most of us will be in that position at some point), we should assess the situation and start thinking, "What if?"

4.12.6 STC: Another Way to Think about What If

Altshuller (1996), the Russian originator of the Theory of Inventive Problem Solving (Section 7.9), refers to the Size-Time-Cost (STC) operator. By radically varying these three parameters one at a time when taking on an IPO, he says that "we are deliberately complicating the problem and, at the same time, we are searching for a simplified solution." He notes that STC is a "tool for your imagination" and is intended to "break up our psychological inertia, which blocks our thinking." The Taco Bell restaurant story is in effect an example of using the Time part of STC. The company was motivated to be innovative by thinking about drastically reducing the normal, multiple-month construction time to a seemingly impossible two days.

Altshuller describes an example in which a pipeline was to be designed so that at any time it could be transmitting, in series at the same time, two or more different liquid petroleum products. The products would need to be separated to prevent mixing, and the separator would need to go through the pumps. The Size part of STC was used: The designers started to think of a separator so small that it would pass through the pumps. How could that be? They thought about tennis balls, smaller balls, pellets, and finally molecules: Molecules would pass through the pump.

Then the question became, molecules of what? The answer was to form a separator out of aqua ammonia because it was nonorganic and therefore would not dissolve in petroleum products; it was safe and inexpensive. As explained by Altshuller, "During transportation, this separator will partially mix with the petroleum . . . At the final station, the ammonia will turn into gas and evaporate," leaving just the desired petroleum product.

4.12.7 Neuroscience Basis

The What If method moves you away from overreliance on your left brain toward engaging your right brain because it temporarily sets aside typical logical constraints provided by your left hemisphere. Therefore, at least temporarily, individuals or members of a team are more likely to think in a whole-brain manner. If the Medici Effect is used to assemble a team, the results will be even better. This method can also offer a means of addressing the brain's negativity bias—that is, the form of negativity bias that is fearful of trying something new and risky. You might offer a thought like this to a person who is reluctant to participate in What If because he or she sees no good coming out of such a ridiculous idea: "Yes, I know that What If sounds silly and risky, but let's proceed just for the fun of it." Finally, the often unusual ideas generated by What If stimulate the subconscious mind to ponder the implications.

4.12.8 Positive and Negative Features

The most positive aspect of What If is the likelihood of engaging both the left and right hemispheres of participants in an unrestrained manner and thus generating creative and innovative ideas. The principal negative aspect of What If is that it often suggests bizarre approaches that stand in strong conflict with left-brain thinking characteristic of the majority of engineers.

4.13 CONCLUDING THOUGHTS ABOUT BASIC WHOLE-BRAIN METHODS

Building on the case for more creativity and innovation presented in Chapter 1 and the brain primer offered in Chapter 2, this chapter offered you eleven easy to learn and use whole-brain methods. They will be followed in Chapter 7 by discussion of nine more advanced methods. However, that chapter aside, you now have the means in your individual and team efforts, within and outside of your studies and eventually in professional practice and beyond, to use one or more of eleven whole-brain methods. You are equipped to more effectively draw on that amazing entity between your ears.

> Today is a new day that has been handed to you for shaping.
> You have the tools; now get out there and create a masterpiece.
> —*Steve Maraboli, speaker and writer*

CITED SOURCES

Adams, R. 2014. "Bar Code 1." About.com. Accessed May 15, 2014. http://www.adams1.com/history.html.

Alessandra, T. 2015. "Using Behavioral Differences to Build Teams That Work." Accessed July 29, 2015. http://www.success.com/article/using-behavioral-differences-to-build-teams-that-work.

Altshuller, G. 1996. *And Suddenly the Inventor Appeared: TRIZ, the Theory of Inventive Problem Solving.* Translated by Lev Shulyak from the original 1984 Russian version. Worcester, MA: Technical Innovation Center, Inc.

American Society of Civil Engineers. 2008. "Attitudes." In *Civil Engineering Body of Knowledge,* 2nd ed., 172–176. Reston, VA: ASCE.

Arciszewski, T. 2009. *Successful Education: How to Educate Creative Engineers.* Fairfax, VA: Successful Education LLC.

Baldwin, N. 2013. "Can You Hear Me Now?" *The Smithsonian,* December.

Bennett, J. 2010. "A Brief History of Micropiles." Accessed July 29, 2015. https://micropileman.wordpress.com/?s=a+brief+history+of+micropiles.

Bennett, J. K., and N. L. Hothem. 2010. "Hollow Bar Micropiles for Settlement Control in Soft Soils." Paper presented at the International Workshop on Micropiles, Washington, DC, September 22–25.

Berra, Y. 1998. *The Yogi Book.* New York: Workman Publishing.

Billington, D. P. 1996. *The Innovators: The Engineering Pioneers Who Made America Modern.* New York: John Wiley & Sons.

Boehler, P. 2012. "N. Joseph Woodland, Co-Inventor of the Barcode, Dies." *Time,* December 14.

Boorstin, D. J. 1985. *The Discoverers.* New York: Vintage Books.

Brenner, R. 2007. "Dismissive Gestures: Part I." *Point Lookout* e-newsletter, vol. 7, no. 12, March 21.

Brenner, R. 2008. "How to Eliminate Meetings." *Point Lookout* e-newsletter, October 1.

Brinkley, D. 2003. *Wheels for the World: Henry Ford, His Company, and a Century of Progress 1903–2003.* New York: Viking.

Brown, J. 2014. "Between Two Oceans: The Panama Canal." *Civil Engineering,* ASCE, July/August: 42–45

Buzan, T. 1984. *Make the Most of Your Mind.* New York: Simon and Schuster.

Buzan, T. 1983. *Use Both Sides of Your Brain*, rev. ed. New York: E. P. Dutton.

Buzan, T. 1991. *Use Both Sides of Your Brain*, 3rd ed. London: Penguin Books.

Byrne, J. 2005. "Brainstorming Helps Engineers Generate New Ideas." *Engineering Times*, December: 6.

Cain, S. 2012. *Quiet: The Power of Introverts in a World That Can't Stop Talking*. New York: Crown Publishers.

Carlson Learning Company. 1994. *Personal Profile System: A Plan to Understand Yourself and Others*. Minneapolis, MN: Carlson Learning Company.

Carter, R. 2009. *The Human Brain Book: An Illustrated Guide to Its Structure, Function, and Disorders*. New York: DK Publishing.

Civil Rights Digital Library. 2014. "Watts Riots." Accessed November 14, 2014. http://crdl.usg.edu/events/watts_riots/?Welcome.

Cooper, R. K. 2006. *Get Out of Your Own Way: The 5 Keys to Surpassing Everyone's Expectations*. New York: Crown Business.

Cross, H. 1952. *Engineers and Ivory Towers*. Edited by R. C. Goodpasture. New York: McGraw-Hill.

Culp, G. and A. Smith. 2001. "Understanding Psychological Type to Improve Project Team Performance." *Journal of Management in Engineering*, ASCE, January: 24–33.

Dhillon, B. S. 2006. *Creativity for Engineers*. Hackensack, NJ: World Scientific.

Fluoride Commission. 2014. *Report from the Fluoride Commission to the Valparaiso City Utilities Board of Directors*. Valparaiso, IN, August 21.

Fogler, H. S., S. E. LeBlanc, and B. Rizzo. 2014. *Strategies for Creative Problem Solving*, 3rd ed. Upper Saddle River, NJ: Prentice-Hall.

Fox, J. 2000. *How to Become a Rainmaker: The People Who Get and Keep Customers*. New York: Hyperion.

Fox, M. 2012. "N. Joseph Woodland, Inventor of the Bar Code, Dies at 91." *The New York Times*, December 12.

Fredrich, A. J., ed. 1989. *Sons of Martha: Civil Engineering Readings in Modern Literature*. New York: American Society of Civil Engineers.

Fruechte, R. 2014. Former director, Electrical and Control Systems Lab, General Motors R&D Center. Pers. comm., August 18 and September 16.

Gelb, M. J. 2004. *How to Think like Leonardo da Vinci: Seven Steps to Genius Every Day*. New York: Delta Trade Paperback.

Goldberg, D. E., and M. Somerville. 2014. *The Whole New Engineer: The Coming Revolution in Engineering Education*. Douglas, MI: ThreeJoy Associates.

Gross, R. 1991. *Peak Learning*. Los Angeles: Jeremy P. Tarcher.

Hensey, M. 1993. "Essential Tools for Total Quality Management." *Journal of Management in Engineering*, ASCE, October: 329–339.

Herrmann, N. 1996. *The Whole Brain Business Book: Unlocking the Power of Whole Brain Thinking in Individuals and Organizations*. New York: McGraw-Hill.

Johansson, F. 2006. *The Medici Effect*. Cambridge, MA: Harvard Business School Press.

Johnson, H. 2010. "Biz Tip of the Day." Email from training@globalteleclass.com, April 12.

King, B. R. 2007. "Virtual Teams Should Have Real Meetings." *COMMUNITYPOST*, e-newsletter, PMI, October 26.

Koberg, D., and J. Bagnall. 1991. *The Universal Traveler: A Soft-Systems Guide to Creativity, Problem-Solving, and the Process of Reaching Goal*. Menlo Park, CA: Crisp Publications.

Kolter, P., and K. F. A. Fox. 1985. *Strategic Marketing for Educational Institutions*. Englewood Cliffs, NJ: Prentice-Hall.

Leeds, D. 2000. *The 7 Powers of Questions: Secrets to Successful Communication in Life and Work.* New York: Berkley Publishing.

Lehrer, J. 2012. *Imagine: How Creativity Works.* New York: Houghton Mifflin Harcourt.

Leonard, D., and S. Straus. 1997. "Putting Your Company's Whole Brain to Work." *Harvard Business Review,* July–August: 1–10.

Liker, J. K. 2004. *The Toyota Way: 14 Management Principles from the World's Greatest Manufacturer.* New York: McGraw-Hill.

Lillibridge, E. M. 1998. *The People Map: Understanding Your People and Others.* Lutz, FL: Lilmat Press.

Macintyre, B. 2012. *Double Cross: The True Story of the D-Day Spies.* New York: Crown Publishers.

May, R. 1976. *Courage to Create.* New York: Bantam Books.

McCullough, D. 1977. *The Path between the Seas: The Creation of the Panama Canal 1870–1914.* New York: Simon & Schuster.

Miles, E. 1997. *Tune Your Brain: Using Music to Manage Your Mind, Body, and Mood.* New York: Berkley Books.

Milosevic, I. N. 2010. "Practical Application of SWOT Analysis in the Management of a Construction Project." *Leadership and Management in Engineering,* ASCE, April: 78–86.

Murray, D. K. 2009. *Borrowing Brilliance: The Six Steps to Business Innovation by Building on the Ideas of Others.* New York: Gotham Books.

Neumeier, M. 2014. "Dreaming: A Metaskill for the Future." *Rotman Management Magazine,* Spring: 24.

Nierenberg, G. I. 1982. *The Art of Creative Thinking.* New York: Barnes & Noble Books.

Oakley, B. 2014. "Learning Paradoxes." *PE,* National Society of Professional Engineers, November.

Osborn, A. F. 1953. *Applied Imagination: Principles and Procedures of Creative Problem-Solving.* New York: Scribners.

Parkinson, J. R. 2009. "Nothing More than Feelings, But that's How to Keep A Client." Show and Tell column, *Herald-Tribune,* Sarasota, FL, March 7.

Pisasale, P. E. 2014. Operations integrated product team lead, Seapower Capability Center, Raytheon Integrated Defense Systems. Pers. comm., October 27.

Prestpin, P. 2011. "Message Marketing with Mind Maps: Interests, Behaviors, Beliefs." *Website Magazine.com,* June 24.

Restak, R. 2009. *Think Smart: A Neuroscientist's Prescription for Improving Your Brain's Performance.* New York: Riverhead Books.

Reynolds, G. 2008. *Presentation Zen: Simple Ideas on Presentation Design and Delivery.* Berkeley, CA: New Riders.

Rhein, B. 2009. "Selling through Curiosity: Why the Right Questions Matter." Barry Rhein and Associates, webinar, July 8.

Rico, G. 2000. *Writing the Natural Way: Using Right-Brain Techniques to Release Your Expressive Powers.* New York: Jeremy P. Tarcher/Putnam.

Roane, S. 1988. *How to Work a Room: A Guide to Successfully Managing the Mingling.* New York: Shapolsky Publishers.

Rogers, J. D. 2014. "Engineering the Panama Canal." *Civil Engineering,* ASCE, October: 72–95.

Sandstrom, G. E. 1970. *Man the Builder.* New York: McGraw-Hill.

Shipping Container Pros. 2014, "Shipping Container Tips." Accessed September 17. http://www.shippingcontainerpros.com/about-us.php.

Singularity HUB. 2011. "10,000 Shipping Containers Lost at Sea Each Year." *Singularity HUB,* April 5. Accessed September 17, 2014. http://singularityhub.com.

Smallowitz, H., and D. Molyneux. 1987. "Marketing Strategies for Engineers." *Civil Engineering*, ASCE, August: 70–72.

Smiles, S. 1997. *The Life of Thomas Telford: Civil Engineer. Project Gutenberg.* Accessed August 5, 2014. https://archive.org/stream/thelifeofthomast00939gut/tlfrd10.txt.

Taco Bell. n.d. "Compton Comeback." Private video.

Tice, L. 2011. "Magic Words." *Winner's Circle Network with Lou Tice*, e-newsletter, July 18.

Tompkins, J. 1998. *Revolution: Take Charge Strategies for Business Success.* Raleigh, NC: Tompkins Press.

Van Doren, C. 1991. *A History of Knowledge,* Ballantine Book, New York, NY.

von Oech, R. 1990. *A Whack on the Side of the Head: How You Can Be More Creative.* Stamford, CT: US Games Systems, Inc.

Walesh, S. G. 1982. "Emergency Floodproofing of the Tecumseh Diecast Plant." Paper presented at the Seminar on Residential and Commercial Floodproofing, University of Minnesota, St. Paul, MN, March 1–2.

Walesh, S. G. 1990. "Water Science and Technology: Global Origins." In *Urban Stormwater Quality Enhancement: Source Control, Retrofitting, and Combined Sewer Technology: Proceedings of an Engineering Conference, Davos, Switzerland,* 1–27. New York: American Society of Civil Engineers.

Walesh, S. G. 2000a. "Decision Economics." In *Engineering Your Future: The Non-Technical Side of Professional Practice in Engineering and Other Technical Fields,* 2nd ed., 209–276. Reston, VA: ASCE Press.

Walesh, S. G. 2000b. *Street Storage System for Control of Combined Sewer Surcharge,* EPA/600R-00/065. Washington, DC: US Environmental Protection Agency.

Walesh, S. G. 2004. "Lesson 15: So, What Do You Know About Bluebirds?" In *Managing and Leading: 52 Lessons Learned for Engineers,* 75–78. Reston, VA: ASCE Press.

Walesh, S. G. 2011. "Project Management and Creativity/Innovation." Part of the graduate course Master of Leadership in Engineering, Civil Engineering School, Castilla LaMancha University, Ciudad Real, Spain, September 19–22.

Walesh, S. G. 2012a. "Building: Construction and Manufacturing." In *Engineering Your Future: The Professional Practice of Engineering,* 283–297. Hoboken, NJ/Reston, VA: Wiley/ASCE Press.

Walesh, S. G. 2012b. "Developing Relationships." In *Engineering Your Future: The Professional Practice of Engineering,* 123–166. Hoboken, NJ/Reston, VA: Wiley/ASCE Press.

Walesh, S. G. 2014. "Five Habits of Highly-Effective Marketers: Engage Your Subconscious Mind." Webinar presented by the American Society of Civil Engineers, September 3.

Walesh, S. G., and R. Carr. 1999. "Street Surface Storage for Control of Combined Sewer Surcharge." In *WRPMD '99: Preparing for the 21st Century,* edited by M. E. Wilson. Proceedings of the 26th Annual Water Resources Planning and Management Conference, Tempe, AZ, June 6–9.

Wankat, P. C., and F. S. Oreovicz. 1993. "Psychological Type and Learning." In *Teaching Engineering,* 244–267. New York: McGraw-Hill.

Wheeler, R. 2014. "The Online Profile of Russell A. Wheeler." Accessed July 17. http://russellawheeler.com/resources/learning_zone/alex_f_osborn/.

Wilson, R. 2011. "The Ohno Circle." *Indiana Professional Engineer,* January/February: 3.

Wolff, J. 2012. *Creativity Now.* Harlow, UK: Pearson.

Yesiller, N. 2015. Director, Global Waste Research Institute, California Polytechnic State University, San Luis Obispo, CA. Pers. comm., May 8.

EXERCISES

Notes:

1. The goal of the exercises is to provide students, usually and preferably working in diverse groups, the opportunity to use all of the chapter's tools. Therefore, most exercises suggest use of a specific whole-brain method described in this chapter

2. However, many circumstances and corresponding teaching-learning opportunities may arise. For example, a team could use a different tool or more than one tool, or the stated issue may be altered to meet specific concerns or needs. Rather than work with the largely hypothetical situation described in a particular exercise, a team may wish to take on an actual issue, problem, or opportunity facing the team or one or more of its members. These and similar variations are encouraged, subject to the concurrence or direction of the instructor.

3. Recall the facilitation discussion in Section 3.8. Each of the team exercises provides opportunities for individual students to apply pre-, during-, and post-facilitation advice. Even if the instructor does not require facilitation, you may want to practice it for two reasons. First, your group will get better results. Second, students who provide facilitation will gain valuable knowledge and skills.

4.1 PREPARING FOR MEETING WITH A CLIENT (ASK-ASK-ASK): You are an engineer working for an engineering consulting firm and just received an email from a client you have worked with before. The client invites you to meet to discuss a problem that must be resolved. You naturally welcome the invitation, contact the client, and set up a time for a face-to-face meeting at the client's office. Read the following list of problems and select one for purposes of this exercise.

   a. An attempt is being made to encourage the cultivation of ginger and turmeric in a floodplain region. Scale-appropriate machinery needs to be designed and developed.

   b. A region known for its annual floods has very fertile lands. The client wants to encourage organic farming in the community and design appropriate machinery.

   c. The client is looking for a women-centered farm machinery and process redesign. The challenge here is also how to attract women to be machine-drivers and make it socially acceptable.

   d. Homestead gardens provide year-round nutrition to the communities of their region. But due to young people migrating, elderly family members are unable to tend properly to their gardens. The client is looking for feasible and low-cost solutions for this problem.

   e. The client owns power tillers and rents them for agricultural activities which are seasonal in nature. Hence the client is interested in exploring avenues for expansion in tiller accessories to make year round earnings.

   f. The client wants a greenhouse with a low cost of setup and operation to create a cooler and less humid environment than the surroundings.

   Draft a list of questions you might ask during the meeting, possibly drawing on principles and tips in Section 4.2. Clearly, you have very limited information about the client, his or her organization, and the issue. However, you should be able to formulate some questions using this chapter's Ask-Ask-Ask ideas. You are most effective if you can go into a win-win, question-asking mode regardless of the situation.

4.2 CONCEPTUAL DESIGN OF A "GREEN" BRIDGE (BORROWING BRILLIANCE): Assume that your multidiscipline consulting team has been retained by a US west coast river city to prepare the conceptual design for a bridge to further connect one side of the community to the other. Figure 4.27 shows the essential details of the valley cross section where the bridge is to be constructed.

Figure 4.27
A bridge needs to be designed to cross this wide valley, provide for various forms of transportation, and generate energy.

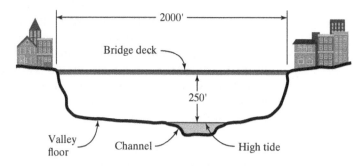

Note: Not to scale: great vertical exaggeration

Community leaders want the bridge to be functional; to generate energy and otherwise be "green"; and to make a statement—that is, become an iconic symbol for the city. Traditional functions to be provided include vehicle traffic, rapid transit, a pedestrian/biking path, and 250 feet of vertical clearance for ocean-going freighters and cruise ships. On the green front, the bridge is to have features such as turbines and/or solar panels, with one goal being to generate part of the community's energy.

The bridge deck shown in Figure 4.27 is meant to show the general location of traditional functions—that is, vehicle traffic, rapid transit, and a pedestrian/biking path. It is not meant to show the actual configuration of the structure that could be provided with various proven bridge structures shown in Figure 4.28, which include suspension, arch, and cable-stayed bridges, as well as piers and trusses.

Use Borrowing Brilliance to prepare a conceptual design. More specifically, for the borrowing part, think of various solar/turbine and other green applications you have seen, and research many more. Then, consider borrowing some of what you have experienced or learned for your conceptual bridge design. To reiterate, this is a conceptual design. Therefore, don't be concerned about cost, benefits, environmental impacts/approvals, and similar practical considerations at this stage. Focus on concepts. Think about what might be even remotely possible rather than what is likely to be practical.

Summarize your conceptual design with a three-part deliverable: a rough drawing that includes a cross section through the valley and shows the essentials of your conceptual design, descriptive text, and a list of all the sources you considered, even though some were not used. Demonstrate that you searched far and wide for concepts, ideas, technology, examples, and so on to borrow from.

Figure 4.28
Proven bridge structures include suspension, arch, and cable-stayed bridges, as well as piers and trusses.

((a) Rootstocks/Fotolia; (b) Elnur/ Fotolia; (c) Gbbrowning/Fotolia; (d) Sonap/Fotolia)

(a)   (b)

(c)   (d)

4.3 ATTRACTING CITIZENS TO PUBLIC MEETINGS (BORROWING BRILLIANCE): Have you ever spoken to a community health worker (CHW)? They are the grassroots force delivering health services to the corners of any country. Since they interact very closely with the community, they are more aware of the needs, wants, ethos, culture, practices and beliefs of the community.

Now imagine that you are assigned a project to improve the health services in your locality. Depending on your specialization, you can try to focus on an engineering solution direction. For example, if you are a computer engineer, you can think of an IT-based solution; if you are a mechanical engineer, you might think of an automotive-oriented health service delivery mechanism, and so on. Engineering aside, first think of strategies and tactics that you can use to interact with all the involved stakeholders through public meetings.

These meetings can be organized in highly mixed groups, homogeneous groups or slightly mixed groups depending on the objective and stage of the project. Assume that you want to collect concerns, difficulties and opportunities in the process of healthcare delivery from all stakeholders. Using the approaches mentioned in Borrowing Brilliance, imagine creative ways of attracting a diverse group of stakeholders and citizens to your public meeting. How could you fill the room with a highly varied and representative audience? More specifically, ask each person in your hopefully diverse group why they go to certain community, business, sporting, entertainment, educational, and other events. What tactics could you borrow to increase the number and variety of individuals who come to your public meetings? Don't be bound by how it has always been done. Summarize your ideas in writing.

4.4 MULTIPLE USES OF HIGHWAY MEDIAN BARRIERS (BRAINSTORM-ING): Concrete and steel barriers, as shown in Figure 4.29, are routinely used to separate opposing lanes of high-speed highways. They serve the single purpose of greatly reducing the likelihood of head-on collisions.

Imagine that your team is in the very early stages of planning and designing a high-speed highway system for a developing country. Median barriers are necessary. However, perhaps the barriers or a barrier system, could provide the opportunity to cost-effectively serve multiple purposes. Maybe the barrier system could fulfill many infrastructure and other functions. Use Brainstorming to identify possible uses of the barriers. Concentrate on developing many ideas; go for quantity, not quality. Summarize your results in a list of the ideas you generated.

Figure 4.29
Barriers are used between opposing lanes of high-speed highways to greatly reduce the likelihood of head-on collisions.

(Kenneth Sponsler/Fotolia; Unclesam/Fotolia)

4.5 POSSIBLE CAUSES OF BRIDGE FAILURE (FISHBONE DIAGRAMMING): A major bridge just failed, as shown in Figure 4.30, with loss of life and great disruption of river navigation and motor vehicle traffic. As an alternative, imagine the catastrophic failure of some other major structure, facility, system, or process; briefly describe or illustrate it; and proceed with the exercise.

Figure 4.30
This bridge failed with catastrophic results, and your team just arrived to begin assessing possible causes.

(Lunamarina/Fotolia)

Your engineering firm has been retained to analyze the failure and determine its cause or causes. Your interdisciplinary team (e.g., engineers, environmentalists, surveyors, divers) just made an initial one-hour visit to the site to view the failure. Before proceeding with determination of possible causes, your team decides to meet to plan its approach.

At the meeting, the group constructs a fishbone diagram. In applying Fishbone Diagramming, you try to imagine all the possible causes of failure. After completing the diagram, you intend to use it to develop your project plan—that is, who will do what, and when and how. However, for the time being, you are concentrating on the diagram. Summarize your results in the form of one fishbone diagram.

4.6 **ASSESSING UNEXPECTED PRODUCT FAILURE RISKS (FISHBONE DIAGRAMMING):** Assume that you are a manufacturer of fuel dispensers for gas stations. These dispensers are supposed to be shipped to different parts of the country with diverse climates and environmental conditions, and stand in the open without protection. For example, the north sees −20°C in winter while the east has very high humidity and flooding. The product has to be tamper-proof. Multiple safety features needs to be incorporated as it handles a highly hazardous product.

- Now your team sees an opportunity in the export market. For this, additional safety standards and regulations need to be considered and certifications obtained. In the international market, legislative measures are stronger and any product failure will mean a long-term legal battle for the company. Also usage and environmental conditions and related product abuse will be different.
- Yours is a small company and does not have the capacity to produce a completely new line of products for the international market. Thus the management decides to have a modular design with the possibility to customize it for the national or international market.
- Thus you invite a diverse group from engineering, marketing, servicing and so on for a meeting. You explain that you need their help in determining what could go wrong if we go ahead with the modular design idea for the national and international market.
- Then, you ask them to use Fishbone Diagramming to define what could go wrong—that is, what would need immediate attention. The head of your fishbone diagram might read "What could go wrong." As all of you work together on this exercise, think about material, weather, corrosion, safety, etc. Summarize your ideas with a fishbone diagram draft.

Note: The purpose is not to determine preventive actions (that would be the next step, and you are not being asked to do that) but rather to define the potential problem areas and problems. Recall that a problem well-defined is half-solved.

4.7 **TEAM FORMATION (MEDICI EFFECT):** Consider the problems mentioned in exercise 4.6. Each of these problems require the formation of a team consisting of experts from diverse disciplines, specialties and positions along with the affected stakeholders who might represent diverse geographies, ethnicities, genders, motivations, ages, experiences and attitudes. Assume that you have been asked to assemble the design team.

Assemble a hypothetical team using the Medici Effect as your guide. As you consider possible members, strive for the types of diversity outlined in Section 4.6 (Medici Effect) of this chapter. Avoid the cloning sameness approach to team formation. Do you think a Novice Effect can be utilized in the problem selected by you? Explain where and how it might be useful in your context.

Now when a team composition plan is ready, plan what steps you will take for team development as mentioned in Section 4.6.5.

4.8 YOUR PERSONALITY PROFILE (RELATED TO THE MEDICI EFFECT): This chapter's Medici Effect discussion mentioned personality (Section 4.6.2), which is in your bundle of habitual responses, and then went on to introduce personality profiles. If you have never had your profile analyzed, you may be interested in doing so, and this exercise provides the opportunity. If you have already been profiled, doing it again would be useful if for no other reason than to see if it changes (my experience and understanding is that it doesn't and therefore we have to work with what we and others have).

Personality profiles—ours and others—help us understand and deal with our feelings and needs and those of the people we work with and serve. The results of this exercise should be confidential, unless you want to share them with your instructor or other trusted persons.

a. Arrange for a personality profile assessment, possibly using one of the personality profiling systems noted in Section 4.6.3. As a student, you might get help from your campus career office or the health center. If you are an employee, seek help from human resources personnel.

b. Study the results, recognizing that there are no right or wrong profiles. They are what they are. Analyze your profile relative to your desired success and significance, as discussed in Section 1.2. What are your strengths and weaknesses or assets and liabilities, and what might you do about it? Also recall and learn from recent positive and negative interactions with students, faculty, coworkers, supervisors, and others in light of the added personal insight. Try to see how you and they might connect or disconnect based on your own profile and what you may be able to deduce about theirs. Going forward, maybe you can be more empathetic and develop or strengthen some of your relationships (Walesh 2012b).

4.9 MULTIPLE USES OF HIGHWAY MEDIAN BARRIERS (MIND MAPPING): See the situation described in Exercise 4.4. Then, apply Mind Mapping instead of Brainstorming. Summarize your results with your actual mind map and a list of ideas generated.

4.10 APPLICATIONS OF SHIPPING CONTAINERS IN DEVELOPING COUNTRIES (MIND MAPPING): A shipping container is "a standardized reusable steel box used for the safe, efficient, and secure storage and movement of materials and products within a global containerized intermodal freight transport system." *Intermodal* means that "the container can be moved from one mode of transport to another (from ship to rail to truck and in reverse) without unloading and reloading the contents of the container." Shipping containers, as shown in Figure 4.31, are seen on land and at sea all around the globe. At any time, about five to six million containers are being transported by ship, and about ten thousand are lost at sea each year as a result of falling off of ships (Singularity HUB 2011).

Figure 4.31
A shipping container is a standardized reusable steel box used for global intermodal shipping.

(Stuart Walesh)

Most shipping containers are eight-feet wide, nine-feet high, and twenty- or forty-feet long. They are constructed of corrugated steel and have large doors at one end. Used twenty-foot containers cost in the $1800 to $4500 range and forty-foot containers in the $2500 to $5500 range, and the cost may include delivery (Shipping Container Pros 2014).

Use Mind Mapping to generate a list of possible uses of shipping containers in poor, developing countries. The uses may be temporary or permanent and may involve one or many containers. Clearly, the containers could be used to provide homes—to provide shelter. However, go beyond that. Concentrate on developing many ideas, and don't evaluate them as they appear. Go for quantity, not quality. In the typical Mind Mapping application, practical considerations are deferred until later. Trying to combine idea generation with idea evaluation leads to neither being done well. Present your results by providing the actual mind map and a separate list of the ideas you generated.

4.11 **APPLICATIONS OF SHIPPING CONTAINERS IN PUBLIC WORKS (MIND MAPPING):** Review the shipping container information described in Exercise 4.10. Use Mind Mapping to generate a list of possible uses of shipping containers in public works. The use may be temporary or permanent and may involve one or many containers. What might you and your team do or want to do that might be accomplished with one or more shipping containers? Concentrate on developing many ideas, and don't evaluate them as they appear. Go for quantity, not quality. In the typical Mind Mapping application, practical considerations are deferred to later. Trying to combine idea generation with idea evaluation leads to neither being done well. Present your results by providing the actual mind map and a separate list of the ideas you generated.

4.12 **EMERGENCY FLOODPROOFING OF A MANUFACTURING FACILITY (MIND MAPPING OR FISHBONE DIAGRAMMING):** A manufacturing facility sits on the floodplain of a river, as shown in Figure 4.32, in a location that experiences severe winters. This 100,000 square foot (9,300 square meter) single-story concrete block building is constructed on a reinforced concrete slab. The principal product of the plant is aluminum castings.

These castings are shipped to two other plants, where they are used to manufacture small gasoline engines. Many containers of molten aluminum, kept molten by electric furnaces, are scattered throughout the plant. This manufacturing facility affects thousands of employees among the three plants and is critical to the local economy.

Figure 4.32
A manufacturing plant sits on the floodplain of a river.

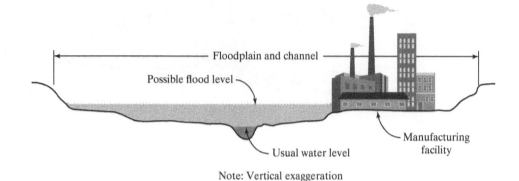

As of February 1, as shown in Figure 4.33, the large watershed tributary to the plant's location contains heavy snow cover, and warmer weather is approaching. Flooding threatened the large single-story building in the past, and in the most serious event flood waters rose within inches of the concrete floor. Given the past history and this year's unusually heavy watershed snow cover, company management wants to take preventive action quickly. They want to keep the manufacturing going as long as possible, balanced by their concern about their employees and the facility.

Figure 4.33
A manufacturing facility that is critical to the local economy sits on a floodplain and is threatened by flooding because of unusually heavy snow cover on the tributary watershed.

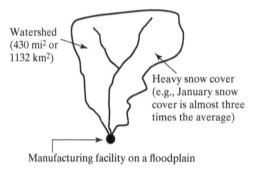

Your engineering firm has been retained as of February 1 to prepare an emergency floodproofing plan to protect the building, its equipment, and employees. Your plan must be ready in two weeks for review by company management, with the idea that if it is accepted it will be immediately implemented. *Note:* This exercise is based on an actual emergency situation and the response to it (Walesh 1982).

Definition of floodproofing: "Floodproofing consists of structural adjustments and other measures undertaken to reduce flood damage to an existing or new residential, commercial, or industrial building, or other facility. Temporary floodproofing measures are those that are implemented for a short period of time, and usually on short notice, to provide protection during floods expected during a particular season or period. Subsequent to that flood threat, some of the temporary measures are typically removed or discontinued. The plan for temporary floodproofing measures, however, may be revised and used again during future flood events" (Walesh 1982).

Additional thoughts about floodproofing: "Regardless of the overall approach taken, the most cost-effective [emergency] floodproofing plan will probably include structural and nonstructural measures. That is, the plan should consider recommendations for temporary structural adjustments to be made to the building as well as recommendations for steps to be taken and procedures to be instituted to supplement structural adjustments" (Walesh 1982).

Use Mind Mapping or Fishbone Diagramming to develop a list of possible structural and nonstructural emergency floodproofing measures. Summarize your results by providing the actual mind map or fishbone diagram, and describe your ideas with text and, as needed, sketches or photos.

4.13 **IMPROVING A TRADITIONAL PROCESS (OHNO CIRCLE):** As individuals or groups, we often continue to carry out processes the way we have always done them. As students or in professional work, the process may be the way we study for examinations, design bridges, conduct meetings, use various materials, carry out laboratory experiments, set up manufacturing processes, or construct office buildings. Other individuals and teams do the same within their worlds of study, work, and beyond. Our and their approaches are comfortable and habitual. Therefore, although minor to major improvements may be possible, even the minor ones are not readily seen. The Ohno Circle, because of its emphasis on really seeing and hearing, can open our eyes and ears.

Select some process that you, as an individual, are interested in and can observe. It could be just about anything. Some examples: a local construction project, a meeting of your campus club, a bus stop with people getting on and off the bus, the first day of classes, or an intersection with pedestrian and auto traffic. The process does not have to have anything to with engineering.

Apply the thirty-minute version of the Ohno Circle method described in Section 4.8.1. Look for minor or major improvement opportunities in the categories defined in the text.

Search for ways to remove the deficiencies and make minor to major improvements, and make some of your suggested changes creative and/or innovative. Prepare a short report that includes the following sections:

- Description of the process you observed, preferably supplemented with photos/sketches.
- Assumptions: You may have been given or been able to obtain minimal information about the process you observed, and therefore you may need to make some assumptions.

- Sources used: If you used one or more outside sources, such as a website, reference book, published article or paper, or an expert, then list your sources.
- Description of suggested improvements categorized as minor and major.

4.14 IMPROVING A CONSTRUCTION OR MANUFACTURING PROCESS (OHNO CIRCLE): This exercise enables you to apply the Ohno Circle and critique a construction or manufacturing process (Walesh 2012).

a. Arrange to observe a manufacturing process that will be operating when you arrive or an active construction site where construction will be occurring while you are there. Inquire about safety measures, and then locate a place from which you can observe and hear all or most aspects of the construction or manufacturing for an extended period.

b. If you selected a manufacturing process, pretend you are its newly appointed manager. If you chose a construction site, imagine that you are the newly appointed construction project manager—that is, on the staff of the general contractor. Either way, you want to improve effectiveness and efficiency; do the right things and do them right.

c. Apply the Ohno Circle method, modified so that you stay at your observation point for perhaps only one hour, rather than the up to eight hours that Ohno required! The objective is to be there long enough to see and hear everything. Look for underutilized resources (e.g., personnel, equipment, materials); excess motion of personnel, unnecessary movement of parts or materials, excessive parts or materials; defects (e.g., production or constructed elements that do not seem to meet requirements); waiting due to materials, information, or resources that are not available where and when needed; and safety and health hazards.

d. Recognize that you are not qualified to do what you are doing, unless you have constructing or manufacturing experience. However, recall the novice effect (Section 4.6.3), because it may serve you well during this exercise. Hall of Fame baseball player Berra (1998) offers this sound advice: "You can observe a lot by watching."

e. Prepare a memorandum that addresses all of the preceding tasks, with emphasis on problems you observed and your ideas for resolving them.

4.15 GENERATING IDEAS (STREAM OF CONSCIOUSNESS WRITING): For this exercise, first use the individual and then the group mode.

In the individual mode, select an IPO. These can be any challenge, like selecting an elective, a career, or an internship; or an issue close to your heart; or a social or political cause. Write or type for ten minutes, recording whatever enters your mind. Don't let your pen or pencil leave the paper or your fingers leave the keyboard. Try not to repeat your thoughts.

You can write about the current problems, your ideas which resolve a part of the problem, a simplistic wishful thinking, or other solutions. You are very likely to gain new and useful insights into the issue. Given the possibly personal nature of the IPO selected, you may choose not to share your results.

In the group mode, form a team and choose an IPO relevant or important to the team. These can be problems related to your projects, a business idea you might have, common problems faced by the class or students group, or current social and political issues and so on. Repeat the 10 minute non-stop writing or typing exercise now followed by exchanging results with others in the group and continuing to write. A team may choose the option of confidentiality in disclosing insights in this case too. Compare the insights obtained in individual and group modes.

4.16 **ANALYZE YOUR TEAM OR GROUP (SWOT):** Imagine that you have to form a team for solving one of these tasks:

- A techno-cultural exhibition in the city.
- A greenhouse for growing tomatoes, which require a cold climate with low humidity, in a place which is hot and humid.
- An on-demand, multi-lingual and remote speech therapy service for people facing speech disorders.
- A piggery which is efficient but does not cause stress to build up in the pigs.
- A software for helping students conduct physics and chemistry experiments remotely.

Select a team or group to analyze and invite a variety of members, Medici Effect style, to join you in an objective analysis using SWOT. Begin by identifying those elements or aspects of your team or group that influence its performance. Some examples might be disciplines or specialties, writing and speaking knowledge and skill, IT capabilities, equipment, education and training programs, budget, mix of full- and part-time personnel, and other experiences. These elements become the rows in your SWOT table, as illustrated in Figure 4.14.

Lead the participants in determining the strengths, weaknesses, opportunities, and threats associated with each element and or aspect; fill in the rows. This process can be difficult, because some of the weaknesses or threats may be explicitly or implicitly directed at one or more participants. Nevertheless, a complete SWOT analysis can be helpful to both individuals and the team or group, assuming everyone is committed to improvement. While performing the analysis phase, do not discuss possible fixes. Separate problem definition from problem solution.

Once the analysis phase is complete, lead the group in prioritizing strengths and opportunities to be celebrated and enhanced and weaknesses and threats to be addressed. Then, generate ideas for building on strengths and weaknesses and for resolving weaknesses and threats. This is the point at which you might use idea-generating tools such as Borrowing Brilliance, Brainstorming, and Mind Mapping. Choose the course of action and develop an action plan.

Prepare a report that names and provides an overview of the team or group; presents the SWOT table; identifies the highest priority strengths, weaknesses, opportunities, and threats; indicates the selected ways to build on strengths and weaknesses and resolve weaknesses and threats; and outlines the action plan.

4.17 **DEVELOPMENT OF SOCIAL MEDIA POLICY (TAKING A BREAK):** Social media are defined as Internet-based means of self-publishing—that is, ways an individual can unilaterally place almost anything in cyberspace with the likelihood that it will be out there and discoverable forever! Examples of social media include LinkedIn, Facebook, YouTube, Twitter, and blogs. The variety and use of social media have exploded in recent years.

Although social media have great collaboration potential, their use by personnel in engineering firms and engineering-oriented government entities can lead to at least the following two types of problems:

- Misuse of time; that is, instead of carrying out job responsibilities, personnel are wasting time using social media.
- Making confidential or sensitive information widely available.

Assume that you work for an engineering firm or a government entity (pick one of the two). Your diverse team (you are the leader) has been assembled and charged with drafting social media policies to be followed by all personnel. The organization's top executive wants a list of creative and innovative social media guidelines that will help personnel make more effective use of their time and social media and also protect confidential information. Your draft will be reviewed by your organization's top executive.

You gather the team, discuss the issue, review the charge, obtain concurrence on team protocol, and then suggest using Taking a Break. Your rationale for that tool is that everyone uses social media. Now, after initially discussing the issue, social media will be on the conscious and subconscious minds of team members as they go about their work and other activities and use social media and see others use it. The next meeting is scheduled, and at that meeting, participants use Brainstorming or Mind Mapping to share ideas. Some of your team's intermeeting communication is very likely to occur via social media.

Play out the preceding two-meeting scenario, with the meetings separated by at least one day. Prepare and submit a list of creative and innovative social media requirements.

4.18 MANAGEMENT OF DISASTER WASTE AND DEBRIS (WHAT IF): Think of the types and huge amounts of waste and debris, as suggested by Figure 4.34, resulting from natural and other disasters. What should be done with it? This is a major problem.

Listen to Yesiller (2015) of the Global Waste Research Institute at California Polytechnic State University: "This is a topic that I have worked on some in the past and there is not really much information on the topic. Significant amounts of debris and waste are generated, in particular, subsequent to major events. Innovative solutions are required for sustainable management of these materials."

Use the What If tool to generate an initial set of ideas. For example:

- What if all the waste and debris was magically sorted? Then we could . . .
- What if all the waste was organic? Then we could . . .

Don't get in the weeds. Just use What If to generate as many ideas as you can. At this stage, go for quantity, not quality, and don't be concerned about practicality. As noted early in this chapter, when seeking creative and innovative solutions to challenges, we want to separate divergent thinking from convergent thinking and engage thoroughly in the former before beginning the latter. Summarize your initial ideas in the form of a list of ideas.

Then, select a few of the initial ideas, including some that appear ludicrous, discuss them, and see what additional related and more practical options might occur to you. Document your initial set of ideas and the results of your subsequent analysis of them.

Figure 4.34
Waste and debris resulting from natural and other disasters presents a major challenge.

(Benjamin Simeneta/Fotolia; Dmitry Naumov/Fotolia; Amelie/Fotolia)

4.19 RENOVATION/REUSE OF A MAJOR STRUCTURE/FACILITY (WHAT IF): The physical life of an engineered structure or facility, or any of its major components, is defined as the time over which the structure, facility, or component could perform its intended functions, assuming reasonable but not extreme care. Economic life is the period of time during which incremental benefits of use are likely to exceed incremental costs. In other words, the economic life of a structure, facility, or component ends when the incremental benefits of use become less than the incremental costs.

Clearly, determinations of physical and economic life are judgments. Of importance here is the observation that the economic life of an engineered structure or facility is usually significantly less than its physical life. For example, tanks, pipes, and other components in a wastewater treatment plant may have physical lives of up to fifty years, but given the rate of change of treatment technology, significant improvements are likely to occur in far fewer than fifty years. Therefore, a structure or facility may be taken out of service when many of its components still have significant physical life. Those parts may have salvage value—that is, monetary value (Walesh 2000a). On the other hand, the entire structure or facility, or major parts of it, might be renovated for a completely new use for public or private benefit.

Select an actual or hypothetical publically or privately owned engineered structure or facility. Some examples follow, but don't necessarily limit your choice to them:

- Airport
- Bridge
- Dam remaining after permanently dewatering a reservoir
- Elevated water storage tank—concrete or metal
- Football stadium
- Manufacturing plant
- Marina
- Nuclear power plant
- Outdoor swimming pool and complex
- Ski jump
- Transmission towers for electric power lines
- Wastewater treatment plant
- Water treatment plant

Temporarily set aside the original use of the selected structure or facility. Take a What If point of view: Figuratively look at it from above, below, inside out, and so on. Imagine other uses. After developing a list of possible reuses, select one. Then, identify some of the technical, economic, environmental, legal, regulatory, and other factors that would have to be addressed to implement it.

Summarize your initial ideas in writing, supplemented with sketches as needed. Describe the potential new use, and list factors that would need to be considered to further explore project feasibility.

Overcoming Obstacles to Creativity and Innovation

*Patience and perseverance have a magical effect
before which difficulties disappear and obstacles vanish.*
—*John Quincy Adams, sixth US President*

Objectives:

After studying this chapter, you will be able to:

- Describe seven likely obstacles to individual and organizational creativity and innovation
- Illustrate at least one remedy for each obstacle

- Apply twenty questions to help you and/or your team more thoroughly define the potential positive and negative impacts of your creative/innovative idea so that you can proactively move forward

5.1 OBSTACLES TO STOP YOU OR ROADBLOCKS TO BE REMOVED?

This chapter addresses the resistance your creative ideas will often encounter and offers remedies. We begin by describing internal and external obstacles; the remainder of the chapter discusses seven obstacles in depth and how you can overcome them.

5.1.1 External Obstacles

On the surface, being individually and organizationally creative and innovative seems very desirable, like favorite desserts, high grade point averages, and long weekends.

Who wouldn't want those things? The popular media frequently extols the need for and benefits of creativity and innovation. Leaders and managers from all sectors of society, including engineering, call for more creativity and innovation, and many imply that they are setting the pace.

However, based on my studies and experiences that focus on the world of engineering, I believe that only a miniscule fraction of engineering firms and engineering-oriented government, academic, volunteer, and other entities take a proactive, system-wide approach to creativity/innovation. Their visions, missions, recruitment, marketing, and other public statements aside, very few such organizations embrace creative/innovative cultures. As a result of their inattention, if not indifference, they are missing much, taking passive or reactive positions, and accepting surviving or risking dying. They could be thriving.

That said, I recognize the good news that there are some of you who, by virtue of personal qualities (e.g., see Chapter 6), will create and innovate no matter what the prevailing environment says. However, my mission (of which this book is a part) is to help many more engineers, and thus their organizations, be even more creative and innovative. A rising tide lifts all boats.

As a young person, whether an engineering student or practitioner, you see, understand, and quickly use new technologies. Accordingly, you may view creativity and innovation very positively and wonder how entire organizations could fail to endorse it or how some individuals could resist it. By raising the issue of obstacles, I do not want to diminish your enthusiasm for creativity and innovation, but rather I want to expose you to some realities that you will need to address if you wish to be creative and innovative. Forewarned is forearmed.

Resistance to establishing a creative/innovative atmosphere and even a tendency to discourage creativity and innovation are understandable, but not productive in the long run. We can collectively offer many reasons, some very well-intentioned (as will become apparent in this chapter), for those oppositional viewpoints. When faced with a challenging IPO, taking a creative/innovative approach presents risks and incurs up-front costs. However, those reasons, risks, and costs often do not tell the whole story.

You've probably noticed as you work through this book that creativity and/or innovation, when they are cultivated and thrive, often yield many and varied benefits for various individuals and organizations and, more importantly, those they serve and society at large. Table 5.1 illustrates this fact by alphabetically listing most of the examples of creative/innovative systems, facilities, structures, products, processes, and approaches that are at least mentioned in this text. The table notes the sections in which they appear and identifies one major benefit of each, recognizing that most have multiple benefits. If a particular item interests you, refer to the indicated section; if you want more information, use the source or sources cited in that section.

Section 1.4 offered reasons that engineers in the United States and other well-developed nations will need to be more creative and innovative. They are meeting grand challenges, doing more conceptual work because algorithmic work is moving to increasingly capable personnel in developing countries, placing more emphasis on pursuing opportunities, addressing wicked problems, practicing better stewardship with the intellectual gifts of student and practicing engineers, and the enjoying satisfaction of doing what has not been done.

In my view, the positives of creativity and innovation offset the negatives. Those who share that view should be aware of the obstacles to creativity/innovation so that they can individually and organizationally deal with them and help themselves and others reap the benefits. What appear to be impenetrable obstacles are often merely

Table 5.1 Many and varied examples of creative/innovative systems, facilities, structures, products, processes, and approaches, along with their benefits, are described in this text.

Creative/innovative system, facility, structure, product, process, service, or approach	Section(s) in book where described	A major benefit
Accelerated bridge construction (ABC)	8.6.2	Greatly reduces traffic disruption
Agriculture: precision	8.3	Reduces cost and risk
Alternating current systems	6.8.3	Enables community-wide electric power
Art museum: Milwaukee, Wisconsin	7.2.3	Unique roof wings that open to the sky
Automobile assembly line	4.3.2	Reduces cost per vehicle
Baby incubator	6.8.1	Saves lives in developing countries
Bar code	4.11.2	Reduced retail costs and increases sales
Barbwire	7.2.5	Livestock control
Book proposal process	4.11.1	Generates ideas for content
Books: Dr. Seuss	6.8.3	Enjoyable children's books
Borrowing geological concepts	4.3.2	Stimulates theory of evolution
Brain-imaging techniques	2.15.3	Reveals how the brain functions
Bridge reuse: temporary	8.6	Reduces public impact during construction
Brooklyn Bridge	6.8.4	First use of twisted wire cable
Cable: twisted wire	6.4.1	Enables design and construction of suspension bridges
Calculator: pocket	6.3.5	Easy access to fast computation
Cardiac pacemaker	3.6.1	Extends life
Cold call ideas: generation	4.7.2	Provides content for presentation
Cotton gin	8.3.1	Revolutionizes cotton production
Course scheduling assistance by novice	4.6.3	Frees department heads to work on higher-level tasks
Desalination	8.5	Expands supply of potable water
Desktop metaphor: Microsoft	4.3.3	Basic structure for personal computer use
Disneyland	4.3.3	First in a series of fun and educational theme parks
Door handles: extra	6.2.2	Accomodates children
Drainage laws	6.3.4	Protect property
Drawings of the inside of the human body	6.3.2	Greatly improves understanding of the body's elements and functions
Energy conservation principle	6.4.2	Improves understanding of the natural world
Enigma code: breaking it	4.6.7	Saves many lives
Evolution: theory of	4.3.2	Improves understanding of the natural world
Facebook	4.3.3	Popular social media
Floor cleaner: Swiffer	4.8.2	More efficient floor cleaning
Fluid flow in open channels: Manning Equation	4.3.4	Channel design
Fluid flow through porous media: Darcy's Law	6.6.4	Design of sand filters for water treatment
Fluoride options: generation of possible consequences	4.7.3	Enables decision making

(Continued)

Table 5.1 (*Continued*)

Creative/innovative system, facility, structure, product, process, service, or approach	Section(s) in book where described	A major benefit
Gas filler door and cap combination	4.12.4	Easier to use
Golden Gate Bridge	6.4.1	Iconic structure
Grass seed in cattle feed	4.12.1	Reseeds range land
Gravitation: universal/mutual theory of	4.3.3	Improves understanding of the natural world
Home battery: Tesla Powerwall	6.8.3	Provides energy when not available or too expensive
Integrated circuit	6.3.5	Simplification
Masking tape	6.6.2	More effective painting
Micropiles	4.12.4	Suitable for use in restrictive situations
Microwave oven	3.6.4	Faster food preparation
Meeting agenda: good news item	7.3.4	Increases awareness of organizational activities
Mental and physical activity studies	2.15.2, 2.16.3	Longer life and less dementia risk
Motion Theory: Newton's laws	4.3.3, 6.3.2	Improves understanding of physics
Music in retail sales	7.5.1	Influences types of purchases
Office layouts	7.8.5	Enhances collaboration
Opera house: Sydney, Australia	7.2.5	Iconic structure
Oxygen produced by photosynthesis	3.6.3	Improves understanding of the natural world
Panama Canal	4.12.5	Reduces shipping time
Penicillin	3.6.5	Widely used antibiotic
Peristaltic pump	7.2.5	Prevents contamination of pumped liquids
Personal computer features and functions	6.7.1	Global impact on personal effectiveness
Phonograph	4.3.4	Entertainment
Pipeline: use of aqua ammonia	4.12.6	Transport different liquid petroleum products serially in the same pipeline
Pond problem: definition of	4.7.1	Enable search for solution
Printing press with reusable type	1.3.2, 4.3.2	Historic global communication impact
Props in presentations	9.3	Holds attention and communicates
Prostheses: neuro	8.4	Enhances tactile, visual, and auditory functions
Q Drum	6.2.1	Improves health in developing countries
Railroad station columns: Lisbon, Portugal	7.2.3	Unusual palm tree forest design
Reward for using public trash containers	4.12.1	Solves refuse problem in public areas
Rover on Mars	8.2	Exploration
Skyscraper: Malmo, Sweden	7.2.3	Unique twisted spine shape
Smartphone	5.6.2	Combines many functions, including voice, photographs, video, and web features capabilities
Soapboxes: detecting empty ones	7.9.3	Cost-effective solution
Split-brain studies	2.15.1	Understanding of left and right hemisphere capabilities
Spoon and fork combination (spork)	4.12.4	Reduces cost
Storm water facility failure assessment	4.5.1	Basis for resolving issue
Storm water management facility	8.7	Multipurpose: recreation and flood control

Table 5.1 (Continued)

Creative/innovative system, facility, structure, product, process, service, or approach	Section(s) in book where described	A major benefit
Storm water runoff formulation: Rational Formula	4.3.4	Design of urban storm water runoff systems
Street storage of storm water	4.12.3	Reduces cost of public works
Structural elements that are honey combed	7.2.5	High strength-to-weight ratio
Suspension bridge: first major one and theory	4.3.4	Widely applicable theory
Taco Bell restaurant : 48 hr. construction	4.12.2	Cost savings on subsequent construction
Telephone	4.3.3	Enhances personal communication
Television	6.3.3	Transmit images
Television network	6.3.3	Massive information sharing
Theory of Inventive Problem Solving	7.9	Leverage the creative/innovative approaches of others
Train: high speed	6.6.3	Noise reduction
Utility office operations assessment	4.10.2	Improves effectiveness and efficiency
University engineering department: ideas	4.7.3	Provides stimulating ideas
Vacuum cleaner: Dyson bagless	6.8.3	Improves carpet cleaning
Velcro	1.3.2	Many useful fastener applications
Visual art techniques	6.3.2	More realistic portrayals of subjects
Vulcanization	3.6.2	Rubber for many uses
Wave theory	6.3.2	Improves understanding of physics
Weed eater	6.6.1	Easier lawn maintenance
Wetlands: floating	7.2.4	Enhances surface water quality
Xerography	6.8.2	Faster copying

temporary roadblocks to be moved aside or barriers to climb over. Accordingly, as suggested by Figure 5.1, this chapter's purpose is to identify seven obstacles or roadblocks to creativity and innovation and then offer suggestions as to how you and your group or team can deal with them for the benefit of yourself, your organization, and society.

5.1.2 Obstacles from within You

The preceding discussion of obstacles to your creative and innovative urges assumes that the obstacles come from outside you. That is, your inclination to explore different approaches to resolving an IPO is hampered by your team, your academic department, your employer, your boss, or some other external entity.

Please recognize that, in contrast to these external impediments, some obstacles will come from within you. You may initially be inclined to take a creative or innovative approach, but when specific opportunities arise you might decide not to do so for any number of reasons, including one or more of the obstacles that are about to be discussed, perhaps fueled by your brain's negativity bias (as explained in Section 2.12).

For example, a professor invites you to take the lead on a small, well-defined part of her research project, but you decline because you fear you lack the innovation ability to contribute to a research effort. You think about taking a

Figure 5.1
This chapter identifies possible obstacles to your and your team's creative and innovative intentions and offers ideas on how to overcome them.

(Suphakit73/Fotolia)

painting class while at the university, but decide not to because you have been told that you are not creative. In your first engineering position, your department head asks for a volunteer to help draft a social media policy for the organization, and you hesitate to get involved because you have never helped develop a policy and fear you might fail. As noted by Pogo, the amiable and philosophical comic strip opossum, "We have met the enemy and he is us."

Hopefully, the following discussion of obstacles to creativity and innovation will help you and your teams recognize the external variety of obstacles, see most of them as temporary roadblocks, and move past them. This discussion should also help you see and deal with the "enemy within."

5.2 FEAR OF FAILURE

We begin our discussion of creativity and innovation obstacles with fear of failure (especially catastrophic failure) of that which is planned, designed, constructed, or manufactured. Engineers, especially in some disciplines such as civil engineering, have traditionally and understandably been risk averse because of the possible disastrous consequences of failure of large, complex, one-of-a-kind structures, facilities, and systems, like that illustrated in Figure 5.2

5.2.1 Concern with Public Safety, Health, Welfare, and Costs

Moving away from the tried-and-true approach and toward an innovative and experimental mode raises the specter of violating the engineer's highest responsibility: protecting the safety, health, and welfare of the public. This paramount responsibility is explicitly prescribed in the ethics codes of essentially all engineering disciplines. For examples, refer to the codes of the American Council of Engineering Companies (ACEC), the American Institute of Chemical Engineers (AIChE), the American Society of Civil Engineers (ASCE), the American Society of Mechanical Engineers

Figure 5.2
Engineers strive to avoid failures of large, complex, one-of-a-kind structures, facilities, and systems.

(Baloncici/Shutterstock)

(ASME), the Institute of Electrical and Electronic Engineers (IEEE), the National Society of Professional Engineers (NSPE), and other engineering societies.

In addition to one-of-a-kind entities, fear of failure also applies to many-of-a-kind products. "When a product engineer at a car company considers making a change to a design or proposing a new approach to an engineering problem, the potential financial impact of being wrong is huge if this results in a costly recall of thousands or hundreds of thousands of cars," according to electrical engineer Fruechte (2014), who worked in automobile research and development. He goes on to explain, "One of the fears is not considering the unintended consequences when taking a new path."

Besides technical failures, we can also have failures in nontechnical areas. As engineers, we may fear situations and events such as exceeding our project budget, missing project and other deadlines, making poor presentations to our peers, and rejections of our proposals. Understandably, fear of failure in nontechnical and technical activities can squelch the inclination to try a new approach; we might not pursue a creative or innovative idea because we fear failure. Perhaps we are controlled by negativity bias (Section 2.12), or we're trapped by the *FUD factor*: fear, uncertainty, and doubt (Carlson and Wilmot 2006).

5.2.2 Remedies

Even when we carefully use traditional, tried-and-true design methods, we risk failure. As explained by Henry Petroski in his book *To Engineer is Human* (1985), using a hypothesis framework, "The process of engineering design may be considered a succession of hypotheses that such and such an arrangement of parts will perform a desired function without fail." He goes on to say the we can never be absolutely certain about the "fail-proofness" of any of our designs because we cannot imagine all the things that could go wrong. In other words, we can never enjoy zero risk of failure in our technical and nontechnical activities.

The risk of failure may seem small with traditional approaches, but it would seem to be greater with creative and innovative approaches. However, consider the following:

- Maybe some of the failures and shortcomings that occur with tried-and-true engineering approaches would be eliminated if we employed creativity and innovation to develop improved analysis, planning, and design methods. Early in my career, I benefited from the then recently developed digital computer watershed hydrologic–hydraulic models, which helped me, my teams, and those we served make better infrastructure and environmental decisions. In return, I wrote and spoke about our applications of the models with the hope of encouraging others to use and benefit from them. The models reduced the likelihood that recommended facilities would fail.

- We routinely benefit from the creative/innovative work of our predecessors. This implies that we in turn have an obligation to advance the engineering profession's approaches and tools for the benefit of our successors and those they serve. Such advances will require creativity and innovation. English scientist and philosopher Bacon, described the obligation this way: "I hold every man a debtor to his profession; from that which a man has course to seek countenance and profit, so ought they of duty to endeavor themselves, by way of amends, to be a help and ornament there unto." In other words, we take much from our profession, so let's give something back—and if it is creative/innovative, all the better.

- The risks associated with creative and innovative ideas and methods can be minimized by cautious measures such as research, testing, pilot studies, prototyping, and phasing. Section 4.12.3 illustrates What If by describing an innovative project in which storm water was intentionally temporarily stored on streets throughout an 8.1 square mile community in order to prevent surcharging of combined sewers and the related widespread basement flooding. Because this was the first major application of street storage, the project presented many risks such as failure to control flooding, pavement deterioration, icing of streets, and interference with movement of emergency vehicles. That risk was defined and reduced by means such as studying smaller-scale efforts elsewhere, fabricating and experimenting with various flow control devices, driving vehicles over trial low water control structures, conducting pilot studies in small drainage areas, and phasing the eventual community-wide construction (Walesh 2000, Walesh and Carr 1999).

5.3 BELIEF THAT CREATIVITY AND INNOVATION ARE NATURAL AND NOT LEARNED

You may hear expressions like "she was born creative" and "he is naturally innovative." As illustrated in Figure 5.3, this suggests that a person's creativity and innovation potential is determined at birth and that this wonderful ability is essentially a matter of nature, not nurture. This line of thinking can be an obstacle to you realizing your potential to think in entirely new ways.

5.3.1 Nurture: The Primary Determinant of a Person's Creative/Innovative Ability

Is it true that creativity and innovation potential is determined essentially by nature? Not according to many researchers and authors. For example, academic researchers Dyer and Gregersen (2011) state, "Our study of over 5000 entrepreneurs and executives shows . . . [that] almost anyone who consistently makes the effort to

Figure 5.3
Some believe that a
person's creativity and
innovation potential is
mostly a matter of nature,
not nurture.

(Svetlana Fedoseeva/Fotolia)

think different can think different." They go on to suggest a few methods to encourage creative and innovative thinking, consistent with the use of the methods presented in this book.

"Although creativity has long been considered a gift of a select minority, psychologists are now revealing its seeds in mental processes, such as decision making, language, and memory that all of us possess," according to researcher Chrysikou (2012). She goes on to say that studies reveal that we can be more creative and innovative if we use "strategies that encourage unconscious thought processes." Many of the methods in Chapters 4 and 7 engage the subconscious mind.

Altshuller (1996), the Russian developer of the Theory of Inventive Problem Solving (TRIZ), which is described Section 7.9, said "The theory of inventing can be taught at any age." He indicated that his creativity and innovation tools were used effectively by children in the fifth and sixth grades, and a major theme in his book is that anyone can be inventive if they are provided with some tools.

Based on the preceding information and my presentation and breakout experiences, I reject the idea that birth defines one's creativity and innovation potential. On the contrary, your ability to think in entirely new ways and directions is determined mostly by nurture and only secondarily by nature. That nurture element should include gaining an understanding of brain basics, as presented in Chapter 2, and the use of whole-brain tools, as discussed in Chapters 4 and 7.

5.3.2 Remedies

Most likely, you or those you work or interact with discount the possibility of being innovative and creative because you or they have heard or believe that a person is either born that way or isn't. I urge you and them to do at least two things, lest you miss some thrilling and satisfying experiences.

First, study at least some of the sources just cited that support the idea that creativity and innovation ability can be learned, that is, it is determined by nurture, not nature. Second, individually or as a group approach, take on some challenging IPOs by drawing on the Chapter 2 brain primer and applying one or more of the whole-brain methods described in Chapters 4 and 7 of this text. Stimulated by those methods, your innate creative and innovative capabilities will become apparent.

5.4 NEGATIVE RESULTS OF THE LEFT-BRAIN EMPHASIS IN FORMAL EDUCATION

Another possible obstacle to creativity and innovation is the left-brain emphasis in US formal education. Artist and author Edwards (1999) wrote the following about the US K–12 and beyond educational system: "Most of our educational system has been designed to cultivate the verbal, rational, on-time, left hemisphere, while half of the brain of every student is virtually neglected." She further notes that although there are a few art, shop, and creative writing K–12 classes, finding courses about imagination, visualization, perception, creativity, intuition, and inventiveness is unlikely.

Others criticize what they see as the tendency of K–12 education to discourage student inquiry and creativity/innovation by focusing students on finding and giving what the teacher wants. Educator and cultural critic Postman suggests that when naturally inquisitive children enter K–12 education, they can be thought of as question marks, but by the time they leave, they look like periods. They spend too much time thinking about what the teacher is thinking and wants, and too little time thinking about what they are thinking and would like to know. The stress is on the teacher's head rather than their own (von Oech 1990). Test the validity of these allegations by thinking about your K–12 experience.

5.4.1 Engineering Education

Might the preceding discussion of K–12 education also generally characterize engineering education? I think so. For example, in late 2014 and early 2015, I studied the Civil Engineering Body of Knowledge (CEBOK), the aspirational "necessary depth and breadth of knowledge, skills, and attitudes required of an individual entering the practice of civil engineering at the professional level [licensure as a professional engineer] in the 21st century" (American Society of Civil Engineers 2008). Knowledge is what you know, skill is what you are able to do with what you know, and attitude is how you respond to various situations.

I took on this project because the CEBOK was about to be reviewed for a possible third edition or at least some revisions. My purpose was to determine if creativity and innovation were present in the CEBOK and to learn the extent to which creativity and innovation were part of the formal education and prelicensure experience of civil engineers.

My study (Walesh 2015a) concluded that the current CEBOK, even though it's forward-looking in many ways, gives minimal attention to creativity/innovation. The investigation, informed by education and practice experience, also led me to conclude that creativity and innovation are not widely taught and learned in CE bachelor programs and that creativity/innovation fundamentals are not acquired during prelicensure experience. I conclude by recommending that creativity and innovation be integrated into the next version of the CEBOK and offer ideas on how this could be done.

I also studied (Walesh 2015b) the aspirational Engineering Body of Knowledge (EBOK), which is defined similarly to the CEBOK but applies to essentially all engineering disciplines and was published by the National Society of Professional Engineers (National Society of Professional Engineers 2013). My analysis indicates that creativity and innovation receive minimal attention in the EBOK.

We could do much more to prepare US engineers, regardless of their disciplines, to be creative and innovative for their own sake and for the benefit of society. One tactic is to include creativity/innovation in the next versions of the CEBOK, EBOK, and other engineering bodies of knowledge or similar documents. Inclusion in these aspirational documents will encourage more explicit treatment of creativity/innovation in the formal education and prelicensure experience of engineers.

Engineering educators Goldberg and Somerville reach a similar conclusion, writing, "It is surprising how little emphasis is placed on imagination, creativity, and design within the standard engineering curriculum today" (Goldberg and

Somerville 2014). After a cursory review of courses required in US engineering schools, they concluded that only a small fraction include the word *design* and address creativity. For the design courses, they observed that many "include very little discussion of creativity and the thought processes that underlie it," which they consider remarkable, "given the importance of this mode of thinking to the fundamental purpose of engineering."

5.4.2 You May Be an Exception

Some of the preceding information may not apply to you, in that you may be deeply involved in creative/innovative whole-brain activities, such as art and music. While working in university education, I collected and analyzed campus data showing that although engineers made up 10 percent of the student body, they comprised more than 20 percent of the campus musical groups and more than 20 percent of the campus leadership positions. Colleagues at other universities have shared similar observations. To some extent, you and other engineering students may have offset the left-brain emphasis of the formal education system. Another possibility is that you may be fortunate to be in an academic program committed to or experimenting with a whole-brain approach, possibly indicated by the use of this text.

5.4.3 Caveat

Lest there be any misunderstanding, nothing in this text is intended to detract from the value of left-brain capabilities. The typical student or practitioner engineer's critical thinking knowledge and skill, which is largely left-brained, is a powerful and often not fully recognized and appreciated force. Critical thinking can be generally viewed as an objective, self-disciplined, and rational thinking process. Critical thinking, which you probably already use when presented with a technical challenge, means defining the depth and breadth of the challenge, obtaining data, asking questions, invoking applicable principles, applying deductive and inductive reasoning, developing hypotheses, drawing conclusions, generating and evaluating options, and selecting and implementing a course of action.

Left-brain capabilities are powerful, and with continued development they will serve you well throughout your career. This text urges you—and shows you how—to celebrate your left-brain capabilities and complement them with right-brain capabilities and interaction between your conscious and subconscious minds so that you acquire whole-brain capabilities. You and your teams and organizations, while in school and beyond, are more likely to be more successful and achieve greater significance if you frequently engage in whole-brain thinking.

5.4.4 Remedies

If you believe that your formal education up to now has been too light on courses and topics that tend to engage the right side of your brain, you can begin to take some remedial actions. For example, enroll in a visual or performing arts class at your college or university; you may experience an awakening of parts of you that you did not know existed. In a similar vein, learn how to play an instrument; sign up for an overseas study, travel, or service experience; or research a right brain-themed topic that interests you.

As you move into professional practice, be aware of the role of creativity/innovation in K–12 education and in engineering education. Consider becoming an advocate for a whole-brain approach and exert influence in engineering education and practice as opportunities arise.

PERSONAL: ART AND MORE APPRECIATION OF MY RIGHT HEMISPHERE

Several years ago, after an over five-decade lapse that began after the third grade, I returned on a whim to art by taking a graphite pencil drawing class, loving it, going to classes, and creating a variety of drawings. I soon moved to colored pencils and discovered that I would draw in graphite or colored pencil, with some acrylic accents, for two or more hours while being oblivious to the passage of time. In returning to art, I initially envisioned no connection to engineering education or practice. This was simply a pleasant diversion. However, in addition to creating pencil drawings that I never envisioned (see Figure 5.4), this return to art had another creative/innovative effect.

As a result of drawing, thinking about drawing, talking to my art instructors and other students, and doing some reading, I began to see possible connections between visual arts and improving engineering education and (ultimately) practice. I was referred to and read Edward's book *Drawing on the Right Side of the Brain* (1999). That led to more research, including on recent neurological discoveries; interacting with colleagues; writing articles; presenting papers; conducting workshops; and writing this book. One thing can lead to another for you, as it did for me—but you have to start the process and be open to possibilities.

In summary, my entry into art on a whim enabled me to draw well, learn about the human brain, and use that knowledge to help engineers be even more creative and innovative. If you venture outside of your comfort zone, you are very likely to have similar eye-opening, whole-brain, and satisfying experiences. You only go around once, as they say, so make it a great trip.

Figure 5.4
Colored pencil drawing of Ize, the author's dog.
(Stuart Walesh)

5.5 RELUCTANCE TO CHANGE

Another possible obstacle to creativity and innovation is simply reluctance to change, or even fear of change. We have a word for that: *misoneism,* which means "a hatred, fear, or intolerance of innovation or change" (Merriam-Webster 2014a).

5.5.1 Why We Resist Change

Why do many of us resist change? The possibility of change causes each of us to compare the way things are to the way things could be. We contrast the familiar and comfortable with the unfamiliar and uncomfortable. I believe that most of us can see and weigh the pros and cons of a proposed change at the cognitive level, especially if thoughtfully presented. However, even if the pros clearly outweigh the cons at the cognitive level, we fear how we are going to get from here to there at the emotional level.

As suggested by Figure 5.5, we recognize the current situation, understand the proposed change, realize it would be better, but tend to be intimidated by that unknown chasm between where we are and where we could be. The trip is scary; therefore, when faced with change, we often revert to fear and other emotions, not reason (Walesh 2012b).

Consider another change-resistance factor. We are characterizing creativity/innovation as requiring a whole-brain approach. To some, this may imply that up to now, they have been using a half-brain approach. By being receptive to a whole-brain approach, might they be refuting what they've done for a long time? Might fear of embarrassment be an obstacle? Do we risk losing face?

Kaplan (2011) offers reasons companies fail at self-reinvention—that is, thinking about new business models, such as (in keeping with this book) a model that expects creativity and innovation. He says: "The most obvious reason companies fail at business model innovation is because CEOs and their senior leadership teams don't want to explore new business models." He goes on to explain that CEOs like the current models and expect the organization's personnel to improve their performance. In other words, let's not change; instead, let's try harder. As a result, according to McArdle (2012), "most companies wait far too long to even recognize

Figure 5.5
Although we may understand that a suggested major change would be a significant improvement, we sometimes resist because of the foreboding chasm between here and there.

(Don Landwehrle/Fotolia)

that they have a problem. . . . Even a dysfunctional culture, once well established, is astonishingly efficient at reproducing itself." For example, Netflix destroyed Blockbuster, digital cameras took Kodak down, and some engineering firms disappeared when they were purchased and disassembled.

VIEWS OF OTHERS: CHANGE IS HARD

Recognizing the frequent initial knee-jerk resistance to change, like that which may result from a creativity/innovation initiative, economist Galbraith said, "Faced with the choice between changing one's mind and proving that there is no need to do so, almost everybody gets busy on the proof." Machiavelli, the Italian politician and writer, explained opposition to change as follows: "There is nothing more difficult to plan, more doubtful of success, nor more dangerous to manage than the creation of a new system. For the initiators have the enmity of all who would profit by the preservation of the old institutions and merely lukewarm defenders in those who would gain by the new one" (Machiavelli 1980). Note, in particular, his mention of the initial "enmity" of many who oppose change contrasted with the "merely lukewarm defenders" of change.

The change associated with your creative/innovative proposal is likely to be vigorously opposed by some while being only casually supported by others. Kettering, engineer and inventor, warned, "If you want to kill any idea in the world, get a committee working on it." In a more positive vein, "All truth goes through three stages," according to German philosopher Schopenhauer. "First it is ridiculed, then it is violently opposed, finally it is accepted as self-evident." Creativity and innovation means change, and change will be opposed by many. Be prepared.

People offer many reasons to resist change, but might a major change now, either personally or organizationally, be better than major regret later? "One of the saddest experiences which can come to a human being," according to Burrows, "is to awaken gray-haired and wrinkled, near the close of an unproductive career, to the fact that all through the years he has been using a small part of himself."

5.5.2 Change Resistance in the Political Environment

Some engineers, especially civil engineers because they often work with elected and appointed public officials, will encounter politically driven resistance to change when they present their creative/innovative ideas. For example, the idea may have merit on all fronts except for timing.

Consider this scenario. You are the city engineer, a position you have held for several years, and the mayor is beginning the second year of her first four-year term. She is cautious, a quick learner, doing well, and already planning to run for a second term.

You and your staff have been working on an innovative energy idea that would provide long-term financial benefits to the city. Your team's idea is to establish a citywide system of solar collectors that would meet most municipal electric energy needs and that would feed energy into the regional network at times of low city energy needs, for which the city would receive monetary credit. Panels would be placed on city-owned buildings and facilities, such as city hall, schools, parking structures and shelters, bus and train stations, utility poles, and public works buildings. Preliminary engineering studies indicate that the system is technically feasible.

Your group also completed a preliminary long-term economic analysis in which you projected annual revenue and costs for the next twenty years. Assuming the project's detailed engineering begins next year and construction and installation get underway in few years, the analysis indicates economic success. That is, the large design and construction/installation costs that would be incurred in the first three years of the project would be offset in the project's first eight years, after which annual energy cost savings plus credits from the local power company would exceed annual operation and maintenance costs. Furthermore, the city could apply for some state and federal grant programs ending in three years to fund design and some capital costs. Because this would be the first project of this type in your state, both state and federal funding are very promising. This is a great project from a technical, economic, and financial perspective.

You meet with the mayor, enthusiastically describe the project, and are surprised at her negative response. She says the project seems risky (you did your homework and believe otherwise), requires too big an investment (yes, but would generate a much bigger return), and "the time is just not right" (state and federal funding are very likely if the city moves quickly). She asks you to abandon the effort and to keep the work that you and your staff performed confidential. You quickly conclude that politics, mainly her reelection, is her principal concern.

These kinds of politically motivated decisions occur often; if you choose to be in the public arena, you will need to deal with them, possibly in a creative/innovative manner. The following are some options for responding to the mayor's position:

- Stress the positive attention that the project would bring to the city.
- Suggest verification of your team's analysis by a consulting firm.
- Convene a public meeting at which the mayor could present *her* idea and gauge the response, especially with respect to timing.
- Conduct a modest pilot project to demonstrate the technology and keep the idea alive.
- Put the innovative idea on the back burner and wait for a favorable political climate.

PERSONAL: POLITICS AND YOU

I do not want to leave the impression that the political process is objectionable. I like this politics definition: "The art and science concerned with guiding or influencing governmental policy" (Merriam-Webster, 2014b). The definition does not attach an ethical or unethical, legal or illegal, or positive or negative quality to the political process. Recognize that politics, like any type of interaction among individuals, can be anywhere on the ethics, legal, or positive/negative scales. In any situation, we the participants place the process on those spectrums by our words and actions.

My hope is that you will participate in politics—that is, "guiding or influencing" public policy—and that you will strive to do it creatively and innovatively. Attend public meetings and share your views, serve on and lead ad hoc committees formed by public bodies, vote, assist candidates running for elected office, and be a candidate. Given your intelligence and knowledge, especially of scientific and technical matters, you have much to contribute.

My views aside, the engineering profession encourages you to positively participate in the political process. For example, the EBOK (National Society of Professional Engineers 2013) defines knowledge, skills, and attitudes appropriate to enter practice as a professional engineer. One of the capabilities in the EBOK is "Public Policy and Engineering," which urges you to understand public policy and consider influencing it. If you seek guidance for a particular political situation, refer to one or more of the engineering codes of ethics referenced in Section 5.2.1.

5.5.3 Remedies

When your creative/innovative approach to an IPO begins to gather attention and, more specifically, resistance, consider responding to and managing the process using the cascading awareness-understanding-commitment-action process shown in Figure 5.6. The process cascades in that it flows from the top to the bottom, the number of participants typically becoming markedly smaller as the process proceeds. However, even so, the number of individuals remaining at the last level (*action*) is often adequate to effect change.

As illustrated, on becoming aware of a possible change, many of us react in a mostly emotional knee-jerk fashion. You should anticipate and gracefully and patiently tolerate knee-jerk reactions. Simply ask for understanding of what is being proposed and the reasons for it. Some knee-jerkers will show you that courtesy and express openness, and on understanding, a portion of them will commit. Finally, for some, commitment will lead to the action needed to advance the creative/innovative effort: They will join you. For a comprehensive discussion of change, see Chapter 15, "The Future and You," in my book *Engineering Your Future* (Walesh 2012c).

5.6 LOSS OF BILLABLE TIME AND OTHER ORGANIZATIONAL IMPEDIMENTS

For engineers working in professional services (such as a consulting engineering firm), maintaining billable time targets is critical. *Billable time* is the time engineers work that can be billed to clients to generate income, in contrast with those hours that are not billable. As the percent of billable time drops, so does profit (Walesh 2012a). Therefore, losing billable hours is a fifth possible obstacle to creativity and innovation. If you are going to enter a professional services firm, be aware of the need to meet billable time criteria and the related creativity/innovation obstacle. The government, academic, or volunteer sector parallel obstacle might be, "time for creativity and innovation is not in our budget; we have more important work to do."

Figure 5.6
As the creator or innovator, you should anticipate and patiently work through the cascading awareness-understanding-commitment-action process.

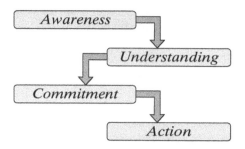

More specifically, an engineering consulting firm could easily experience the following two short-term billable time (and profit) hits if it tries to be more creative and innovative:

- Nonbillable time incurred by individuals working on creativity/innovation tasks not billable to clients
- Time and other resources needed to implement a team's promising idea

5.6.1 Business Realities

I empathize with managers in engineering firms, as a former department manager in one. They need immediate results in terms of time utilization and other metrics, and *immediate* typically means *this week* or *this month.* "So even though managers know that innovation is necessary," according to consultant Ashkenas (2012), "most do not have the patience [or flexibility] to wait [months or] years for results. Consequently, they say innovation is important, but they don't back it up with time or resources." His comments remind us that even when billable time is not a major productivity metric, the uncertainty of the results of a proposed creative/innovative effort will be an obstacle to initiating it.

When any of us learn to think differently as individuals or teams, we act differently; this may incur short-term costs—but, and this is a big *but*, the long-term return on that investment of occasional billable time hits and other disruptions could be tremendously positive. Clearly, we need both short-term thinking, like billable time tracking, and long-term activities, like strategic planning. "But the safety of the short term is an illusion," warns innovation expert Kao (2007). "The hot winds of disruption swirl all around us, whether they be in the form of new competitors, business models, technologies, consumer preferences, or geopolitical factors."

Billable time and other considerations aside, some managers may oppose creativity and innovation to protect their turf. Ashkenas argues that although a particular innovative idea might give the manager's firm an edge over competing firms, it may also adversely affect the manager's department or other unit vis-à-vis other departments or entities. "In other words, while managers might want to disrupt their competitors, they are less comfortable disrupting themselves."

A final manager thought: The admirable slow, continuous improvement philosophy, which thrives in a few business, government, academic, and volunteer organizations or portions of them, can be an impediment to typically disruptive creativity/innovation initiatives. Therefore, "managers who have grown up in a continuous improvement culture may be uncomfortable with change that doesn't happen step-by-step" (Ashkenas 2012). This is not meant to be critical of continuous improvement but to suggest that managing it and creativity/innovation side by side can be a challenge.

5.6.2 Remedies

Recognize that the return on the resources invested in creative/innovative initiatives may be tremendous. Think back to the year 2000: What tools and techniques that you and other engineering students and practitioners use today existed then? The following did not: iPod, iTunes, iPhone, iPad, readily available GPS, the Google search engine, building information modeling (BIM), 3-D printing, and social media (Isaacson 2011).

Perhaps the most significant electronic advancement in the past decade is the smartphone, which gained popularity with the advancements of the iPhone, introduced by Apple in 2007. It "turned mobile phones into music, photography, video, email, and web devices" (Isaacson 2011). It also spawned numerous competitors, such as Google's Android phones and Microsoft's Windows phones, and begat thousands of application developers. The smartphone changed how people relate to each other (e.g., texting versus email or the telephone) and how people acquire information (Fruechte 2014).

What might be the equivalent successful, creative, and innovative products or services in your business, government, academic institution, or other organization? Do you really want to forgo finding out? If not, you and your organization need to take the long view, need to invest in the quality of people you assemble, the leaders you identify, and the creative/innovative ideas you encourage. Given the smart people typically found in engineering-oriented organizations, you never know what they might come up with.

For some practices that could help to strengthen an existing innovation culture or develop one from scratch, refer to Section 7.8. These are ways to offset impediments to creativity/innovation in all types of organizations, including on-campus student organizations. I am not suggesting that your organization do all of them. Instead, think of the list as a smorgasbord of ideas that you could choose from or that might stimulate other approaches.

5.7 MISCONCEPTIONS ABOUT ARTISTS

Another possible obstacle to having some engineering students and practitioners embrace creativity and innovation initiatives is that mentioning *creativity* may engender a negative reaction about alleged "creative" types. As stated by author Miles (1997), creativity's "association with a marginalized artistic life-style devalues its worth." This suggests that some of us think that creativity is for free-spirited, brush-wielding, devil-may-care "artistic" types with lots of time on their hands. In stark contrast, we engineers have real, practical work to do!

Or, we may have observed that a few of the highly creative people we have known or are aware of are somewhat eccentric. The famous engineer Tesla developed the first practical commercial use of alternating current motors, generators, and transmission lines. His eccentricities included loving pigeons and the dark, and fearing germs and round objects. Kamen, inventor of the Segway scooter, never takes vacations, and Einstein "picked up cigarette butts off the street to get tobacco for his pipe" (Pickover 1998). Researcher Carson (2011) says, "The incidence of strange behavior by highly creative individuals seems too extensive to be the result of mere coincidence." According to psychology professor Simonton (2012), "top performers are not a very normal bunch."

5.7.1 Free the Artist Within

Recall the *free to be foolish* discussion (Section 3.2.4), which argues that the path to creatively and innovatively resolving an IPO requires the freedom to be foolish, daring, unreasonable, unconventional, and eccentric and to at least temporarily think counter to reason, authority, and common sense. Although it does not suggest that we need to be inherently eccentric, that section suggests that being temporarily so is likely to be fruitful.

Carson goes on to share the hypothesis that "reduced cognitive filtering could explain the tendency of highly creative people to focus intensely on their inner world at the expense of social and even self-care needs." She explains that "reduced cognitive filtering" means that some individuals are more likely to benefit from the cognitive processing that "goes on in our brains behind the scenes," in their subconscious minds. This can lead to exceptional insights that flow from the subconscious into the conscious mind. *Bottom line:* Highly creative individuals may be somewhat eccentric; let's welcome them and their contributions so that all may benefit: us, them, our organizations, and, most importantly, those we serve.

Consider another perspective. We may narrowly associate creativity with visual or performing arts—rather than, much more broadly, as a way of thinking. I suspect that many of you can envision an artist coming to his or her studio in the morning and saying, "What painting or sculpture will I create or start today?" In contrast, how many of us, when we come to school or work, will say, "What concept, idea, process, or thing will I create or start today?" Do you have a creative/innovative mind-set? McCuen (2012), a civil engineering professor, offers this thought: "The attitude that creative thinking is fun, but unnecessary to solve today's problems, needs to be replaced with the attitude that creative thinking is an essential problem-solving tool." What are you going to create today?

PERSONAL: ENGINEERS AND ARTISTS HAVE MUCH IN COMMON

As a professional engineer and an amateur artist, I understand how some very pragmatic engineers may not see or feel a connection to artists or to creativity. However, engineers and artists have much in common:

- We both study and apply fundamentals. In my first graphite pencil drawing class, the instructor explained that a successful drawing required three basics that proved to be widely applicable. First, the principal subject should not be in the center. Second, if I am drawing a duck, it should look like a duck; for me to do that, I had to really see, not just look at, a duck. Third, use various intensities of graphite to achieve a three-dimensional effect on a two-dimensional medium. In Static Mechanics, one of my first engineering classes, we also learned widely applicable fundamentals.
- We both should be very careful observers; we can't just look, we must see. In art, failing to see means missing and failing to portray the richness of the subject. In engineering, failing to see means misdiagnosing the IPO.
- We both produce one-of-a-kind results.
- We both can appreciate the historic and linguistic connections between engineering and creativity (Section 1.5).

5.7.2 Remedies

If you are inclined to resist creative/innovative urges or efforts (yours or others) because they suggest frivolity, then visit an art gallery or museum and see, not just look at, the displayed works. Attend a concert and really listen. Ask artists and musicians what they view as the fundamentals that enable them to do their work, and think about the fundamentals that enable you to do yours. You may find, as I have, that most artists rely on fundamentals and embrace a whole-brain approach.

Perhaps you are uncomfortable with your eccentricities or those of others. Look for the positives. Be guided by essayist and poet Thoreau, who wrote: "If a man does not keep pace with his companions, perhaps it is because he hears a different drummer. Let him step to the music he hears however measured or far away." We achieve the desirable Medici Effect (Section 4.6) when we gather a group of individuals, many of whom are marching to different drummers.

5.8 COMPLACENCY

My last potential obstacle to creativity and innovation to discuss is already having achieved success, which may lead to your organization not being compelled to continue to move forward because it will bask in its accomplishments. Recent and current success becomes an impediment to future success. "Even if you are on the right track," according to humorist and social commentator Rogers, "you'll get run over if you just sit there." Cooper (2006) wrote, "Good and great are the enemies of the possible."

5.8.1 The Success Trap

Current success in the absence of creativity and innovation may be an impediment to future success, or even to future existence. Examples of organizations that seem to have slipped into complacency, some of which were noted in Section 5.5.1, include Kodak, Blockbuster, Borders, HP (Ante 2012), and various engineering firms, manufacturing companies, university engineering departments, government units, and other entities that are no longer with us or barely surviving.

Complacency and its negative effects can sneak up on us. A product engineer who led a successful design, one that is doing well in the marketplace, may be reluctant to rock the boat or mess with success. After all, the product is as good as, or maybe better than, the current competition, and he or she has many other matters to deal with. Meanwhile, the competition may be about to launch a new and better product, and the product engineer's organization will be caught flat-footed (Fruechte 2014).

See Sections 7.8.1 and Sections 7.8.2 for an expanded discussion of organizational culture and its tremendous influence; the forces that seek, intentionally or unintentionally, to kill creativity and innovation; the tendency of dysfunctional organizations to perpetuate themselves; and the consequences. The benefits of countering complacency with a culture and physical environment supportive of creativity and innovation and the means to achieve them are presented in Sections 7.8.3 through Sections 7.8.8.

5.8.2 Remedies

Business, government, academic, volunteer, and other entities should celebrate their individual and organizational successes. Reflect on the causative factors and positive lessons learned. Also note failures and the related lessons learned. Then, ask what you will do for an encore. More specifically, individually and collectively ask and answer the following three questions (based, in part, on Carlson and Wilmot 2006):

1. Who do we serve? Every organization serves someone; otherwise it would not exist for long.
2. What is the greatest current or near-future unmet need among those we serve and would like to serve? If we don't know, let's ask them, perhaps using some of the question-asking concepts and methods in Section 4.2.
3. How will we meet that need? Then, get on with applying the concepts and tools in this book to proactively, and hopefully creatively/innovatively, define and meet that need.

Working through the preceding seemingly simple steps won't be easy, in part because of complacency. You and others are likely to encounter one or more of the obstacles described in this chapter. However, whatever pain you and others feel as you seek to define and meet the next needs of those you serve or want to serve, it will be less than the pain caused by a dying business, governmental, academic, volunteer, or other entity.

5.9 POINTS TO PONDER

In summary, you and/or your team may encounter the following obstacles to your creative/innovative efforts:

- Fear of failure
- Belief that creativity and innovation are natural and not learned
- Negative results of the left-brain orientation in formal education
- Reluctance to change
- Loss of billable time and other organizational impediments
- Misconceptions about artists
- Complacency

The preceding discussion of obstacles makes you aware of them and offers some remedies, with the hope that they may be converted to temporary roadblocks that can be moved or circumvented. Motivated by the obstacles discussion, perhaps you can think of other obstacles and remedies to them.

5.10 TWENTY QUESTIONS

Assume that you and perhaps a core group are working on a creative/innovative project. You have identified a challenging IPO facing your team, department, campus organization, or other entity and think you have a fresh way to resolve it. You also realize that the new direction and its inevitable changes are likely to engender opposition for reasons such as some of the obstacles discussed in this chapter, at least initially. You've considered some of the suggested remedies. However, you want to do more. Therefore, you and your team will ask many questions to help thoroughly define the impact of your project so that you can proactively move forward.

As a guide, refer to the twenty questions listed ahead, which are based in part on Maxwell (1993), Russell (2006), and Walesh (2012b). The list is provided to motivate question asking; it is not all inclusive. Quiz yourself and many others about the possible implications of your creative/innovative ideas, and thus begin to address what should be changed, why it should be changed, who would be or thinks they would be affected, and how and when the change might occur.

1. Are you advocating this new approach primarily for the organization's benefit, or are you doing so mainly to elevate/bring attention to yourself?
2. What is the challenging IPO, and how will you communicate it so others understand it?
3. Is your commitment to your creative/innovative solution sufficient to deal with likely prolonged apathy and/or opposition?
4. Is the change compatible with the organization's mission and vision, or do you propose to change the organization's mission and vision?

5. Who will be positively affected by the change, and what are the actual or perceived benefits?
6. Who will be negatively affected by the change, and what are the actual or perceived costs?
7. What are the long-term implications for the organization of not changing, of proceeding in the current mode?
8. Who will not be impacted, positively or negatively, by the contemplated change but is likely to initially think they are stakeholders?
9. What unexpected changes could occur as a result of implementing your creative/innovative solution?
10. Is the contemplated change visionary enough to excite and engage other leaders, or are you aiming too low?
11. Can you confidently identify likely co-leaders and the reasons they will be supportive?
12. How will the core team learn more about the change process, and how will the group be expanded?
13. Who will be the principal opposition—at least initially—and why?
14. What individuals and/or organizations outside of your organization might assist?
15. Can you point to similar or related changes made elsewhere to use as examples and/or learning experiences?
16. What messages and media will comprise your contemplated communication program?
17. What are some of the major milestones and metrics needed to indicate that the desired change is occurring?
18. What are some small successes that will demonstrate commitment and progress?
19. How will you fund, finance, and/or obtain resources for the change effort?
20. Could your creative/innovative idea be applied on a trial or pilot basis, or would the change be irreversible once it begins?

VIEWS OF OTHERS: VALUE OF QUESTIONS

Let's begin with actor Alda, who offers this advice: "I found I wasn't asking good enough questions because I assumed I knew something," suggesting that we should not inflate our understanding of a new situation, at least initially. Ruskin, an English philosopher, provides this guidance: "To be able to ask a question clearly is two-thirds of the way to getting it answered." "The important thing is to not stop questioning," according to Einstein. An African proverb says, "The one who asks questions doesn't lose his way." Finally, Dell, founder of the company of the same name, said that the idea to start his company was driven by him asking why the cost of a computer was five times the cost of the sum of its parts (Dyer, Gregerson, and Christensen 2014). For additional thoughts about asking questions, see Views of Others in Section 4.2.1.

Opportunity is missed by most people because
it is dressed in overalls and looks like work.
—*Thomas Edison, inventor*

CITED SOURCES

Altshuller, G. 1996. *And Suddenly the Inventor Appeared: TRIZ, the Theory of Inventive Problem Solving.* Translated by Lev Shulyak from the original 1984 Russian version. Worcester, MA: Technical Innovation Center, Inc.

American Society of Civil Engineers. 2008. *Civil Engineering Body of Knowledge for the 21st Century,* 2nd ed. Reston, VA: ASCE.

Ante, S. E. 2012. "Avoiding Innovation's Terrible Toll." *The Wall Street Journal,* January 7–8.

Ashkenas, R. 2012. "Managers Don't Really Want to Innovate." *Harvard Business Review,* May 1.

Carlson, C. R., and W. W. Wilmot. 2006. *Innovation: The Five Disciplines for Creating What Customers Want.* New York: Crown Business.

Carson, S. 2011. "The Unleashed Mind." *Scientific American Mind,* May/June: 22–29.

Chrysikou, E. G. 2012. "Your Creative Brain at Work." *Scientific American Mind,* July/August: 24-31.

Cooper, R. K. 2006. *Get Out of Your Own Way: The 5 Keys to Surpassing Everyone's Expectations.* New York: Crown Business.

Dyer, J. and H. Gregersen. 2011. "Learn How to Think Different(ly)." *Harvard Business Review,* September 24.

Dyer, J. H., H. B. Gregerson, and C. M. Christensen. 2014. "The Innovator's DNA." *Harvard Business Review OnPoint,* Winter: 122–128.

Edwards, B. 1999. *Drawing on the Right Side of the Brain.* New York: Jeremy P. Tarcher/Putnam.

Fruechte, R. 2014. Former director, Electrical and Control Systems Lab, General Motors R& D Center, pers. comm., August 18 and September 16.

Goldberg, D. E., and M. Somerville. 2014. *The Whole New Engineer: The Coming Revolution in Engineering Education.* Douglas, MI: ThreeJoy Associates.

Isaacson, W. 2011. *Steve Jobs.* New York: Simon & Schuster.

Kao, J. 2007. *Innovation Nation: How America Is Losing Its Innovation Edge, Why It Matters, and What We Can Do to Get It Back.* New York: The Free Press.

Kaplan, S. 2011. "Five Reasons Companies Fail at Business Model Innovation." HBR Blog Network, *Harvard Business Review,* October 12.

Machiavelli, N. 1980. *The Prince.* Translated by E. R. P. Vincent. New York: New American Library.

Maxwell, J. C. 1993. *Developing the Leader within You.* Nashville, TN: Nelson Business.

McArdle, M. 2012. "Why Companies Fail." *The Atlantic,* March: 28–32.

McCuen, R. H. 2012. "Creativity: An Important Problem-Solving Tool for Water Resources in 2050." In *Toward a Sustainable Water Future: Visions for 2050,* edited by W. M. Grayman, D. P. Loucks, and L. Saito, 313–321. Reston, VA: ASCE.

Merriam-Webster. 2014a. "Misoneism." Accessed November 15, 2014. http://www.merriam-webster.com/medical/misoneism.

Merriam-Webster. 2014b. "Politics." Accessed November 22, 2014. http://www.merriam-webster.com/dictionary/politics.

Miles, E. 1997. *Tune Your Brain: Using Music to Manage Your Mind, Body, and Mood.* New York: Berkley Books.

National Society of Professional Engineers. 2013. *Engineering Body of Knowledge.* Alexandria, VA: NSPE.

Petroski, H. 1985. *To Engineer Is Human: The Role of Failure in Successful Design.* New York: St. Martin's Press.

Pickover, C. A. 1998. *Strange Brains and Genius.* New York: William Morrow and Company.

Russell, J. 2006. Professor and Chair, Civil and Environmental Engineering Department, University of Wisconsin–Madison, pers. comm., March 13.

Simonton, D. K. 2012. "The Science of Genius." *Scientific American Mind,* November–December: 35–41.

von Oech, R. 1990. *A Whack on the Side of the Head: How You Can Be More Creative.* Stamford, CT: US Games Systems, Inc.

Walesh, S. G., and R. Carr. 1999. "Street Surface Storage for Control of Combined Sewer Surcharge." In *WRPMD '99: Preparing for the 21st Century,* edited by M. E. Wilson. Proceedings of the 26th Annual Water Resources Planning and Management Conference, Tempe, AZ, June 6–9.

Walesh, S. G. 2000. *Street Storage System for Control of Combined Sewer Surcharge,* EPA/600R-00/065. Washington, DC: US Environmental Protection Agency.

Walesh, S. G. 2012a. "Basic Accounting: Tracking the Past and Planning the Future." In *Engineering Your Future: The Professional Practice of Engineering,* 299–327. Hoboken, NJ/Reston, VA: Wiley/ASCE Press.

Walesh, S. G. 2012b. "The BOK and Leadership Lessons Learned." Paper presented at the American Society for Engineering Education Annual Conference, San Antonio, TX, June 10–13.

Walesh, S. G. 2012c. "The Future and You." In *Engineering Your Future: The Professional Practice of Engineering,* 431–454. Hoboken, NJ/Reston, VA: Wiley/ASCE Press, Reston, VA.

Walesh, S. G. 2015a. "Creativity and Innovation as Part of the Civil Engineering BOK." Paper presented at the American Society for Engineering Education Annual Conference, Seattle, WA, June 14–17.

Walesh, S. G. 2015b. "Comparison of Today's EAC/ABET Engineering Degree Criteria to Future Capabilities Recommended in NSPE's Engineering Body of Knowledge." White paper prepared for the ASCE's Task Committee on Educational Requirements for Licensure, April 1.

EXERCISES

Notes:

1. The goal of the exercises is to provide students, usually working alone, the opportunity to think about and use the ideas, principles, and information offered in this and earlier chapters.

2. However, many circumstances and corresponding teaching/learning opportunities may arise. For example, a stated situation may be altered to meet specific concerns or needs. Such variations are encouraged, subject to the concurrence or direction of the instructor.

5.1 BOOK REVIEW: The purpose of this exercise is to provide you with an opportunity to study one book in depth about change and how to either respond to it or help direct it. Do so by identifying the book's key ideas and information, summarizing the book, critiquing it, and determining the book's relevance to your study and work. In doing so, you will be further introduced to a broad range of change literature and other sources, with the hope that you will continue to read critically in this area as one means of growing professionally. Suggested tasks are as follows:

    a. Tentatively select one change book. Some possible sources are books reviewed in newspapers and magazines; books recommended by others; and books you find by searching the Internet.

    b. Request approval of the book from your instructor.

    c. Read the book and prepare a review in which you do the following: a) cite your book (e.g., name, author, publisher, date); b) describe some of the key information, ideas, and/or theses presented in the book; c) identify the supporting evidence; d) indicate whether or not you agree with the key ideas or theses; and e) comment on the book's relevance or lack thereof to your study and work.

5.2 CREATIVITY/INNOVATION: NATURE OR NURTURE: Organize a debate with friends who are not part of this study group. The topic of debate will be "Creativity/ Innovation: Nature or Nurture." Arrange for five participants in to be in favor of nature while five will be in favor of nurture. Now try to summarize the issues raised by each group into clusters and report the reasons why people held such views. Analyze the results.

5.3 AN OBSTACLE YOU ENCOUNTERED: Consider one of your creative/innovative ideas which might have failed or was partially successful. Was the idea radically new in terms of technology or application area? Analyze all the factors that led to its failure. Usually one tends to identify external causes with much greater ease. Identifying the "within me" causes are more difficult as one needs to accept that they exist. Identify all external and internal causes. Describe the solution with due respect to your privacy and that of the others involved.

    Now assume that you have to make a presentation of this idea of yours in front of a Venture Capitalist jury team. You hardly know the profile and background of the jury members. From your previous experience and the seven obstacles discussed in this chapter, plan for tackling all the probable obstacles. Also plan for how you will fight the "within me" enemy to gain the necessary confidence in your idea.

5.4 AN OBSTACLE SOMEONE ELSE ENCOUNTERED: Interview a person (preferably someone local, for convenience) who is recognized as being creative and/or innovative. Perhaps someone on the faculty can help you identify and connect with an appropriate person. Ask the person if he or she would share an obstacle encountered and how he or she responded. With the person's permission, prepare a summary of what you learned.

5.5 FEAR WITHIN ME: Go through Section 5.1.2. Now make a list of all mental boundaries that you have created for yourself. These can be: "I can only go for jobs that pay me a certain amount"; "I can only go to a certain type of graduate school"; "I can't dance well"; "I am not good at making friendships"; and so on.

    Take one of these boundaries which you want to proactively and creatively tackle. Which one of the following four obstacles discussed in this chapter is most likely to deter you in breaking your mental boundary: fear of failure, belief that creativity and innovation are natural and not learned, reluctance to change, or complacency? What will you do about it? You may choose to keep the plan to yourself.

6

Characteristics of Creative and Innovative Individuals

The role of the human is not to be dispassionate, depersonalized, or neutral . . . emotive traits are rewarded: the voracious lust for understanding, the enthusiasm for work, the ability to grasp the gist, the empathetic sensitivity to what will attract attention and linger in the mind.
—*David Brooks, columnist*

Objectives:

After studying this chapter, you will be able to:

- Illustrate seven characteristics often exhibited by creative/ innovative individuals
- Analyze your profile relative to the seven characteristics and infer your readiness for creativity and innovation

- Explain your strengths and articulate your weaknesses relative to your creativity/ innovation potential
- Show further insight into how to apply the Medici Effect
- Recognize at least ten creative/innovative individuals and describe their contributions

6.1 INTRODUCTION TO CHARACTERISTICS

Section 1.4 provided six reasons that you should study creativity and innovation starting now, as part of your formal education, and continuing through your career: meeting grand challenges, doing more conceptual work because algorithmic work is moving to increasingly capable personnel in developing countries, placing more emphasis on pursuing opportunities, addressing wicked problems, practicing better stewardship with your intellectual gifts, and enjoying the satisfaction of doing what has not been done before.

Being more creative and innovative—taking a more whole-brain approach—requires personal growth, including learning the basics of how the human brain functions (Chapter 2), obtaining whole-brain tools (Chapters 4 and 7), and overcoming obstacles (Chapter 5). Enhancing creativity and innovation also requires recognizing, strengthening, or acquiring certain personal characteristics conducive to creativity and innovation, as discussed in this chapter, and perhaps being further inspired by the Chapter 8 case studies and the implementation ideas offered in Chapter 9.

I trust that you welcome learning about these personal qualities because you want to be more creative and innovative and wonder if you have it in you. Furthermore, in keeping with the Section 4.6 discussion of the Medici Effect, when you are invited to join a team or have the opportunity to form one, I hope you want diversity. The seven personal characteristics discussed in this chapter are a set of diversity factors that are important to consider when forming a team or, more broadly, establishing an organization.

I've studied what research has revealed about the characteristics of creative and innovative individuals in various professions and specialties. I've also reflected on my experiences and observations. Some of the findings are to be expected and others may be surprising. At best, we are talking about favorable tendencies—not a definitive personality profile prescription. For example, as you will soon see, innovative individuals tend to be empathetic—but of course, not all empathetic people are innovative. Few of us will be strong in all of the characteristics that I describe. However, each of us can determine the extent to which we do exhibit some of the characteristics, consider the possibility of embracing more of them, and bring appropriate characteristics to bear as situations require.

6.2 EMPATHETIC

The creative and innovative person is *empathetic*—that is, he or she recognizes the wants and needs of others. More specifically, that person thinks about ideas that may help fulfill those wants and/or needs (Canales 2011). Innovation educator Wagner (2012) defines empathy as "the ability to imagine the world from multiple perspectives and having an attitude that puts others first." From an engineer's perspective, *others* might be existing or potential clients, customers, owners, or colleagues who may be down the hall or halfway around the globe.

PERSONAL: MAJOR DAILY EFFORT TO OBTAIN POTABLE WATER

My wife and I visited Tanzania a few years ago. We were immediately shocked and saddened to notice that many people, mostly women and children, spent a good part of their day carrying containers of potable water from streams and community wells to their homes, often leading to debilitating back and neck injuries resulting from carrying heavy loads, frequently on their heads. In general, the load for an individual is limited at best to about four gallons (or 33 pounds), which could mean many trips each day for a family (Innovative Concepts Group 2014).

Figure 6.1
In some developing countries, people—mostly women and children—spent a good part of their day carrying containers of water from sources to their homes.

(DiversityStudio/Fotolia)

6.2.1 Q Drum Meets a Major Need

How could the major load-carrying problem in Tanzania (Figure 6.1) be solved? How could the weight per trip be increased and the number of trips be reduced at minimal cost?

One answer is the Q Drum, shown in Figure 6.2, which addresses the problem of reducing the load while increasing the volume (by a factor of four) by rolling the

Figure 6.2
The Q Drum addresses the challenge of reducing the water-carrying load for individuals, increasing the volume they can transport, reducing the number of trips, and making their lives more tolerable.

(P J Hendrikse/MCT/Newscom; CB2/ZOB/WENN/Newscom)

water in a simple cylindrical vessel (GreenUpGrader 2014). The vessel is a wheel; the wheel is a vessel. The idea of the Q Drum is credited to Piet Hendrikse and his brother Hans, who empathetically watched South African natives use wheelbarrows and old water drums to transport drinking water (Murray 2011).

A Q Drum carries 13.2 gallons and weighs about 120 pounds when filled. The drums are manufactured in Johannesburg, South Africa, and cost about $70 US dollars. The challenge shifts from the design of the drum to raising funds to purchase and distribute them. "The people that need them can't afford them and must rely on people who can afford them but don't need them" (Innovative Concepts Group 2014).

6.2.2 Additional Examples of Empathy-Driven Creativity and Innovation

Recognizing wants and needs enables us to help others and maybe do it in a creative/innovative manner. Many instances of known or implied empathy in action appear in this book. For example, in addition to the Q Drum, the invention of the weed eater, masking tape, and a special baby incubator (all of which are discussed later in this chapter) were initially motivated by empathy.

Biologist Medina (2008) recalls a shoe store he visited when he was five years old that had a front door with three handles: low, middle, and high. He described it as "a door [he] could actually reach" and went on to observe that anyone, "regardless of the strength or age of the customer," could reach a handle. This anecdote suggests that when we plan or design a structure, facility, system, product, or process, we should empathetically put ourselves in the shoes of intended users and search for creative/innovative—and maybe simple—ways to meet their needs. It also illustrates a pattern: innovation is often simple, in retrospect, and often low tech.

Speaking of being aware of wants and needs of others, Schultz, CEO and chairman of Starbucks, said, "We're in the people business serving coffee, not the coffee business serving people" (Behar 2009). Let's paraphrase that for our profession: "We are in the people business serving engineering, not in the engineering business serving people."

6.3 STUDIOUS

As used here, *studious* is broadly defined to mean observant, curious, and desirous to learn. Being studious includes zealously digging deep for new knowledge. Former educator turned consultant Wagner (2012) refers to the "exponential growth of information" and says that "all successful innovators have mastered the ability to learn on their own in the moment" and then "apply the knowledge in new ways." Presumably, their education taught them how to learn. According to Samuel Johnson, English lexicographer and writer, "Curiosity is the permanent and certain characteristic of the vigorous mind"—and, might I add, the whole-brain mind.

6.3.1 Always a Student

Study is essential in our rapidly changing world. Individually and organizationally, we must avoid exhausting our intellectual capital (Sanborn 2006). The creator or innovator is a perpetual student of things and people who, while continuing to develop his or her area of expertise, also observes, reads widely, engages diverse individuals in conversation, asks questions, participates in seminars and webinars, travels, plans new experiences, and seeks varied assignments.

The capital letter *T* nicely captures the essence of being studious. The vertical line represents one's specialty, which results from focused study and provides expertise to help resolve challenges. The horizontal line reflects the studious person's range of interests, knowledge, and skills and enables him or her to recognize, value, and integrate the different and potentially supportive expertise of others.

Curiosity may have killed the cat, but curiosity stimulated by observation cultivates creativity and innovation. Recall electrical engineer de Mestral's curiosity about the burrs that were attached to his and his dog's coat, the miniature hooks he discovered with his microscope that could attach to a surface bearing hoops, and the resulting creation of Velcro, as discussed in Section 1.3.2. Think also about Joseph Priestley's interest in what happens when living things are sealed in glass jars and the resulting discovery of oxygen (Section 3.6.3).

Creative and innovative people frequently ask questions (Canales 2011) motivated by their observations and curiosity. Sometimes, the frequency and/or intensity of the questions borders on annoying, especially when they challenge the status quo. That may be a small price to pay for the resulting creative/innovative thinking. Consider some examples of such questions:

- We've developed a great system to quickly repair products that come off the assembly line with flaws. Shouldn't we invest as much effort in finding and fixing the causes of those flaws?
- Why do we always wait for our competitors to use new technology or offer new services before we do?
- This process requires major manual effort. Could we automate it or write software to do it? (If this software-oriented topic interests you, read *Automate This* by engineer Steiner [2012].)
- Why don't we give selected personnel bonuses at the beginning of the year conditioned on defined performance, with the provision that if those individuals do not perform during the year, the bonuses would be taken away at the year's end? This unusual idea is based on the loss aversion phenomenon, which means that we typically dislike losing what we have more than not getting what we want (Brooks 2014).
- Why are my major course assignments thrown together at the last minute so that they do not reflect my best effort?
- Most of what our consulting firm does is routine, algorithmic. Aren't we at risk? Shouldn't we be trying to provide higher-level services that other firms are not providing?
- If we announced tomorrow that we were closing our business, government agency, university, or professional society who would notice and why?
- Why do we make the same mistakes over and over and over? How can we break this pattern?

PERSONAL: ONE WAY TO BE A STUDENT

Especially after you enter engineering practice, you may feel that you do observe and are curious, but that you don't have time to study! A participant in one of my webinars said the following about the list of study materials I provided: "With everyone working fifty to sixty hours per week, this reading becomes another item at the bottom of an ever-expanding to-do list."

That's like being too busy driving across the country to stop and buy gas (Clarke and Crossland 2002). You need to refuel, especially if you want to be creative and innovative. Refueling means staying current, but it also means satisfying your observations and curiosity. You owe it first to yourself, then to your employer, and then to the clients and stakeholders you serve. Take and make the time to study what you have observed and what captures your curiosity!

Let me share a mechanism I've frequently used to "make the time" to study something I've observed that has stimulated my curiosity. Select a topic that interests you and about which you want to learn much more, and set up a forum at which you will share what you do not yet know. For example:

- As a student member of a senior project team, volunteer to design an intriguing laboratory apparatus for your project, even though the topic is new to you, and commit to doing it in one month.
- As a co-op student, sign up to give a lunchtime presentation at your temporary employer one month from now to speak about a newly developing technology you recently heard about but do not fully understand.
- As a practitioner, submit an abstract to present a paper at next year's state geotechnical conference about a subsurface exploration technique that is used in your firm and about which you want to learn more.
- Also as a practitioner, join a committee of a professional or business society and volunteer to take on a specific task or function related to a topic that piqued your curiosity.

When we make these kinds of commitments, we are relying on a basic human characteristic: We do not want to embarrass ourselves. Therefore, we will do the study necessary to follow up on what we have observed and are curious about and learn much in the process. It works for me!

6.3.2 Leonardo da Vinci: Exemplar of Studiousness

Based on my experience and research for this book, no one was more observant, curious, and desirous to learn than artist, scientist, and engineer Leonardo da Vinci (Figure 6.3). His breadth and depth of curiosity are evident in his writings, his drawings and paintings, and the testimonials of those who knew him. About seven thousand pages of his notes and drawings, which is estimated to be about half of what he produced, still exist, along with about fifteen of his paintings. He was born in 1452 out of wedlock, near the tiny village of Vinci, Italy, about one day's travel by horse from Florence. Poor and raised mostly by his mother, da Vinci had little formal education, partly because his illegitimacy prevented him from entering the cathedral schools connected with churches.

Fortunately, he was apprenticed at the age of fifteen to a master sculptor and painter, Andrea del Verrocchio, in Florence, which started his painting career. His early artistic success introduced him to a community of artists, scientists, poets, mathematicians, philosophers, and financiers, in addition to less well-known skilled craftsmen that the powerful Medicis had assembled in Florence, marking the beginning of the Renaissance. The stage was set for da Vinci to become the ultimate perpetual student. His search for knowledge was reflected in his belief that if someone had information he wanted, he went to them and asked for it and his view that knowledge of all things was within his reach (Gelb 2004; Shlain 2014; Wallace 1966).

Let's consider some examples of da Vinci's curiosity, boundless studiousness, and creative and innovative results, all of which are based on books by Gelb (2004), Shlain (2014), and Wallace (1966). His interest in music led him to

Figure 6.3
Artist, scientist, and engineer da Vinci exemplifies studiousness.

(Mates/Fotolia)

design, craft, and play musical instruments, and he enjoyed paradoxes and wrote books of riddles.

Da Vinci was a superb and trend-setting artist. He showed other artists how to beautifully portray three-dimensional effects with a two-dimensional medium. He championed strongly contrasting areas that were illuminated with those that were shadowed, and he introduced the idea of having the sky in the background be brightest on the horizon and gradually become darker with elevation. He worked in varied media, such as pen and ink, silverpoint (using a silver point on a surface prepared with a primer), frescoe, chalk, pencil, and paint, and sometimes used more than one on a project. However, his favorite medium was pen and ink because he could quickly alternate between drawing something and then annotating it, the result of which is evident in most of his drawings.

His fascination with human anatomy motivated him to dissect more than thirty human cadavers and many animal corpses. He conducted the first documented autopsy, was the first to diagnose arteriosclerosis, and can be considered pathology's founder. As a result of these investigations, da Vinci was the first artist to create highly detailed drawings of the inside of the human body. He used cross sections and exploded views, and he showed the same muscular structure from varying viewpoints on the same page (Figure 6.4), simulating what a moving viewer would see. His cross-sectional drawing of the human skull was the first in anatomy's history.

He became interested in what we now call *cartography*, as evidenced by his detailed maps of parts of Italy, which accurately depicted the landscape as would be

Figure 6.4
Based on his autopsies, da Vinci creatively depicted muscular structure from various viewpoints.

(Kmiragaya/Fotolia)

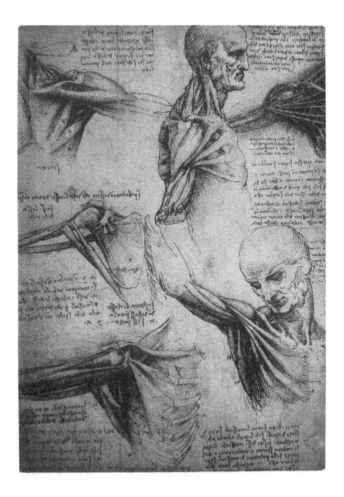

seen from a high altitude. Artistic zeal led da Vinci to develop a means of depicting distant objects when painting landscapes. His technique, called *sfumato* and widely used today, involves using less distinct borders—a misty and hazy effect—and more muted colors for distant landscape elements.

We engineers often use Newton's three laws of motion, which were described in the seventeenth century. Almost two centuries earlier, da Vinci described the essence of Newton's first law (an object tends to stay at rest or in motion) and third law (action and reaction). He also described the essence of the principle of conservation of mass, another foundation of engineering analysis and design. By observing water waves, da Vinci correctly postulated that when a wave moves through a medium, the molecules of the medium do not transfer with the wave. He established the basis for wave theory.

Leonardo da Vinci's observational powers, curiosity, and engineering-like desire to meet human needs resulted in many original ideas and ideas for inventions, some of which have come to fruition. For example, he suggested the possibility of contact lenses, conceived of windmills as power sources, provided a design for a double-hulled ship (an idea that eventually became the standard for oil tankers), and provided ideas for scissors and folding furniture. He also offered ideas for the machine gun, a huge crossbow, a bombshell, an army tank, a parachute, the helicopter (Figure 6.5), a bicycle, ball bearings, the universal joint, an anemometer, pontoon bridges, a fortress, swing bridges, life preservers, diving suits, a cathedral

Figure 6.5
Da Vinci used freehand detailed drawings annotated with his unusual backward (right to left) writing to present his creative ideas, such as for the helicopter.

(Janaka Dharmasena/Fotolia)

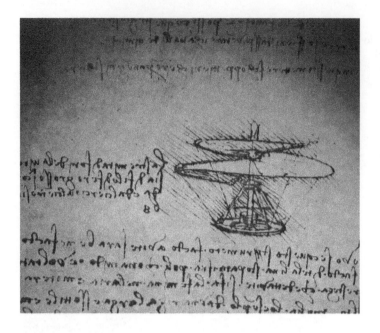

dome, waterway locks, stone-cutting machines, shoes for walking on water, and metal-boring machines.

6.3.3 Philo Farnsworth: Crop Rows and Television

In 1920, an observant and curious fourteen-year-old farm boy, Philo Farnsworth, observed neat parallel rows of crops on his uncle's Idaho farm. This caused him to think of electronically capturing an image in line-by-line slices, transmitting the slices, and reassembling them into the original image. He shared the concept (illustrated in Figure 6.6) with his high school chemistry teacher, who Farnsworth later credited with providing key inspiration and knowledge.

Farnsworth persisted, continued his study and experimentation, and, at the age of twenty, demonstrated the first working television, which used electronic scanning of both the pickup and display devices. As you may have guessed, the father of television was just beginning his creative/innovative work: He eventually received over 130 patents for his many and varied inventions (Brigham Young University High School 2014; Michalko 2001). Dhillon (2006) mentions the invention of the mechanical television—a very different approach—in Great Britain at about the same time, in 1926.

As is often the case, one invention leads to another. Farnsworth's 1920s creation of television was built on Crooke's 1878 invention of the cathode-ray tube in Great Britain (Dhillon 2006) and possibly the invention of the mechanical TV. In turn, Farnsworth's television prompted another creation: Sarnoff, leader of the Radio Corporation of America (RCA), developed a television broadcasting system that brought black-and-white television to consumers beginning in 1939 (Carlson and Wilmot 2006).

6.3.4 Arthur Morgan: Twentieth-Century Renaissance Engineer

Engineer Arthur Morgan (1878–1975) was an unusually creative and innovative person. His accomplishments include the following (Leuba 1971):

- Authoring new drainage laws for Minnesota
- Founding an engineering firm

Figure 6.6
Studious and observant
Farnsworth was inspired by
a field of row crops to
invent television.

*(Andrii Salivon/Fotolia;
Sebastian185/Fotolia)*

- Establishing the Miami Conservancy District, "the first time [in the United States] that plans would be made for an entire river valley in a comprehensive and thorough fashion"
- Rescuing Antioch College
- Organizing the Tennessee Valley Authority

Note that he created and innovated in the private, public, and academic sectors and in technical and nontechnical spheres. His creativity and innovation were based in part on his widespread observations, intense curiosity, and thorough follow-up actions. In reflecting on his childhood, he said: "I was inordinately curious. When older people were talking, I had an irresistible urge to 'listen in,' and if I did not understand, to ask questions." He went on to say, "Much of my free time as a boy was spent in the woods and swamps about St. Cloud, Minnesota, where curiosity took the form of observation of earth and sky, streams, plants, and animals. As a result of this habit of curiosity and observation, my mind was stored with a vast miscellany of facts which served as the material for thinking" and, I might add, for lifelong creating and innovating.

Note that he says that his observation tendencies and curiosity were habitual. According to his biographer, Morgan was "observant of, and sensitive and open to, a wide variety of physical and social phenomena," and he read widely and was always "wanting to know" (Leuba 1971).

Are you curious as a result of your observations, maybe even "inordinately curious"? Good: Curiosity is a trait conducive to being creative and innovative. If not, you might consider developing the curiosity and observation habit, like Morgan, using the habit-changing process presented in Section 2.10.5; it could redirect your career and life.

6.3.5 Jack S. Kilby: Simplification and the Integrated Circuit

Useful but heat-producing, energy-hungry, fragile, unreliable, and bulky vacuum tubes dominated the electronic industry for the first half of the last century. Invention of the much smaller transistor—an efficient way to amplify and switch electronic signals—by Bell Telephone Laboratories in 1947 offset many of the vacuum tube disadvantages, but the assembly of complex circuits still required tedious hand-soldering to interconnect the transistors, diodes, rectifiers, and capacitors (Beakley, Evans, and Keats 1986; Johnson 2010; Texas Instruments 2014).

Jack S. Kilby, a newly hired and very observant electrical engineer at Texas Instruments (TI), spent two weeks in the company's shop in July 1958 while everyone else was away on the traditional two-week vacation; he had not yet earned vacation time. He became curious while working on circuits that had thirty parts, and asked himself, what if they only had one part? He later wrote: "Further thought led me to the

Figure 6.7
Electrical engineer Kilby's curiosity led him to invent the integrated circuit.

(Edelweiss/Fotolia)

conclusion that semiconductors were all that were really required—that resistors and capacitors [passive devices], in particular, could be made from the same material as the active devices [transistors]." He also recognized that all of the components could be made of one material and be interconnected to form a complete circuit. In September 1958, Kilby's curiosity and persistence enabled him to successfully demonstrate the first working integrated circuit, built on a piece of germanium (a semiconductor material); it eventually evolved to today's chip (Figure 6.7).

Of course, this creativity/innovation story continues. In order to stimulate commercialization of the integrated circuit, Kilby was challenged by TI to design a pocket-sized calculator based on the integrated circuit, one that could replace then-common desktop calculators: Kilby coinvented the TI pocket calculator. Mine was purchased in 1975 for $175 ($780 today accounting for inflation) and immediately replaced my slide rule, which I bought in 1959 for $29 ($240 today; see Figure 6.8). Today, the integrated circuit is everywhere. Engineer Kilby received the Nobel Prize in Physics in 2000 for his part in creating the integrated circuit in 2005 (Texas Instruments 2014).

6.4 PASSIONATE

Wagner (2012) argues that passion is essential to creativity and innovation. *Passion*, which may be defined as "a strong feeling of enthusiasm or excitement for something or about doing something" (Merriam-Webster 2014), can be a powerful aid when resolving issues, solving problems, or pursuing opportunities. Passion may also include an aversion to boredom and an accompanying deep-seated need to take on new challenges and eventually realize the thrill of making new things happen.

Pink (2009), author of *Drive: The Surprising Truth About What Motivates Us*, supports the importance of passion with this statement: "For artists, scientists, inventors, school children, and the rest of us, intrinsic motivation—the drive to do something because it is interesting, challenging, and absorbing—is essential for

Figure 6.8
Creation of the integrated circuit led to the invention of many devices, including this pocket calculator, purchased by the author in 1975 to replace his slide rule, purchased in 1959.

(Stuart Walesh)

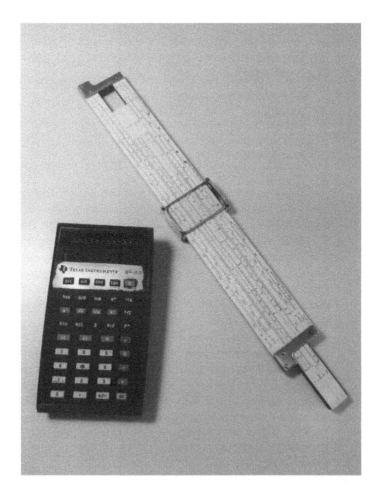

high levels of creativity." Pink does acknowledge that extrinsic motivation—carrots and sticks—"can work nicely for algorithmic tasks," but he goes on to suggest that although offering bonuses or threatening firing will usually increase productivity in more routine work, at least for some time, it will not stimulate creativity and innovation. The latter stimulation needs to come from within, and its driving forces include passion.

Without passion, creativity and innovation are likely to escape us. "A [person] without passion is only a latent force, only a possibility," according to the Swiss philosopher Amied, "like a stone waiting for the blow from iron to give forth sparks." Passion helps us to persist in spite of obstacles and setbacks. The passionate person is less likely to be deterred by failures, lack of support, negative criticism, and other setbacks. Passion will help you deal with the external obstacles described in Chapter 5. Passion revealed in your speaking and writing will also help you engage others, stimulate them to consider your ideas, and join you and others in exploring those ideas and implementing the best of them.

6.4.1 Joseph Strauss: Golden Gate Bridge

The story of engineer and poet Joseph Strauss demonstrates the power of creativity and innovation driven by passion. He dreamed of bridging San Francisco's Golden Gate (Figure 1.6) and knew how it could be done. For two decades, and in the face of widespread skepticism, Strauss lived his dream by leading the planning, design, finance, and construction of the now-famous bridge.

The intensity of his passion is suggested by these lines from his poem "The Mighty Task Is Done":

> Launched midst a thousand hopes and fears,
> Damned by a thousand hostile seers,
> Yet ne'er its course was stayed,
> But ask of those who met the foe
> Who stood alone when faith was low,
> Ask them the price they paid.

Strauss saw the 1937 opening of the bridge and then died approximately one year later. Strauss' passion is recognized with a statue at the south end of the bridge, dedicated to *The Man Who Built the Bridge* (Fredrich 1989; Walesh 2011).

As an example of how today's creative and innovative results, such as the Golden Gate Bridge, depend on earlier ones, consider the work of civil engineer Roebling in the mid-1800s. He was employed as a canal engineer when he observed horses pulling boats along canals. The hemp ropes connecting the horses to the boats often broke, so Roebling created a cable composed of twisted wire that moved the boats faster and safer.

This invention moved him towards a higher goal: the design and construction of suspension bridges. Eventually, he, his engineer son Washington Roebling, and Washington's wife Emily accomplished the design and construction of the Brooklyn Bridge in New York City, which opened in 1883 (Section 6.8.4). Its four twisted wire cables were the first to be used in a suspension bridge. Similar cables were then used on many other suspension bridges around the world, such as the previously discussed Golden Gate Bridge and the Menai Straits Bridge in Wales (Section 4.3.4), which was upgraded in 1941 (Fredrich 1989; Weingardt 2005).

6.4.2 Hermann von Helmholtz: Conservation of Energy Principle

Hermann von Helmholtz is the creative and prolific German scientist who made contributions in mathematics, biology, and physics. In 1847, he published his formulation of the conservation of energy, a principle that is widely used in engineering (Koenigsberger 1906).

Consider his description of passion in action—desire to reach a goal (Stuewer 2013): "I must compare myself to a mountain climber, who without knowing the way climbs up slowly and laboriously, must often turn around because he can go no farther, discovers new trails sometimes through reflection, sometimes through accident, which again lead him forward a little, and finally, if he reaches his goal, finds his shame on a Royal Road on which he could have traveled up, if he would have been clever enough to find the right starting point."

6.5 INTROVERTED

Creative and innovative individuals are often *introverts*—that is, people who are drawn to the "inner world of thought and feeling," contrasted with *extroverts*, who are drawn to their "external life of people and activities" (Cain 2012). By *introvert*, I do not necessarily mean *shy*.

One-third to one-half of Americans are introverts (Cain 2012; Culp and Smith 2001). In contrast, engineers tend to be significantly more introverted. For example, over 60 percent of engineering project team members are introverts (Culp and

Smith 2001); engineers as a group are more introverted than the population at large. However, don't make the mistake of denying the creativity and innovation potential of introverts (more on this shortly).

In her book *Quiet: The Power of Introverts in a World that Can't Stop Talking*, Cain (2012) says this about introverts: "Of course, there's another word for such people: thinkers." She goes on to state, "Introverts are not smarter than extroverts. According to IQ scores, the types are equally intelligent. . . . But introverts seem to think more carefully than extroverts." By the way, if you are an introvert and have been made to feel uncomfortable about it, read Susan Cain's book. Her message? Count your blessings!

Cain claims that "some of our greatest ideas, art, and inventions . . . came from the quiet and cerebral people who knew how to tune in to their inner worlds and the treasures to be found there. . . . Without introverts, the world would be devoid of these creations/innovations." Some of those introverts and their creations and innovations are featured in Table 6.1.

Cain (2012) describes the introvert approach to problem solving relative to the extrovert approach this way: "Extroverts are more likely to take a quick-and-dirty approach to problem-solving, trading accuracy for speed, making increasing numbers of mistakes as they go, and abandoning ship altogether when the problems seem too difficult or frustrating." In contrast, she says that "introverts think before they act, digest information thoroughly, stay on task longer, give up less easily, and work more accurately."

Table 6.1 Introverts contributed some of civilization's greatest creations and innovations.

Introvert	Example of creation/innovation
J. M. Barrie	*Peter Pan*
Lewis Carroll	*Alice in Wonderland*
Frederic Chopin	His nocturnes
Marie Curie	Pioneering radioactivity research
Charles Darwin	*On the Origin of Species*
Thomas Edison	Phonograph (Buelow 2015)
Albert Einstein	Theory of relativity
Bill Gates	Microsoft (Buelow 2015)
Theodore Geisel (Dr. Seuss)	*The Cat in the Hat*
George W. Goethals	Panama Canal (Fredrich 1989)
Sir Isaac Newton	Universal gravitation
George Orwell	*1984*
Larry Page	Google
J. K. Rowling	Harry Potter series
Steven Spielberg	*Schindler's List*
James Watt	Steam engine (Billington 1996)
Stephen Wozniak	Apple Inc.
Mark Zuckerberg	Facebook (Buelow 2015)

Source: All items provided by Cain 2012, except where other sources are indicated.

I'm not suggesting that I agree with Cain's views that introverts have a creativity/innovation edge. However, her ideas remind all of us—especially we introverts—that introverts have a fabulous creativity/innovation track record, as suggested by centuries of engineering creations/innovations. Furthermore, we tend to be very comfortable in the garden of the mind—the place where creative/innovative seeds are planted. Let's celebrate our introversion—not apologize for it—and create and innovate!

6.6 EXPERIMENTALIST

Creative/innovative persons are experimentalists. *Experimentalism* can be defined as "a process of trial and error that explores problems and possible solutions in new and creative ways" (Wagner 2012). In addition to thinking of new ways to do things, creative/innovative individuals act; they are willing to try ideas—that is, experiment, prototype, and pilot.

Although creative and innovative individuals appreciate and often engage in in-depth analysis, they also know when to avoid analysis paralysis and *just do it*. They conduct laboratory experiments, pilot new project management processes, build prototypes to see what their ideas might look like and how they could work, try different marketing tactics, or apply new design approaches. Sometimes, the experiments succeed; sometimes they fail. Although success is appreciated, the creative/innovative person never truly fails because what others may view as failure, he or she sees as a valuable lesson learned. As engineer Weingardt said, "It's only a mistake if you don't learn from it."

HISTORIC NOTE: LEONARDO DA VINCI KNEW HOW TO EXPERIMENT, SUCCEED OR FAIL, AND LEARN

Speaking of experimentation sometimes leading to insightful failure, consider the experimental philosophy and experiences of the genius da Vinci during the fifteenth and sixteenth centuries. He experimented in the very late 1400s with a new way of fixing the paint on a huge refectory wall in a Milan monastery as he created *The Last Supper*. Instead of painting fresco-style on wet plaster, he painted experimentally on a dry surface. The work soon started to fade and flake; the experiment failed, but useful lessons were learned. The painting has been restored many times and survived major bomb damage to the refectory in August of 1943.

As noted earlier, da Vinci is credited with being the first to describe the essence of the principle of conservation of mass and is credited with laying the foundation for wave theory.

He confirmed his initial hypotheses about these phenomena with experiments. Perhaps in the spirit of encouraging experimentation and the resulting learning, da Vinci said, "The greatest deception men suffer is from their own opinions." (Gelb 2004; Shlain 2014; Wallace 1966). In other words, ideas that seem to have value warrant experimentation.

6.6.1 From Car Wash to Weed Eater

The story of the invention of the Weed Eater, as summarized in Figure 6.9, illustrates early experimentation or prototyping. George C. Ballas, who ran a dance stu-

Figure 6.9
The Weed Eater story illustrates experimentalism as well as empathy and Borrowing Brilliance.

(Volodymyr Khodaryev/Fotolia; Photoiron/Fotolia; Dave Willman/Fotolia)

dio in Houston, was concerned when a poisonous snake bit a worker who was using hand shears to trim the edges of Ballas's lawn.

Shortly thereafter, in 1971, while moving through an automatic car wash, Ballas observed large, rotating nylon bristles that cleaned but did not scratch cars. He took a popcorn can, attached wires radially, connected it to a rotating edger, and experimented. This prototyping evolved into the commercial Weed Eater device introduced in the early 1970s, and "by 1976 [he] was selling $40 million worth of them annually" (Miller 2011). Note that in addition to illustrating experimentation, the Weed Eater story also provides examples of empathy (Section 6.2) and Borrowing Brilliance (Section 4.3).

6.6.2 From Sandpaper to Masking Tape

About a century ago, Dick Drew was a sandpaper salesperson for what is now 3M, and he called on auto body shops to ask mechanics to buy his brand. He gradually noted a problem common to body shops when they performed two-tone paint jobs: Because the tape they used was too sticky, it removed some of the paint on previously painted sections of vehicles, which required wasteful and frustrating rework.

Committed to solving this problem, which was not directly related to sandpaper, Drew began to experiment in 1925. He started with what he knew best: sandpaper, which was manufactured by coating strong paper with glue and then rolling it in crushed minerals. He omitted the crushed minerals and experimented with progressively less sticky sheets of paper. As he moved toward an optimum stickiness, he was increasingly challenged by how to store and handle the sticky sheets of paper. He continued to experiment, and then hit on an idea: Apply the adhesive to a strip of paper and roll it up so that auto body experts could unwind it as needed.

He called his creation *masking tape*. It may seem commonplace now, given the plethora of specialty tapes on the market, but masking tape came into being because of Drew's persistent experimentation in spite of setbacks. In fact, Drew's boss ordered him to stop the project, but Drew simply continued to experiment on his own time until he produced a tape of "pressure-sensitive adhesive that could be applied to metal and then ripped off without damaging the paint." By 1928, 3M's masking tape sales exceeded its sandpaper sales (Lehrer 2012).

6.6.3 From Bird Beak to High-Speed Train

Japan's high-speed trains are known for their safety, efficiency, and comfort. However, until the late 1990s some lines were also criticized for the loud noise they made on exiting the country's many tunnels. "When a train entered a tunnel, its bullet-shaped nose compressed the air into something like a tidal wave; when the wave exited the tunnel, it expanded so rapidly it set off what is known as a tunnel boom" (Vanderbilt 2012).

Consider the long, tapering beak of the kingfisher, a bird that dives quickly and quietly into water to catch fish (Figure 6.10). The bird and its beak were known to Eiji Nakatsu, Chief Engineer of the West Japan Railway Corporation, because he was a birder. His engineers experimented by firing variously shaped bullets into a pipe until they found the shape that caused the least tunnel boom. The new kingfisher-beak-shaped trains entered service in 1997 (EarthSky 2012; Vanderbilt 2012).

PERSONAL: WORDS MATTER WHEN CONSIDERING CHANGE

I like to use the word *experiment* when offering a new idea or suggestion to an individual, team, or organization. Rather than say, "I suggest that you implement this new project management process across your company," I prefer to say, "I suggest that you experiment with this process for a specific period in one part of your company and then evaluate."

The word *experiment* and alternatives such as *prototype*, *trial*, and *pilot* seem less threatening. Such words suggest that the idea may work, while recognizing that it may not work. Although we prefer the former, the latter is OK, especially if we find failure early on so that we can learn from it and direct our creative/innovative efforts in a modified or new direction.

Figure 6.10
The kingfisher's beak inspired the new shape for the lead unit on a Japanese high-speed train and solved the problem of loud noise when exiting tunnels.

(Massimhokuto/Fotolia; SCPhotos/Alamy)

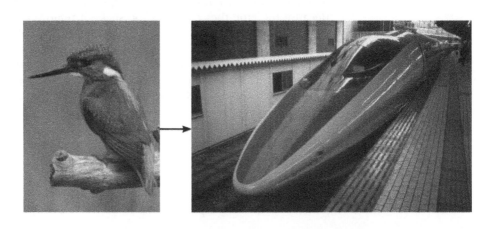

6.6.4 From No Theory for Flow Through Porous Media to a Widely Used One

Henry Darcy was a member of the French civil engineering corps. Born in Dijon, France, he returned there after his education in Paris in the early 1800s and was given responsibility for designing and constructing the municipal water supply system. To gain further insight into the behavior of sand filters, which were one component of the Dijon water supply system, Darcy conducted experiments on flow through porous media. His experiments demonstrated that energy loss is proportional to velocity, as stated in what is now called Darcy's Law—that is, $v = k$ (dh/dl), where

> v = apparent velocity (volumetric discharge divided by total cross-sectional area),
>
> k = coefficient of permeability with dimensions of velocity,
>
> h = head with dimensions of length, and
>
> l = distance in the direction of flow with dimensions of length.

In 1856, Darcy published the results of his experiments and the equation he developed, thus enabling others to benefit from his creative/innovative work as they design water treatment plants, analyze groundwater flow, and take on other flow through porous media challenges. Similar creative/innovative theoretical and experimental efforts driven by pragmatic needs gave us the Manning Equation for open channel flow, the Rational Formula for storm water system design, and the Darcy-Weisbach pipe flow equation (Walesh 1990).

6.7 COLLABORATIVE

Although creative/innovative individuals certainly value personal study and reflection and use them wisely, they also frequently reach out to and interact with others in many ways (Canales 2011; Wagner 2012). Their *collaboration* may be informal, like when individuals exchange ideas with various members of their networks, or more formal, like when they serve on teams or groups formed to address an IPO. Creative/innovative individuals highly value and proactively apply the Medici Effect discussed in Section 4.6 because they recognize that diversity of education, experiences, viewpoints, and other characteristics stimulate creativity and innovation. Some ways in which creative/innovative individuals collaborate informally are as follows:

- Seek to understand the wants and needs of prospective clients and customers.
- Ask questions of and offer ideas to members of their professional and personal networks using email or other electronic media.
- Arrange and participate in group sessions that use the kinds of whole-brain tools described in Chapters 4 and 7.
- Study new topics and share and test their preliminary findings by writing articles, papers, and blogs and speaking to various groups. By offering and testing new concepts, ideas, processes, and methods, these proactive collaborative communications benefit both the presenter and the audiences/readers.
- Find partners with whom to seek research and development funding.

6.7.1 Birth of the Personal Computer System

As an example of fruitful collaboration, consider the birth of the personal computer system. On December 9, 1968, electrical engineer Englebart, leader of a thirteen-person team at the innovative consulting organization SRI spoke at the San Francisco Fall Computer Conference. His topic: the team's development of basic computer functions that exist in computers today.

After describing and demonstrating the "computer mouse, multiple windows, on-screen editing, hypermedia, context-sensitive help, distributed collaboration, and shared-screen video teleconference," Englebart and his team received a standing ovation. Today, essentially every personal computer uses those interface features (Carlson and Wilmot 2006). This event was almost a decade before the 1977 San Francisco release of the Apple II, the first ready-to-run, out-of-the-box personal computer (Isaacson 2011). Because commercializing inventions was not part of SRI's mission, the company licensed the computer mouse to Xerox, Apple, and others.

Douglas Englebart's team exhibited highly productive collaboration. Their successful collaboration is attributed to factors such as selecting an important and challenging need; assembling a team of software and hardware personnel with complementary expertise; Englebart's passionate championing of his ideas; thinking of prospective customers; integrating ideas from around the globe; and leveraging what Engelhart referred to as the team's *collective intelligence* through frequent interaction (Carlson and Wilmot 2006).

6.7.2 Other Collaboration Examples

Many collaboration examples are noted in Chapter 4, including the cardiac pacemaker, Shakespeare's writing, Thomas Edison's devices, Steve Jobs' electronic inventions, breaking the German Enigma code, defining a pond problem, building a Taco Bell restaurant in forty-eight hours, temporarily storing storm water on streets, and the Panama Canal. Collaboration examples cited in this chapter include an adaption of the shape of the kingfisher beak to the high-speed train (Section 6.6.3) and development of a baby incubator for developing countries (Section 6.8.1).

PERSONAL: THREE ESSENTIAL FACTORS FOR SUCCESSFUL COLLABORATION

Having experienced many successes and a few failures in collaborative efforts in the business, government, academic, and volunteer sectors, I am convinced that three qualities lead to productive collaboration. These three qualities, which are consistent with the factors noted in the Douglas Englebart example, are as follows:

- **Vision:** The first quality is a strong and shared commitment to an ambitious vision—the bolder, the better. The vision should initially appear highly desirable and perhaps unachievable. Sometimes, groups take on less aspirational but nevertheless challenging tasks. In these situations, the word *vision* may not be appropriate. Instead, use an end-point term, such as *objective* or *goal*, and as with vision, seek a strong and shared commitment to it.
- **Diversity:** An optimum mix of participants is the second collaboration factor. Diversity characteristics to consider when forming a team are discussed in the Medici Effect portion of Section 4.6. When a group is care-

fully constituted, each member is important. This idea is explained in one of my favorite statements from former US Secretary of Health, Education, and Welfare Gardner, who said: "The society which scorns excellence in plumbing as a humble activity, and tolerates shoddiness in philosophy because it is an exalted activity, will have neither good plumbing nor good philosophy: Neither its pipes nor its theories will hold water."

- **Trusting, communicative structure:** Trust and open, ongoing, intrateam communication is the third collaboration success factor. With this factor, the emphasis moves from the characteristics of the team members to the relationships among them, which must be respectful and trusting.

All three qualities are necessary; none is sufficient alone. An aspirational vision without diverse players is a pipe dream. A talented team toiling without a shared vision or goal is poor stewardship. A superb organizational structure without talented players degenerates into bureaucracy.

6.7.3 Additional Thoughts about Trust

The previous personal note asserts that trust is one of three essentials in collaboration, which warrants elaboration. Each member of a team that is taking on a challenging IPO must be able to trust and be trusted by all other participants. Mutual trust is crucial in creative/innovative efforts because much is often at stake; the initiative could fail at great cost or succeed and provide great benefits. You may be tempted to hoard the essentials of your creative/innovative idea because you don't trust others; some of them may do the same because they don't trust you and others. A team's success is jeopardized when it does not have access to all of its intellectual and other resources. In keeping with the theme of this book, your desired success and significance are frustrated when you don't engage all of your intellectual resources—that is, your whole brain.

Trust can be difficult to define, but we know at the gut level when it is present. I try to keep it simple by defining *mutual trust* as meaning that you and I view each other as being honest and as practicing integrity. Honesty and integrity, which are essential for mutual trust, are different but complementary and may be described as follows:

- *Honesty* is telling the truth. It's retrospective; it's how we report the past. For example, if while in high school your dog ate your homework and you told your teacher that, then you are being honest.
- *Integrity* is keeping promises. It's prospective; it's how you keep your commitments. To continue the homework example, if you then promised your teacher that you would redo the homework and hand it in at the beginning of the next class and then did as you promised, that's integrity. People of integrity live by the DWYSYWD principle: "Do what you say you will do."

Let's not distinguish between little promises and big promises. They are viewed the same; more specifically, you are viewed the same way by team members who receive your promises, whether big or small. It's like when your doctor says he or she will be performing only "minor" surgery. You still want him or her to be just as careful as if it were "major" surgery (Sheth and Sobel 2000). Each promise you or I make, large or small, should be treated habitually with the same seriousness.

Motivational writer Anderson (2007) says this about trust: "Contrary to what most people believe, trust is not some soft, illusive quality that you either have or don't have; rather trust is a pragmatic, tangible, actionable asset that you can create." Think about it. We follow the trusted leader, we seek help from the trusted friend and advice from the trusted professor, clients retain the trusted firm, employers hire and promote the trusted engineer, and citizens support the trusted official (based, in part, on Horsager 2012). You can take trust to the bank—symbolically and literally. Once you earn the trust of others, doors will open, opportunities will arise, your recommendations are more likely to be accepted, sole-source consultant selection will occur more often, and so on.

Notice I said you must *earn* trust. You can't buy it. You must build it piece by piece by your words and actions. If you discipline yourself to habitually tell the truth and keep your word, many good things will come your way, not the least of which is being an effective player on teams that seek to creatively and innovatively resolve issues, solve problems, or pursue opportunities.

6.8 PERSISTENT

The final characteristic of creative and innovative individuals is *persistence*.

This attribute follows from but is different than being passionate (Section 6.4). We hear about fabulous ideas that supposedly came out of the blue, but the accounts of actual creative/innovative contributions are very different. They are admirable human stories reflecting many qualities like those discussed in this chapter, with persistence perhaps being the most important.

VIEWS OF OTHERS: STICK WITH IT

The amazing scientist/artist/engineer da Vinci credited persistence for his creative and innovative successes, writing, "I do not depart from my furrow" next to a drawing of a plow in one of his notebooks and also stating, "Every obstacle is destroyed though rigor" (Gelb 2004). Einstein shared his faith in persistence by saying, "It's not that I'm so smart; it's just that I stay with problems longer." Coolidge, the thirtieth US president, said this about the power of persistence: "Nothing in the world can take the place of persistence. Talent will not; nothing is more common than unsuccessful men with talent. Genius will not; unrewarded genius is almost a proverb. Education alone will not; the world is full of educated derelicts. Persistence and determination alone are omnipotent." Michelangelo, Italian painter and sculptor and contemporary of da Vinci, stated, "If people knew how hard I work to gain my mastery, it would not seem so wonderful at all."

Assume you are succeeding as an engineering student or have already earned one or more engineering degrees. You probably are persistent and have other admirable qualities discussed in this chapter, because the formal study of engineering and similar disciplines requires above-average effort. If that applies to you, then celebrate your demonstrated persistence and continue to use it in all that you do, including finding ways to work smarter and to be more creative and innovative.

6.8.1 Baby Incubator for Developing Countries

Infant incubators (heated cribs for newborns) were first created by French medical doctors in 1881 and were inspired by the use of an incubator for baby birds. Given the number of extra years of life they provide, baby incubators may be one of the greatest medical creations. However, today almost two million newly born babies die each year, mostly in developing countries, because the infants lack a consistent heat source. A standard modern incubator, as used in an American hospital, costs roughly $40,000 and requires careful maintenance.

Even if funds are available to purchase and send incubators to developing countries experiencing high infant mortality rates, the devices soon fail because of power fluctuations, high humidity, and other complications. They are rarely repaired due to lack of expertise, absence of instructions in native languages, and shortage of parts. Up to 98 percent of the medical technology donated to developing countries fails within five years of its first use. For example, eight incubators were sent to an Indonesian city following the 2004 Indian Ocean tsunami. By the end of 2008, none of the eight were working.

On learning about this dilemma in 2008, mechanical engineer Prestero committed to finding a solution. He and his team were inspired by an idea offered by Boston doctor Rosen, who observed that people in the developing world knew how to keep automobiles running. The team persisted until they designed and created an incubator that is readily assembled with many automobile or similar parts (Figure 6.11). For example, a sealed beam headlight supplies heat, a dashboard fan circulates heated air, and a motorcycle battery provides power during a power outage or when an incubator is being transported (Design that Matters 2014; Johnson 2010).

In summary, a critical medical device originally created in 1881 that gradually improved and naturally became very complex and widely used was, through persistence, successfully recreated in a vastly different and simpler form for a very special environment. Like the development of the cardiac pacemaker described in Section 3.6.1, the design of the special-purpose incubator is another example of the potential for collaboration between engineers and medical professionals.

6.8.2 Xerography

In the late 1940s, inventor Chester Carlson visited the laboratories of a major photography company. He met with a company researcher and demonstrated step by

Figure 6.11
Persistence-driven innovation led to the development of this life-saving baby incubator that can be maintained in developing countries using readily available automobile and motorcycle parts.

(Design that Matters, Inc.)

step the quick electrostatic photography process that he had created. Carlson envisioned his process as replacing the then-cumbersome copying method—that is, the film-developer-darkroom process.

He was shown the door because his imaging process did not fit the paradigm of the time—that is, exposing film using a developer solution and working in a dark-room. Being persistent, Carlson presented his ideas to forty-two other companies, including IBM and Kodak; unbelievably in retrospect, all rejected it. His persistence paid off, however, because his electrostatic photography process was finally accepted by what was then the Halloid Corporation, which eventually changed its name to the Xerox Corporation. Carlson's process became known as xerography, which is the basis for today's omnipresent copy machines (Barker 1989).

On hearing this story, you may be tempted to say, "I can see that some companies wouldn't get it, but forty-two?!" Keep that in mind when someone presents an idea to you, whether as a student or practitioner or member of any community, and your first inclination is to say, "That's not how we do things."

6.8.3 From Car Batteries to Home Batteries

Elon Musk, who was born in South Africa and completed his formal education in Canada and the United States, exemplifies the highest form of persistence, accompanied in good measure by other characteristics presented in this chapter. He takes on a creative/innovative challenge, carries it to completion or a major milestone, and then moves forward to a new challenge, sometimes in a very different area of technology. There seems to be no limit to his apparent desire to do what has not been done. Consider some of his creative/innovative accomplishments, portions of which were achieved in parallel (Biography.com 2015a):

- Launched the online payment system PayPal in 2000 as the result of a merger.
- Started Space Exploration Technologies (Space X) in 2002; in 2012, under contract to NASA, Space X launched a rocket that was the first to send a commercial vehicle to the International Space Station.
- Cofounded Tesla Motors in 2003, which designs and manufactures all-electric cars. Its first version, a sports car, went into production in 2008, and a four-door luxury sedan was introduced in 2012.

Described as "an earnest entrepreneur," Elon Musk explains his persistence this way: "If I am trying to solve a problem, and I think I've got some elements of it kind of close to being figured out, I'll pace for hours trying to think it through." One can only imagine the intense and productive interaction between Elon Musk's conscious and subconscious minds (Biography.com 2015a).

In 2015, Musk announced that Tesla Energy, the battery unit of the company, would offer batteries for residential, business, and utility use. Building innovatively on what the company learned about lithium-ion battery technology in its automobile business, Tesla began offering Powerwall batteries, which are wall mounted, inside or outside of a building, and connect to solar and/or grid power systems.

The Powerwall stores energy that can be used when other energy is temporarily not available or too expensive. Control devices direct the flow of energy among solar panels, the grid, and the Powerwall. Initial challenges included the high cost of the Powerwall, which was expected to decline; the cost of other parts of a system, such as solar panels; dealing with competitive products; and determining the roles of electric utilities (Shandrow 2015; Smith and Sweet 2015).

HISTORIC NOTE: NIKOLA TESLA

Tesla Motors' namesake is the creative and innovative electrical and mechanical engineer Nikola Tesla. Born in Croatia in the mid-1800s, Tesla was educated and worked in Germany, Austria, the Czech Republic, and Hungary. He came to the United States in 1884 and worked briefly with Edison. However, the two parted ways after several months and later became adversaries: Edison advocated direct current (DC) power systems, whereas Tesla promoted alternating current (AC) systems. Tesla won in the sense that AC became dominant worldwide beginning in the twentieth century.

The creative and innovative Tesla founded the Tesla Electric Company in 1885, and there he began to develop AC electrical systems. In 1895, Tesla designed an AC hydroelectric plant at Niagara Falls, which was one of the first such power facilities in the United States. It powered Buffalo, New York, and was viewed worldwide as an amazing feat. Tesla was also involved in the development of radar, X-ray, remote control, and wireless transmission of energy (Biography.com 2015b).

6.8.4 Brooklyn Bridge: It Took a Family

Returning to the Brooklyn Bridge (Section 6.4.1) after noting its innovative first use of twisted wire cable, now consider the persistent family effort that brought this iconic bridge to reality (Fredrich 1989, Weingardt 2005). For decades, the idea of the bridge, like many creative/innovative ideas, was widely dismissed as impossible. Challenges to crossing New York City's East River from Manhattan to Brooklyn included deep water and severe weather that moved up the river from the Atlantic Ocean. However, if anyone could get the job done, engineer Roebling could.

He completed overall plans in 1865. At about that time, Roebling sent Washington, his just-married son, and Emily, his new daughter-in-law, to Europe and around the world to study deep-water caisson foundations. The senior Roebling invested the next four years to getting support for the project from city, state, and federal officials.

Unfortunately, as construction began in 1869 and Washington and Emily Roebling returned home, the family experienced the first of a pair of disasters. John Roebling died as the result of an accident at one of the bridge's abutments. Exemplifying persistence, Washington Roebling took over as chief engineer, and his wife helped with labor, materials, political, and public relations challenges. Emily Roebling also began to study civil engineering topics, including mathematics, strength of materials, catenary curves, and cable and bridge construction. The seeds of these studies would soon bear great fruit.

In 1872, three years into what would be a thirteen-year project, Washington, who was a hands-on professional, suffered caisson disease, leaving him paralyzed, partly blind, deaf, and usually unable to speak. He and his wife were determined to persist and complete the bridge. Washington used binoculars to watch construction progress from his bedroom window on the Brooklyn side of the river, while Emily visited the site daily to observe details and deliver and receive messages. She gradually took on increased responsibilities, such as dealing with construction workers, material suppliers, assistant engineers, and public officials. Functionally,

Figure 6.12
New York City's iconic and innovative Brooklyn Bridge was constructed largely through a persistent and strong family effort.

(Mike Liu/Fotolia)

Emily became the chief engineer. The Brooklyn Bridge, shown in Figure 6.12, opened in 1883.

The Roeblings moved on, with the ailing Washington involved in the family's cable business and Emily, in addition to being a wife and a mother to their son, John, taking on many new endeavors and challenges. For example, she earned a law degree, was a much-in-demand speaker, wrote many articles, traveled worldwide, and championed various causes. She wrote her husband's biography, which barely describes her own role in building the bridge but lauds the contributions of her husband and the assistant engineers.

However, history reminds us of Emily Roebling's leadership role. The Brooklyn Bridge story reminds us that when we take on creative/innovative endeavors, our immediate families may be among our most important supporters; they can enable us to persist.

6.8.5 Other Persistence Examples

Consider some other examples of persistence leading to creative/innovative results:

- Engineer de Mestral worked ten years to bring Velcro to market (Section 1.3.2).
- Goodyear devoted ten years to experimentation and other efforts to obtain his vulcanization patent (Section 3.6.2).
- From concept to implementation, development of the now-omnipresent bar code required twenty-six years (Section 4.11.2).
- Starting at the age of fourteen, Farnsworth worked for six years to be the first to demonstrate a very simple version of what he is reported to have called *electronic television* and then worked many more years to commercialize it (Brigham Young University High School 2014; Section 6.3.3).
- In spite of many unsuccessful experiments and lack of support from his boss, sandpaper salesperson Drew continued with his experiments and eventually created masking tape (Section 6.6.2).
- Theodor Geisel, more popularly known as Dr. Seuss, is considered a premiere author of children's books. He was a pioneer in linking drawings to text, an approach that appeared in his first book. That innovative book was rejected by

twenty-nine publishers before being accepted thanks to the author's persistence (Walesh 2011).

- James Dyson, inventor of the dual-cyclone bagless vacuum cleaner, worked through more than five thousand designs before achieving success (Forbes 2014).

6.9 CHARACTERISTICS: CONCLUDING THOUGHTS

This chapter discusses recognizing, strengthening, or acquiring seven personal characteristics conducive to being creative and innovative:

- Empathetic
- Studious
- Passionate
- Introverted
- Experimentalist
- Collaborative
- Persistent

On seeing the list of characteristics after our review of each, and recognizing that the list reflects the thinking of many individuals, you may have had a number of reactions. Maybe you expected a silver bullet, or perhaps, like me at first, you thought that this is an interesting list, but you sort of expected at least some unusual characteristics that clearly set apart creative/innovative individuals. However, based on my studies and observations, that's not the case.

Or you may be saying to yourself that creative/innovative people have a set of normal human characteristics. There is nothing exotic or unusual about the components of their profiles. Creative/innovative individuals simply stand apart because they focus on a mix of appropriate characteristics in a given situation and apply them more intensely. Therefore, you and others possess most of these characteristics, and you can celebrate those that are strong and strengthen those that are weak. We have great potential!

Perhaps this is just another way of declaring, in keeping with the evolving theme of this and previous chapters, that anyone can be creative and innovative. The essentials: Take a more whole-brain approach by learning the basics of how the human brain functions; obtain whole-brain tools; overcome obstacles; and recognize, strengthen, or acquire certain personal characteristics, as noted in this chapter.

> The real contest is always between what you've done
> and what you are capable of doing.
> You measure yourself against yourself and nobody else.
> —*Geoffrey Gaberino, Olympic swimmer*

CITED SOURCES

Altshuller, G. 1996. *And Suddenly the Inventor Appeared: TRIZ, the Theory of Inventive Problem Solving*. Translated by Lev Shulyak from the original 1984 Russian version. Worcester, MA: Technical Innovation Center, Inc.

Anderson, M. 2007. *You Can't Send a Duck to Eagle School and Other Simple Truths of Leadership*. Naperville, IL: Simple Truths.

Barker, J. A. 1989. *Discovering the Future: The Business of Paradigms*. St. Paul, MN: ILI Press.

Beakley, G. C., D. L. Evans, and J. B. Keats. 1986. *Engineering: An Introduction to a Creative Profession*. New York: Macmillan Publishing Company.

Behar, H. 2009. *It's Not About the Coffee: Leadership Principles for a Life at Starbucks*. New York: Penguin Group.

Billington, D. P. 1996. *The Innovators: The Engineering Pioneers who Made America Modern*. New York: John Wiley & Sons.

Biography.com. 2015a. "Elon Musk: Engineer, Inventor, Explorer." Accessed May 6, 2015. http://www.biography.com/people/elon-musk-20837159.

Biography.com. 2015b. "Nikola Tesla: Engineer, Inventor." Accessed May 6, 2015. http://www.biography.com/people/nikola-tesla-9504443.

Brigham Young University High School. 2014. "Philo Taylor Farnsworth: Mathematician, Inventor, Father of Television." Accessed November 17, 2014. http://www.byhigh.org/History/Farnsworth/PhiloT1924.html.

Brooks, D. 2014. "In Praise of Small Miracles." *The New York Times,* December 14.

Buelow, B. 2015. "The Introvert Entrepreneur." Accessed April 12, 2015. http://theintrovertentrepreneur.com/resources/introvert-info/.

Cain, S. 2012. *Quiet: The Power of Introverts in a World That Can't Stop Talking*. New York: Crown Publishers.

Canales, K. 2011. "Finding Creative People Is Easy (and Here's How)." June 7. Accessed November 17, 2014. http://www.theatlantic.com/life/archive/2011/06/finding-creative-people-is-easy-and-heres-how/240069/.

Carlson, C. R., and W. W. Wilmot. 2006. *Innovation: The Five Disciplines for Creating What Customers Want*. New York: Crown Business.

Clarke, B., and R. Crossland. 2002. *The Leader's Voice*. New York: SelectBooks.

Culp, G., and A. Smith. 2001. "Understanding Psychological Type to Improve Project Team Performance." *Journal of Management in Engineering*, ASCE, January: 24–33.

Design that Matters. 2014. "Work and Vision." Accessed June 11. http://www.designthatmatters.org.

Dhillon, B. S. 2006. *Creativity for Engineers*. Hackensack, NJ: World Scientific.

EarthSky. 2012. "Sunni Robertson on How a Kingfisher Inspired a Bullet Train." June 21. Accessed November 17, 2014. http://earthsky.org/earth/sunni-robertson-on-how-a-kingfisher-inspired-a-bullet-train.

Forbes. 2014. "The World's Billionaires: #351 James Dyson." *Forbes*. Accessed August 3, 2015. http://www.forbes.com/profile/james-dyson/.

Fredrich, A. J., ed. 1989. *Sons of Martha: Civil Engineering Readings in Modern Literature*. New York: American Society of Civil Engineers.

Gelb, M. J. 2004. *How to Think like Leonardo da Vinci: Seven Steps to Genius Every Day*. New York: Bantam Dell.

GreenUpGrader. 2014. "Q Drum: Water Transportation Made Easier." Accessed November 17. http://greenupgrader.com/3934/q-drum-human-water-transportation-made-easier/.

Horsager, D. 2012. "Trust." Audio CD, *Success Magazine*, December.

Innovative Concepts Group. 2014. "Q Drum." Accessed November 17. http://www.qdrum.co.za.

Isaacson, W. 2011. *Steve Jobs*. New York: Simon & Schuster.

Johnson, S. 2010. *Where Good Ideas Come From: The Natural History of Innovation*. New York: Riverhead Books.

Koenigsberger, L. 1906. *Hermann von Helmholtz*. Translated by F. A. Welby. London: Claredon Press.

Lehrer, J. 2012. *Imagine: How Creativity Works.* New York: Houghton Mifflin Harcourt.

Leuba, C. J. 1971. *A Road to Creativity: Arthur Morgan—Engineer, Educator, Administrator.* North Quincy, MA: The Christopher Publishing House.

Lumsdaine, E., M. Lumsdaine, and J. W. Shelnutt. 1999. *Creative Problem Solving and Engineering Design.* New York: McGraw-Hill.

Medina, J. 2008. *Brain Rules: 12 Principles for Surviving and Thriving at Work, Home, and School.* Seattle: Pear Press.

Merriam-Webster. 2014. "Passion." Accessed November 17. http://www.merriam-webster.com/dictionary/passion.

Michalko, M. 2001. *Cracking Creativity: The Secrets of Creative Genius.* Berkeley, CA: Ten Speed Press.

Miller, S. 2011. "Dance Studio Owner Invented Weed Eater." *The Wall Street Journal,* June 30.

Murray, P. 2011. "The Wheel Reinvented: The Q-Drum is an Easy Way to Transport Water in Developing Countries." *Singularity HUB*, October 24. Accessed November 17, 2014. http://singularityhub.com/2011/10/24/the-wheel-reinvented-%E2%80%93-the-q-drum-is-an-easy-way-to-transport-water-in-developing-countries-video/.

Pink, D. H. 2009. *Drive: The Surprising Truth about What Motivates Us.* New York: Riverhead Books.

Sanborn, M. 2006. *You Don't Need a Title to Be A Leader.* New York: Currency Doubleday.

Shandrow, K. L. 2015. "Elon Musk Unveils Clean, Green Batteries to Power the World." *Entrepreneur.* Accessed May 6, 2015. http://www.entrepreneur.com/article/245713.

Sheth, J., and A. Sobel. 2000. *Clients for Life: Evolving from an Expert for Hire to an Extraordinary Advisor.* New York: Simon & Schuster.

Shlain, L. 2014. *Leonardo's Brain: Understanding da Vinci's Creative Genius.* Guilford, CT: Lyons Press.

Smith R., and C. Sweet. 2015. "Will Tesla's Newest Battery Pan Out?" *The Wall Street Journal,* May 2–3.

Steiner, C. 2012. *Automate This: How Algorithms Came to Rule the World.* New York: Penguin Group.

Stuewer, R. H. 2013. "The Joy of History." 2013 Pais Prize Lecture, American Physical Society, forum on the history of physics. Accessed April 12, 2015. http://www.aps.org/units/fhp/newsletters/fall2013/pais.cfm.

Texas Instruments. 2014. "The Chip that Jack Built." Accessed November 17, 2014. http://www.ti.com/corp/docs/kilbyctr/jackbuilt.shtml.

Vanderbilt, T. 2012. "Better Living through Imitation: Biomimicry Engineers Are Finding the Designs of the Future in the Greatest Field Laboratory of the Past: The Natural World." *Smithsonian*, September: 50–53.

Wagner, T. 2012. *Creating Innovators: The Making of Young People Who Will Change the World.* New York: Scribner.

Walesh, S. G. 1990. "Water Science and Technology: Global Origins." In *Urban Stormwater Quality Enhancement: Source Control, Retrofitting, and Combined Sewer Technology: Proceedings of an Engineering Conference,* Davos, Switzerland. New York: American Society of Civil Engineers.

Walesh, S. G. 2011. "Creativity Plus Persistence Equals Breakthroughs." *Leadership and Management in Engineering,* ASCE, April: 222.

Wallace, R. 1966. *The World of Leonardo 1452–1519.* Alexandria, VA: Time-Life Books.

Weingardt, R. G. 2005. *Engineering Legends: Great American Civil Engineers.* Reston, VA: ASCE Press.

EXERCISES

Notes:

1. The goal of the exercises is to provide students, sometimes working alone and sometimes as teams, with the opportunity to think about and use the ideas, principles, and information offered in this and earlier chapters.

2. However, many circumstances and corresponding teaching-learning opportunities may arise. For example, a stated situation may be altered to meet specific concerns or needs. Such variations are encouraged, subject to the concurrence or direction of the instructor.

6.1 RESEARCH PAPER (INDIVIDUAL STUDENT VERSION): Identify two-person creative teams: a. a professional; b. a student. These two person teams can be identified on the basis of your knowledge regarding their exemplary work in developing creative and innovative facilities, structures, systems, products, or processes. The intent of this exercise is to study what goes behind the scene of innovation. The following steps are suggested:

- Select the two person teams and get an approval from the instructor.
- Prepare an interview questionnaire with open-ended questions using the principles discussed in the chapters till now.
- Conduct the interview and make a recording of the session with permission.
- Go through these recordings again and again to identify keywords or phrases that describe creative/innovative results, operable personal characteristics and training, inspirations or methods used. Write each keyword/phrase on a sticky note.
- Now for each team, cluster the sticky notes on the basis of affinity. You can identify affinity as per your choice.
- Compare the professional against the student and identify similarities and differences.
- Write the paper. Provide a complete description of the creative/innovative result and identify operable personal characteristics. Assume your principal readers are engineering or other technical profession students who know very little about your topic.

6.2 INTERVIEW AN ENTREPRENEUR: Ask around and identify one or more widely recognized creative/innovative individuals in or near your community. I suggest that you use the term *entrepreneur* because people you talk to are more likely to relate to that word than to *creative/innovative person.* Be assured that most entrepreneurs are creative and innovative.

Select one of the identified individuals, contact him or her, and ask if you could have a half hour to an hour of his or her time for an interview. Then, prepare some questions, possibly drawing on Section 4.2 for some ideas. In addition to formulating questions about the interviewee, you might include some queries helpful to your career plans.

Conduct the interview and write a summary that stresses what you learned about the characteristics of the interviewee and how they compare to one of more of the seven characteristics discussed in this chapter. Thinking about your career, what might you do differently as a result of the interview? This interview exercise reflects my belief that we can learn a lot by conversing with accomplished people. Ask questions and listen carefully.

6.3 **WIDENING YOUR CREATIVITY (WHAT IF):** How can a man get a clean and smooth shave? As an individual or a team, explore possible ways you can provide a better shave for a man using What If (Section 4.12).

One can think about making sharper blades, increasing the number of blades, adding vibrations along with blade movement. But What If we put aside the word shave and replace it with remove facial hair or eliminate facial hair or groom facial hair. Does that trigger new ideas or ways for look-ing at the age-old problem of facial hair? For example, there are several ways to remove facial hair such as shaving, waxing, and threading. Laser treat-ment can be seen as eliminating facial hair permanently. Grooming facial hair can be interpreted as trimming it so that it is still visible. Summarize your initial ideas in writing and include a list of scenarios, supplemented with sketches as needed.

6.4 **RASPBERRY SYRUP IN CHOCOLATE BOTTLES (MIND MAPPING):** At a birthday party, each child received a piece of novelty candy consisting of a tiny chocolate bottle containing raspberry syrup. Being inquisitive, the chil-dren began discussing how the candy was made while enjoying it.

One idea was that someone made the tiny chocolate bottles and then filled them with the raspberry syrup. An adult who knew the candy-making process indicated it was not done that way; the bottles would be too fragile, and pour-ing the thick syrup would take too long. The children's discussion continued; they suggested warming the syrup to make it flow easier, but the adult said that was not what was done: The warm syrup would melt the chocolate bottle.

Eventually, the children described how it was done and they were correct. What was the process (adapted from Altshuller 1996)? How could that process be scaled up and used in engineering? Work as an individual or in a team; con-sider using Mind Mapping (Section 4.7) to find answers to both questions.

6.5 **FINDING THE MISSING OIL (FISHBONE DIAGRAMMING):** Each week, a manufacturing company receives numerous shipments of fuel oil deliv-ered by a tanker truck driven by the same person. The tank's capacity is fif-teen thousand gallons, and the tank is completely filled and sealed when it leaves the seller—that is, the oil company.

However, the buyer—that is, the manufacturing company—gradually realizes that when the truck arrives and is unsealed and unloaded, there is always a shortage of three hundred gallons, or 2 percent. The buyer's repre-sentative begins to ask questions and check measuring devices at the seller and at the manufacturing plant; all are in order. There is no leakage from the tank truck, and even a thin oil film left on the inside walls of the truck's tank would not explain the shortage. Temperature change effects are ruled out (adapted from Altshuller 1996).

What's going on? *Hint:* The tank truck driver is dishonest. You or your team might want to use Fishbone Diagramming (Section 4.5) to search for possible explanations to generate ideas.

6.6 **YOUR LOGO:** You just joined a company known for its creativity and inno-vative work. As part of the first-day orientation, you learn that you will be given a security card to enter certain project areas. You are asked to design a logo for your card that expresses one or more of your creativity/innovation strengths. Design your logo, perhaps using some of the seven creativity/innovation characteristics discussed in this chapter as the starting point (adapted from Lumsdaine, Lumsdaine, and Shelnutt 1999).

6.7 **THE NEED FOR EMPATHY:** Recall your last visit to a doctor's clinic. Reflect on the setting, the behavior of the medical staff, the doctor, and the tools and equipment used. Now imagine a ten-year old child who is unwell and has to come to see a doctor. Do you think the medical environment lacks empathy for the child? How can you fix the situation?

Think critically about a 10-year old child's behavior, wants, and needs, and ideate on an empathetic design solution.

6.8 **LEARN ABOUT AND EXPLAIN THE USE OF CAISSONS:** As noted in this chapter's discussion of building the Brooklyn Bridge (Section 6.8.4), part of the process included underwater construction using caissons, and Washington Roebling was seriously injured as a result of working within a caisson. Study caissons, and then describe them and how they are used via a series of simple, freehand drawings (Section 7.4).

7

Advanced Whole-Brain Methods

Today is a new day that has been handed to you for shaping.
You have the tools, now get out there and
create a masterpiece.
—*Steve Maraboli, motivational speaker and writer*

Objectives:

After studying this chapter, you will be able to:

- Explain further the universality of the divergent–convergent thinking process when resolving an issue, solving a problem, or pursuing an opportunity
- Describe how whole-brain tools stimulate creativity and innovation
- Demonstrate understanding and use of nine more advanced whole-brain tools when working on a project
- Illustrate the applicability of some of this chapter's tools to nontechnical challenges
- Discuss the positive and negative features of each tool
- Give examples of the connections between neuroscience and each whole-brain tool

7.1 RESUMING DISCUSSION OF WHOLE-BRAIN METHODS

We know that more ideas are better, and this chapter describes nine more whole-brain methods. You, or you and your team, can use these methods as you work through the divergent–convergent process with the goal of being more creative and innovative.

7.1.1 The More Divergent the Ideas, the Better Their Convergence

As explained in Section 3.1, when an individual or team takes on an issue, problem, or opportunity (IPO), they typically work through the divergent–convergent process.

Whole-brain methods enable us to generate many more ideas and options within the divergent portion of the divergent–convergent process and to analyze those ideas and options within the convergent part. The common feature of these methods or tools is their ability to stimulate you and, more powerfully, your group to think more deeply and widely—to generate more ideas and then more thoroughly analyze them. Whole-brain methods help us work smarter, including being more creative and innovative. This *early on, more is better* concept applies whether we strive to *define* an IPO or endeavor to *resolve* one.

7.1.2 Two-Chapter Approach

As explained in Section 3.3, the twenty whole-brain methods offered in this book are presented in two chapters: Chapter 4 and this one, Chapter 7. This two-chapter structure will help you appreciate the diversity of the described tools as revealed by factors such as the effort required to understand and apply them, the many functions they perform, their positive and negative features, and the kinds of results they produce.

Accordingly, Chapter 4 includes eleven methods that can be quickly learned and rapidly applied to yield useful results. As indicated by Table 4.1, which includes a list of the Chapter 4 methods, a few methods address IPO definition or IPO resolution alone, but most are applicable to both functions. Essentially all of the Chapter 4 methods can be used by an individual or by a team, and that chapter offers a powerful toolbox by itself.

For those who want an even larger toolbox, this chapter offers nine additional, more advanced methods, the names of which are also listed in Table 4.1. As with the Chapter 4 methods, most of the Chapter 7 methods apply to IPO definition and resolution, and most can be applied by an individual or a group. These advanced methods typically take more time to understand and effectively apply, and that effort might be rewarded by even better results.

For example, Six Thinking Caps, a team method, requires special props, a detailed explanation, and an effective facilitator. However, in return, this method can fully engage participants by expecting the entire team to serially focus on these specific aspects of an IPO: information, emotion, logic, hope, and creativity. Similarly, establishing a supportive culture and physical environment requires a sustained, major, and organization-wide effort, with the hoped-for results being more creativity and innovation in all functional areas.

Accordingly, and as noted in Chapter 3, you as an undergraduate student are less likely to have opportunities to use the whole-brain methods presented in this chapter. However, you could readily apply these advanced tools in graduate courses and in professional practice.

7.1.3 The Ideas of Just "Tools" and the Use of Multiple Methods

Chapter 3 stressed that this text's whole-brain methods are just tools: readily available aids that you select and use as appropriate. As noted in that chapter, you and your team might use several software tools to work through a class project or tools available on your home workbench to do repairs. In a similar fashion, you can use a series of creativity/innovation tools to conduct a project. For example, and referring to some of the methods discussed in this chapter, your team might use Six Thinking Caps to thoroughly define all aspects of a complex technical challenge, Biomimicry to explore some possible conceptual solutions, and TRIZ to further develop one or more of the most promising ideas.

7.1.4 Final Thoughts Before Introducing More Whole-Brain Methods

As an aid to studying this chapter's whole-brain methods, I suggest that you briefly skim the following sections of Chapter 3:

- Section 3.4: Avoiding the Einstellung Effect Trap
- Section 3.5: How Do We Know the Methods Work?
- Section 3.7: Caveats
- Section 3.9: Format Used to Present Each Method

7.2 BIOMIMICRY

Recall from Section 1.3.2 how the Swiss engineer George de Mestral was inspired to create the now almost omnipresent Velcro. He observed how burdock burrs stuck to his clothes and to his dog, studied the burrs, noted the hooks, and the rest was history. This example nicely introduces us to *Biomimicry*.

7.2.1 Description

Natural sciences writer Benyus (1997), in her book *Biomimicry: Innovation Inspired by Nature*, defines *biomimicry* as "a new science that studies nature's models and then imitates or takes inspiration from these designs and processes to solve human problems." She says that her book describes the exploration of "nature's masterpieces—photosynthesis, self-assembly, natural selection, self-sustaining ecosystems, eyes and ears and skin and shells, talking neurons, natural medicines, and more—and . . . copying these designs and manufacturing processes to solve our own problems." Benyus offers a fresh view of nature. She sees nature as a mentor, noting that biomimicry "introduces an era based not on what we can extract from the natural world, but on what we can learn from it." Nature becomes a teacher.

In a similar vein but with reference to engineering, research scientist Bar-Cohen (2012) states that "biomimetics [his term for biomimicry] is the field of science and engineering that seeks to understand and to use nature as a model for copying, adapting, and inspiring concepts and designs." He views nature as a "giant laboratory" in which "trial and error experiments" occur within the evolutionary process. The evolutionary process occurs on a wide scale, ranging from nano and micro (e.g., bacteria) to macro and mega (e.g., whales). That process produces a myriad of results available to us for copying, adapting, and otherwise using.

How can we transfer what we learn from nature's components, organisms, and systems to the design of engineered structures, facilities, systems, products, and processes? The challenge is "quantifying the processes involved and deriving from them systems that are adaptable, constructible, and cost-effective" (Sarkisian et al. 2011). Which of nature's structures, processes, or systems might you learn from and then mimic to resolve an issue, solve a problem, or pursue an opportunity?

7.2.2 Graduated Materials

Mechanical engineering professor Torres-Sanchez said: "We mechanical engineers are obsessed with how solid, homogeneous materials behave, but when you look at nature, there's nothing that is really homogenous out there." She advocates porosity graduation, meaning that we should design structural materials with advantageous cavities similar to those found in bamboo, tree trunks, bones, and beehives. This encourages a higher strength-to-weight ratio, efficient transfer of forces, and less cost. One challenge (besides the design process) is how to manufacture graduated, heterogeneous materials (Czyzewski 2011).

Figure 7.1
The design of this Malmo, Sweden, skyscraper (left) was influenced by the human spine, and that of this Lisbon, Portugal, railroad station (right) by palm trees.

(Piotr Wawrzyniuk/Fotolia; Txakel/Fotolia)

7.2.3 Calatrava's Nature-Inspired Designs

Calatrava, a famous Spanish engineer and architect, produced many works that illustrate the structural and aesthetic benefits of biomimicry (Tischler 2010). For example:

- A Malmo, Sweden, skyscraper is twisted, as shown in Figure 7.1, because its design was influenced by the human spine.
- Also shown in Figure 7.1, columns in the Lisbon, Portugal, train station look like a palm tree forest.
- The ceiling in a portion of a Milwaukee, Wisconsin, art museum has wings that open up to the sky.
- Valencia, Spain, contains a planetarium influenced by the human eyeball.

Calatrava said, "In my hands, there is a little bit of architecture and engineering. What architecture does is what a coat does for our body. It wraps us" (Tischler 2010). Does this mean that architecture addresses aesthetics while engineering provides the substance, with the latter being sometimes influenced by nature?

7.2.4 Floating Wetlands

This innovative idea began in 2000 with Bruce Kania, who was concerned with surface water pollution caused by excessive nutrients. As a former fishing guide in northern Wisconsin, he recalled the natural floating peat bogs that had often surrounded him. Kania assembled a team of scientists and engineers to focus on biomimicking the productive natural floating island ecosystems (Klatt 2011).

As illustrated conceptually in Figure 7.2, the team developed a floating matrix made from recycled, shredded plastic bottles. Vegetation placed on top of the floating matrix provides habitat and food for a variety of wildlife, including waterfowl, songbirds, turtles, and frogs, as well as an aesthetic cover for the island. Plant roots exposed beneath the floating matrix uptake nutrients, provide cover and food for fish, and provide additional substrate for beneficial microbe colonization.

Figure 7.2
Artificial floating wetlands remove potential pollutants from ponds and lakes.

Source: Adapted from Headley and Tanner 2008.

Figure 7.3
A constructed floating island can provide various benefits, such as water quality, habitat, aesthetics, and absorption of wave energy.

(Floating Island International, Inc.)

For a constructed floating wetland, as shown in Figure 7.3, the multilayer biomesh island provides structural strength, huge surface area for beneficial microbe colonization, and rooting matrix for vegetation. These floating "water treatment facilities" can be placed in natural and artificial ponds and lakes. In addition to benefitting water quality, habitat, and aesthetics, the floating wetlands can be placed to absorb wave energy, thus reducing shoreline erosion (Floating Island International 2014; Klatt 2011).

Studies indicate that *microbes*—that is, microscopic single-celled organisms—within the floating matrix remove potential contaminants from water, such as carbon, phosphorus, heavy metals (e.g., copper and zinc), nitrogen, and ammonia. Microbes consume nutrients that would otherwise produce algae. Adding plants on top of the floating matrix adds a whole new dimension. The plant roots provide more surface area for microbes. Plants themselves take up nutrients, but only 15 to 20 percent of the total. Microbes do most of the work. Carbon is sequestered in terrestrial growth on top of the floating matrix, in microbes growing within the matrix, in roots hanging beneath the matrix, and in organic debris accumulating below the matrix (Floating Island International 2014; Klatt 2011).

7.2.5 More Biomimicry Examples

To further suggest the creativity/innovation potential of biomimicry, consider the following observations (from Bar-Cohen 2012 unless noted otherwise):

- Seashell shapes inspired the design of the Sydney Opera House (see Figure 7.4).
- The peristaltic pump, as also shown in Figure 7.4, squeezes liquids in the desired direction, functioning like the valves and chambers in animal and human hearts.

Figure 7.4
Seashell shapes inspired designers of the Sydney Opera House (left), and peristaltic pumps (right) mimic the valves and chambers in animal and human hearts.

(Paul Liu/Fotolia; Beerkoff/Fotolia)

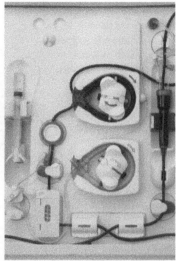

- Barbs on roses and other plants may have stimulated the design of barbed wire.
- Nature's honeycomb objects, such as the hexagonal cellular structure within beehives, inspired the design of aircraft structural elements because of the need for high strength and low weight, or what was referred to earlier in the discussion of graduated materials as a high strength-to-weight ratio (Section 7.2.2).
- The gecko's wall-clinging ability inspired scientists to develop a sticky substance similar to that used by the gecko (Anft 2012).
- The beak of the kingfisher inspired the design of the lead unit on the Japanese high-speed train in the late 1990s, as described in Section 6.6.3 (EarthSky 2012; Vanderbilt 2012)
- Bird beaks, in general, could have motivated the design of all types of tongs.
- Spider webs, which are composed of fiber extruded by spiders and have tensile strength greater that of than steel of similar weight, probably led to the creation of fishing nets, kitchen strainers, and screen doors.
- Membranes on the feet of frogs and swimming birds such as geese, ducks, and swans probably inspired the flippers used by divers—and also the term *frogmen.*

7.2.6 Neuroscience Basis

Assume that you are faced with a challenge and begin to consciously see and comprehend, not just look at, the natural world in an attempt to resolve the challenge. You are committed to finding some potential solutions within nature. With focus, you are likely to see some initial ideas. Given your intensity, your subconscious mind is very likely to work on your project and occasionally provide you with Biomimicry ideas.

7.2.7 Positive and Negative Features

Biomimicry's most positive feature is that it invites ideas for addressing IPOs from the vastness of the natural world. Another plus is that biomimicry can be applied individually or by a team. This tool's biggest drawback is that it requires unrestrained whole-brain thinking to make the leap, metaphorically and literally, into and then back from nature.

7.3 CHALLENGES AND IDEAS MEETINGS

Let's define a meeting as three or more people, talking face-to-face or connected electronically, discussing business or professional work or some aspect of one or more organizations. Some meetings are necessary because they are the most effective way to enable groups of people to carry out their responsibilities and achieve their objectives. However, "meetings are often a waste of time and excessively frustrating because of poor planning, execution, and follow-up that sometimes indicates lack of respect for the time, talent, and feelings of others" (Walesh 2012a).

Because so much time is devoted to meetings, and because so much important work can be accomplished at meetings, careful meeting management is preferred. Basic meeting management tips structured as a planning/conducting/following-up process are discussed elsewhere (e.g., Walesh 2012a). In contrast, this section offers ideas for how to use meetings to discover more creative and innovative approaches to IPOs. *Challenges and Ideas Meetings* can help offset the natural tendency of most groups, especially when very busy, to settle into routines and not think and talk about important changes and trends that could adversely affect organizations or offer them fruitful opportunities.

7.3.1 Challenges Meetings

Meetings in all types of organizations—business, government, academic, and volunteer—are often devoted to reporting on progress in a *show-and-tell* mode. Some reporting of routine matters is necessary, but it gets too much attention and some of it could be more efficiently shared in other ways. Instead of extensive reporting, and in the interest of making optimum use of the brain power in the room and to stimulate creativity and innovation, start the meeting with—and focus on—real, serious challenges.

Go around the room and ask each person to share a major IPO he or she faces, and then expect others to offer at least initial ideas for resolving the challenge. The expectation to offer ideas coupled with the hoped-for diversity of the group is likely to lead to a plethora of IPOs, synergistic interaction, and generation of some potentially creative/innovative approaches. Such short, intense collaborative efforts also plant the various IPOs and the need to resolve them in the subconscious minds of participants. Some of this "planting" may lead later to the unexpected growth of more creative/innovative thoughts and suggestions that turn problems into opportunities.

7.3.2 Ideas Meetings

Consider an even more aggressive, creativity/innovation-oriented approach to meetings, as offered by de Bono (2010). He states that "to get creativity [and innovation] into an organization, you must make it an expectation," and then he suggests dedicating the last fifteen minutes of a meeting to considering anyone's new idea. His view is that "if new ideas are an expectation . . . then people will make an effort to have new ideas."

A variation on this idea is to be even more specific. Ask each person to be prepared to offer answers to one of more of the following questions:

- What could we do much better?
- What should we stop doing?
- What should we start doing?

Why these three questions? Consider this answer from management consultant and writer Drucker: "If you want something new, you have to stop doing something old." Or consider this anonymous thought: "If you do what you did, you'll get what you got."

Depending on the circumstances, answering such questions may be awkward. If that is the case, then ask each participant prior to the meeting to anonymously submit answers to all three questions. Devote the entire meeting or a series of meetings to discussing those answers. Regardless of the process used, when a group takes on these three questions, lively discussions will occur, partly because the possibility of change will be in the air. These exchanges will provide many opportunities for creative/innovative thinking. More fundamentally, the organization will be better prepared to create its future instead of, in the vacuum of business as usual, having others create it for them.

7.3.3 Keystone Habits

Ending each meeting with idea sharing might be referred to as a *Keystone Habit,* as suggested by Charles Duhigg, author of the *Power of Habit* (2012). These habits "start a process that, over time, transforms everything." Keystone Habits ripple through the organization.

As an example, consider the story of Paul O'Neill and the Aluminum Company of America (Alcoa). It's a cold October 1987 day in New York, and O'Neill is being introduced to investors and stock analysts as the new chief executive officer of the huge and financially troubled Alcoa. How would he save the company? His first comment flabbergasted the audience. He said, "I want to talk about worker safety. I intend to go for zero injuries." (Duhigg 2012). Noble as his safety concern may have been, what about saving the company!? O'Neill stuck with his safety-first message. He instituted this requirement: "Any time someone was injured, the unit president had to report to O'Neill within twenty-four hours and present a plan for making sure the injury never happened again."

In order for that to happen, all of the units in the huge company "had to build new communication systems that made it easier for the lowliest worker to get an idea to the loftiest executive, as fast as possible." The company's rigid hierarchy and traditional practices had to change in response to O'Neill's safety program. For example, unions no longer resisted measuring worker productivity because such monitoring helped to identify safety risks. Managers gave workers more autonomy in shutting down production lines when faced with risky situations (Duhigg 2012).

The new communication system extended into all aspects of the company and led to improvements in many areas. By the time O'Neill retired thirteen years later, Alcoa had

- become one of the world's safest companies, with injuries one twentieth of the US average, and
- increased both its annual net income and its stock value by a factor of five.

As summarized by Duhigg, O'Neill's innovative focus on immediately reporting and addressing injuries instituted a Keystone Habit. That habit influenced how essentially everyone worked and communicated, transforming everything. The safety habit reduced injuries and improved business performance.

7.3.4 How You Might Use the Keystone Habit Idea

You can apply the innovative Keystone Habit idea now, while you are student within a student organization, and/or later during your career. Consider some possibilities for the latter. Assume that you as a professional eventually become a member of a department in a business, a university, or a government entity. The group decides that whenever it meets, each member will report on one thing that is occurring in his or her community, with *community* broadly defined. Depending on the individual and the nature of the department, his or her community might be a subset of a business, a neighborhood, a campus, a condo complex, a subdivision, a village, or a city.

Exercising this innovative *what's going on* Keystone Habit will have a ripple effect in that everyone will eventually and habitually be even more aware of what is going on around them—issues to resolve, problems to solve, and opportunities to pursue—and sharing that information is likely to stimulate some creative/innovative ideas. Furthermore, many of the meeting participants will seek help by regularly asking other personnel for briefings about what is happening. These requests are likely to extend laterally and trickle down to the lowest level in the organization. The organization's communication culture might be enhanced as a result of the sharing habit.

Recall Section 3.6, which includes some examples of how an error or accident led to unexpected creative and innovative results—for example, the cardiac pacemaker, vulcanization, photosynthesis, microwave oven, and penicillin. This suggests acquiring the Keystone Habit of sharing error/accident stories at meetings. Yes, we don't like to share such stories, for fear of embarrassment, but when heard by others they may lead to creative/innovative ideas for either preventing similar errors or accidents or capitalizing on the results of the reported incidents. Maybe, just maybe, that personal or organizational error or accident hides a powerful opportunity to head in a new direction underneath all its negatives. Look for that new direction; it may be right in front of you. I've had exactly that happen in my professional life and believe it could happen in your student and professional life.

PERSONAL: THE GOOD NEWS HABIT

My career included eight years as an engineering dean, during which I and three or four department heads met weekly during the academic year and every other week during the summer. We started each meeting with a Keystone Habit called *good news*. We each reported on one good thing that happened, or was happening, in our area of responsibility. Our focus was on the faculty, staff, or students responsible for those good news items. The following three benefits resulted from the good news habit:

- Each of us always managed to find something to report. We didn't want to be embarrassed! I became even more aware of what was going on around me because I was searching for something to report and received help from my administrative assistant because she knew what I needed to do.
- Meetings started positively because each of us always heard several good news stories.
- We subsequently expressed appreciation for the good things that were happening. They were noted in the meeting minutes, cited in the college's newsletter, and recognized by personal congratulations and with special opportunities for achievers.

Not only did it generate three benefits, this innovative good news effort also required only a few minutes at the beginning of our meetings. We devoted most of our time to IPOs. You are already in or soon will be in many and varied groups that meet regularly. Try the innovative good news habit or another Keystone Habit and reap the benefits. Incidentally, you won't need a "bad news" agenda item; that topic will take care of itself.

7.3.5 Neuroscience Basis

Consciously devoting significant portions of regularly scheduled meetings to challenges, ideas, and/or Keystone Habits and knowing that we need to be prepared to contribute will engage our powerful subconscious minds. For each of us, that faithful servant—along with our conscious mind—will identify challenges, generate ideas, and respond to the Keystone Habit. As a result, each of us will be prepared for meetings, and both we and our colleagues will benefit.

7.3.6 Positive and Negative Features

Personal experience, such as my good news story, and research, such as the O'Neill and Alcoa account, suggest that challenges, ideas, and/or Keystone Habits meetings will help teams, groups, and organizations work smarter and be more creative and innovative. On the negative side, such systematic efforts are difficult to start, because they are suspect and require a high degree of self-discipline and organizational discipline to maintain—until they become personal and organizational habits, of course.

7.4 FREEHAND DRAWING

Sometimes, we can discover new approaches and use them to move forward by first looking back. In introducing *Freehand Drawing* as a creativity/innovation method, let's begin with the simple pencil and its use throughout much of engineering's history.

7.4.1 Back to the Pencil

In a return-to-basics spirit, consider another way to engage the right hemisphere to supplement the left hemisphere: the simple pencil, as illustrated in Figure 7.5, or similar hand tools that can be used for Freehand Drawing.

Think about the pencil in the context of the US K–12 educational system. Begin with the earlier comments (Section 5.4.1) by artist and author Edwards (1999). She concluded that K–12 education gives major attention to the left hemisphere, while the right hemisphere of students is "virtually neglected."

Noting the growing importance of right-brain capabilities, Edwards offers a solution—an option—for educators. She suggests going back to the humble pencil by including Freehand Drawing education and training in the curriculum because it is "an efficient, effective way to teach thinking strategies suited to the right brain."

Figure 7.5
The simple pencil, when used for Freehand Drawing, helps engage the brain's right hemisphere.

(Roman Pyshchyk/Fotolia)

Recall my personal note in Section 5.4.2 about taking up formal art instruction after an over five-decade lapse. More specifically, I studied and practiced first graphite pencil drawing and then colored pencil drawing, supplemented with acrylic and ink. I offered this personal note because I have experienced the creative/innovative benefits of Freehand Drawing, some of which are discussed ahead, and want to share those benefits with you. In addition, I use my experience as the basis for a suggestion: If you are not involved in the visual or performing arts, try it. You are very likely to experience an awakening of your brain (especially the right hemisphere) and, equally important, to enjoy and otherwise benefit from the results of your efforts.

7.4.2 Drawing on the History of Drawing and Its Impact on Engineering

Drawing, which can be defined as converting "a mental image into a visually-recognizable form" (Beakley, Evans, and Keats 1986), has been used for over two millennia by the predecessors of what are now engineers, architects, and other similar technical professionals. Almost everyone has seen some of da Vinci's sixteenth-century freehand drawings, which exemplify a whole-brain approach in their composition and detail.

Within engineering, freehand drawing was largely replaced with the more formal projection drawing and other technical drawing methods; projection drawing was developed in France in the eighteenth century by Gaspard Monge (Beakley, Evans, and Keats 1986). As suggested by Figure 7.6, this systematic manual drawing method used tools like straight edges, triangles, and circle guides and was a primarily a left-brain, less spontaneous process than freehand drawing. However, it was an effective way to describe a design so that it could be manufactured, constructed, or otherwise brought into reality.

Near the end of the last century, the drawing component of engineering education and practice changed drastically in that systematic, manual drawing was gradually eclipsed by computerized graphics tools (Figure 7.7). Computer-aided graphics replaced graphite graphics (Lumsdaine, Lumsdaine, and Shelnutt 1999). Therefore, manual drawing instruction of any kind is rare in US engineering and

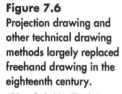

Figure 7.6
Projection drawing and other technical drawing methods largely replaced freehand drawing in the eighteenth century.

(Olga Galushko/Fotolia)

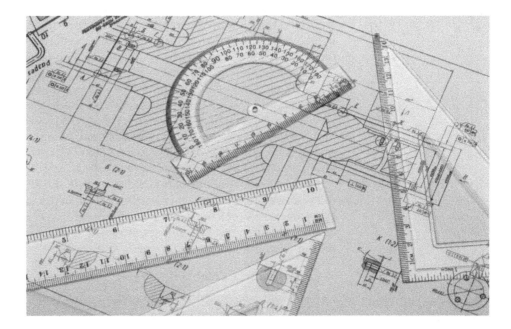

Figure 7.7
Computer-aided drawing is now widely used in engineering.

(Marzky Ragsac Jr./Fotolia)

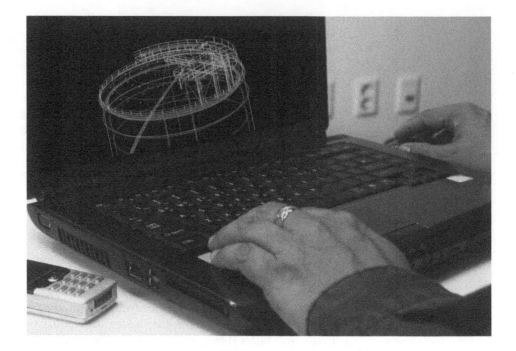

scientific/technical education today and not widely used in practice. Advances in drawing, from freehand to the more disciplined projection drawing and into today's computerized drawing, have been largely beneficial, mainly because they increased the efficiency of drawing and the use of drawings.

However, these changes have had the negative effective of removing some right-brain stimulus potential from education and, as a result, from practice. Although computer-aided design and drafting (CADD) tools are more sophisticated than freehand drawing, they share one characteristic: they are primarily left-brained. In contrast, "freehand drawing, being free of technical symbols, is dominated by the right hemisphere of the brain" (Beakley, Evans, and Keats 1986). As further explained by Arciszewski, Grabska, and Harrison (2009), "The spontaneity of free-hand design, rather than being superfluous, permitted direct expression by parts of the brain that are not engaged by computer-aided drafting tools."

According to consultant Roam (2008), "Computers make it easy to draw the wrong thing." Computer-aided drawing tools might also tempt us to draw the same old things or stop too soon in our creative/innovative efforts. "Technically-perfect, computer-generated drawings always seem to be complete and imply that the work is over," according to Arciszewski, Grabska, and Harrison (2009). They indicate that these technically perfect drawings limit a student's or practitioner's creativity and innovation because of the "limited number of objects available in a given computer tool."

In summary, although we should recognize the advantages of computer-aided drawing, we should also recognize the disadvantages of over- or sole reliance on it. Why? Because Freehand Drawing, when used in series or parallel with computer-aided drawing, offers engineers, scientists, and other technical professionals significant benefits, as discussed in the next section.

7.4.3 Benefits of Freehand Drawing

Let's explore ways in which engineers and other scientific/technical professionals, first as students and later as practitioners, can benefit as a result of learning and applying Freehand Drawing principles (Walesh 2012b). As a result of Freehand Drawing, and thus being more likely to engage both brain hemispheres, you are likely to be even more effective in resolving issues, solving problems, and pursuing opportunities. As noted in this book's discussion of the left-brain emphasis in formal education (Section 5.4.1), a "half a brain is better than none; a whole brain would be better" (Edwards 1999). That observation is illustrated within the following discussions of three benefits of Freehand Drawing.

7.4.4 Benefit 1: Seeing—Not Just Looking

A principle guiding Freehand Drawing is to draw what we see, rather than draw something the way we think it should look. For example, before taking pencil drawing lessons, if I were asked to draw a boat, tree, dog, or other object, I would start thinking mainly about what such an object should look like and try to draw it in that preconceived manner. Now, after drawing lessons, I draw what I see—that is, composition, shapes, and values.

Artists first carefully examine the object or thing to be drawn and then—and only then—draw what they see. Although each artist has his or her own style of converting what is seen to pencil strokes on paper, the process is driven by careful observation. Even if the resulting artwork is not successful, the artist will still have really seen the object, probably for the first time. British Prime Minister Churchill (2013), who took up art at age forty, expressed the intensity of that "first-time" seeing by saying, "I found myself instinctively, as I walked, noting the tint and character of a leaf, the dreamy purple shades of mountains, the exquisite lacery of winter branches. . . . And I had lived for over forty years without ever noticing any of them except in a general way."

Artists see more than they did in their pre-artist days. When I look consciously at any object, even if I have no interest in drawing it, I see more—especially shapes, shadows, and details—then I used to. Nagle (1998) draws a parallel between artists and writers by observing that both think first and then act. She recalls an incident when a painter and art critic asked a little girl how she approached drawing. Her answer: "First I have a think and then I put a line around it."

For example, assume that prior to my drawing studies you put me in an essentially empty, mostly white room—white walls, ceiling, and floor—like that shown in Figure 7.8 and asked me what I saw. I suspect I would have noted the three frames, the ceiling beams, and the wooden floor. Now, as an amateur artist, my observation would include seeing a wide spectrum of shades of white—that is, a range of values. This value spectrum would be prominent in my observation because drawing the room (or anything else) in two dimensions on a sheet of paper so that it appears three dimensional requires applying pencil strokes that capture the value variations. I would make this observation now even if you did not ask me to draw the room or any part of it.

Da Vinci (Section 6.3.2) exemplifies the seeing—not just looking—concept; he was said to have *quickness of vision*. This unusual ability is illustrated by his drawings of turbulence caused by water flowing around obstacles and his drawing of the movement of birds' wings during flight. The accuracy of his drawings was substantiated in modern times by slow-motion cameras (Wallace 1966). Much more recently and in a similar spirit, baseball Hall of Famer Berra (1998) said, "You can observe a lot by watching."

In my view, enhanced observation is an inevitable byproduct of practicing visual arts such as drawing, painting, and sculpture. Really seeing gradually becomes habitual for artists. When looking at anything, artists tend to see the previously

Figure 7.8
The artist goes beyond just looking to really seeing— for example, noting the infinite shades of white in this room.

(WavebreakmediaMicro/Fotolia)

mentioned values plus shapes and details more than others do. As someone noted, once your mind is stretched in a new way, it never returns to its original dimensions; so it is once we practice visual arts.

VIEWS OF OTHERS: ART'S GIFT TO SIGHT

"Art does not reproduce the visible; rather, it makes visible," according to German/Swiss painter Klee. "Drawing is the discipline by which I constantly rediscover the world," as noted by Dutch medical doctor and artist Franck, who also wrote "I have learned that what I have not drawn, I have never really seen," and "drawing is the discipline by which I constantly discover the world." Confucius said, "A common man marvels at uncommon things; a wise man marvels at the common place." "Discovery consists not in seeking new landscapes," according to French essayist Proust, "but in having new eyes." Perhaps Freehand Drawing and, more broadly, practicing the visual arts, enables us to make the invisible visible, see more, discover more, appreciate more, and, as result, be less common and more wise, for our benefit and for the benefit of those we work with and serve.

What does enhanced seeing and not just looking, derived from Freehand Drawing and other visual arts, have to do with engineering? Improved seeing—whether literally as described here or possibly, by extension, figuratively—further enables you to more completely and accurately define an issue to be resolved, a problem to be solved, or an opportunity to be pursued. To paraphrase and expand the expression "a problem well-defined is half-solved," an IPO more completely and accurately seen, both physically and figuratively, is half-resolved, solved, or pursued. Engineering and other scientific/technical profession students are likely to gain valuable enhanced literal and metaphorical diagnostic vision as a result of participating in Freehand Drawing or other visual arts.

Consider a related example from another profession. In the interest of enhancing the observational abilities of medical students, Yale's School of Medicine started a program that includes asking first-year medical students "to look at and then describe paintings . . . with whole people in them." Why? To improve their diagnostic ability. A three-year study reported in the *Journal of the American Medical Association* concluded that students are "10 percent more effective at diagnosis." The Yale program has expanded to more than twenty medical schools (Finn 2012). One argument for having future medical doctors examine paintings is the fear that increased use of MRIs, CAT scans, and other imaging and technological devices (Section 2.15.3) will diminish their visual diagnostic ability (Marcus 2015). All of that aside, recall that I am advocating going way beyond looking at visual arts; I'm urging you to engage in them. If viewing art works during your education will improve your ability to see, I assure you that performing art during and after your education will greatly increase that ability. Furthermore, you will have the satisfaction of creating originals.

Da Vinci's art illustrates the value of performing art to enhance seeing. He used the process of drawing or painting to illuminate his search for truth, to get beyond just looking. Then, having really seen, he used his drawing and painting to share what he was studying and what he saw. Examples include the muscular structure of the human body, Mona Lisa's smile, elements of the natural landscape, the intricacies of the human hand, eddies in turbulent flow, and the flight of a bird (Gelb 2004; Shlain 2014).

PERSONAL: YES, YOU CAN DRAW

You may appreciate the enhanced-seeing benefit of Freehand Drawing but, like many others (including me a few years ago), doubt that you can draw in a credible, satisfying manner. My experience, and that of many others, indicates that essentially anyone can draw if they are willing to see (not just look) and practice.

Chapter 4 in Edwards' book (1999), "Crossing Over: Experiencing the Shift from Left to Right," includes drawing exercises designed to cause a mental shift from what the author calls left-mode thinking to right-mode thinking. One exercise, one of several I completed when I took up drawing years ago, asked me to start with a complex line drawing depicting Picasso and indicated that I could draw it. The author said to turn it upside down, take a pencil and a sheet of paper, and, starting anywhere, move "from line to adjacent line, space to adjacent space," draw the shapes, and "try not to figure out what you are looking at in the upside-down image. It is better not to know." For example, instead of thinking of hands, arms, and face, try to view these parts just as shapes. The instructions concluded by stating that "everything you need to know in order to draw the image is right in front of your eyes."

I did as suggested: turned the Picasso drawing upside down and went from space to adjacent space, using my pencil to draw shapes on my paper. I tried not to think about "hands, arms, and face"—just shapes. When finished, I turned my drawing right side up, compared it to the original line drawing of Picasso, and I was pleased; I missed some hair and a few other details—but it wasn't bad. Still think you can't do Freehand Drawing? The principal points of sharing this personal experience are that Freehand Drawing causes you to see, not just look, and to strongly suggest that you can draw.

7.4.5 Benefit 2: Increased Awareness of the Right Brain's Powerful Functions

As a result of learning and applying Freehand Drawing principles, or studying and doing other visual arts, you are likely to become more aware of the different and valuable functions of the brain's right hemisphere relative to the left hemisphere. This enhanced awareness may be implicit, as in increasingly viewing IPOs more intuitively and holistically. Furthermore, as in the example of my experience, enhanced right-brain appreciation may also result from studying literature that connects art and education (e.g., Arciszewski 2009; Beakley, Evans, and Keats 1986; Edwards 1999). This may lead you and others to imagining how fuller use of right-hemisphere functions by students and practitioners of engineering and scientific/technical professions could enhance individual and group effectiveness.

This curiosity may in turn lead to discovery, study, development, and application of many tools, in addition to those presented in this chapter and in Chapter 4, to assist individuals and groups to further engage the brain's right hemisphere. Expanded right-mode thinking, coupled with typically strong left-mode thinking, will enable individuals and groups to more creatively and innovatively address issues, solve problems, and pursue opportunities.

Benefit 2 is admittedly more esoteric and nuanced than Benefit 1. However, to the extent it manifests itself in more students becoming students of brains—of their own brains—it is a potentially powerful benefit.

7.4.6 Benefit 3: Enhanced Group Collaboration

Suggesting the power of Freehand Drawing in a group setting, Roam (2008) says: "Visually representing someone or something, regardless of actual likeness or detail, always triggers insights that writing a list alone cannot achieve." Simple freehand drawing, in the form of simple shapes, lines, arrows, stick people, and things visible to all participants, enhances each person's ability to really see the physical, environmental, health and safety, sociopolitical, socioeconomic, financial, and other aspects of pressing IPOs. Additional simple Freehand Drawing facilitates generation of ideas for moving forward. The idea is to engage both of the brain's hemispheres because a whole brain is best.

As indicated in Table 3.1, about one-half of the creativity- and innovation-stimulation tools presented in this book have strong visual components. Examples used in this and other chapters employ a wide variety of drawn objects, such as mind maps, wagon wheels, fish bones, and process diagrams.

PERSONAL: WRITING ON THE WALL

I recall meeting with several client representatives in their conference room. The front wall was a whiteboard—floor to ceiling and wall to wall. Fantastic! As we all began to talk and share questions and ideas, I got up and began to make what turned out to be a rough, evolving, visual record of our conversation. *Seeing* what we were saying and *envisioning* where we might go seemed to help everyone.

7.4.7 Neuroscience Basis

Freehand Drawing, especially when one is striving for an attractive and uplifting result, is the ultimate whole-brain activity. Metaphorically, the left hemisphere guides color selection, while the right hemisphere blends colors to obtain the desired hues. The left brain determines the content of the overall composition, the right brain guides the emotional impact of the result, and both hemispheres execute it. Freehand Drawing draws heavily on vision, the most dominant of the six senses directed by the human brain.

7.4.8 Positive and Negative Features

Positive aspects of Freehand Drawing are mainly the three described previously:

- Seeing, not just looking
- Increased awareness of the right brain's powerful functions
- Enhanced group collaboration

The principal negative feature of Freehand Drawing, if you aspire to produce satisfying results, is the study needed to understand fundamentals such as composition and value and the time required to practice them. That study and practice should take place with the help of one or more teachers. However, very simple stick persons and similar Freehand Drawing techniques are all that is needed to achieve the third benefit noted.

7.5 MUSIC

I suspect most of us would agree that *Music*, which was defined by composer Varese as organized sound (Levitin 2006), affects our mood and perhaps our thinking and action. Maybe some of us intuitively believe that music can help us be more creative or innovative. Let's consider what musicians, neuroscientists, and other experts tell us about the brain and music. Building on those basics, we'll explore how we can use music to enhance our creativity and innovation.

However, before proceeding, let's recognize that music may be on our minds even more than we realize, in that we often use music terms in our daily conversation. As a student, you seek *sound* advice from a professor, you and your senior project team are on the same *wavelength*, and when thinking about the weekend you decide to *play it by ear*. Over the weekend, your favorite team suffers a *ringing* defeat, you get frustrated with too many *pitches* from telemarketers, and, on the positive side, you *orchestrate* a deal for a summer job with an engineering firm (Campbell 1997).

7.5.1 Description

Although highly subjective, music affects most of us in various ways. For example:

- **Music accesses both hemispheres.** "Music and language circuits are found in both cerebral hemispheres," according to Miles (1997), an ethnomusicologist—that is, one who studies music in its cultural context. Rocker turned neuroscientist Levitin (2006) says that "musical activity involves nearly every region of the brain that we know about." For example, the left brain identifies familiar tunes, as in *I remember that*, and the right brain makes pitch judgments or mentally generates music (Miles). The two-hemisphere aspect of music is demonstrated in part by the finding that the corpus callosum (Section 2.3.1) of musicians is thicker and more complex than in other people (Campbell 1997).

   Music and the previously discussed Freehand Drawing are similar in that both draw on the brain's left and right hemispheres; they are interhemispheric activities and thus support a whole-brain creative and innovative approach.

- **Music enhances listening.** Just as performing Freehand Drawing, as opposed to viewing drawing, is more beneficial for our brains, so playing music, as opposed to listening to music, is more beneficial for our brains. According to Levitin, "Music lessons teach us to listen better." However, for those of us who do not play an instrument, he says, "Even those of us who lack explicit training in music theory and performance have musical brains, and [can be] expert listeners." Music expert and classical musician Campbell (1997) uses the word *passive* to describe hearing and *active* to describe listening; he urges us to do more of the latter. Listening, whether to people or things, is an important part of defining an IPO prior to seeking a creative or innovative resolution of it.

- **Music enhances memories.** Do you wonder why we remember certain songs, say from our teenage years? Or why hearing some musical pieces causes us to recall a long-ago event? The reason is that the circumstances surrounding us hearing the music were emotionally charged. "We tend to remember things that have an emotional component because our amygdale and neurotransmitters act in concert to 'tag' the memories as something important," according to Levitin (2006). Recall, from Section 2.3, that the amygdale is the small structure near the base of the brain that influences emotion and behavior. In addition, a neurotransmitter is a chemical released from a nerve fiber to create a message that passes from one nerve to another or to a muscle. Levitin also says that "the types of sounds, rhythms, and musical textures we find pleasing are generally extensions of previous positive experiences we've had with music in our lives."

- **Music affects our mood, thinking, and action.** "Music can make a difference in how you feel, think, and act," according to Miles (1997), who goes on to ask, "But which music, why, and how?" She and Levitin (2006) begin to answer the question by listing the following factors or building blocks that determine a musical piece's psychophysiological impact:
  - **Tempo:** Speed or pace at which the music moves. A steady tempo can be quantified in beats per minute.
  - **Pitch:** The frequency of a note's or tone's sound wave quantified in hertz, or cycles per second. A tuba's range is low pitch, whereas a piccolo's is high. By the way, we see or read a note and we hear a tone, with both referring to the same entity.
  - **Loudness or volume:** The energy created by an instrument, which is also referred to as the amplitude of the tone and is quantified in decibels.
  - **Rhythm:** "Patterns made by the lengths and accents of sounds" (Miles 1997).
  - **Harmony:** Two or more notes simultaneously producing a chord.
  - **Melody:** A series of attention-getting tones that is distinguished from the rhythm and harmony; "the part you sing along with, the succession of tones that are most salient in your mind" (Levitin 2006).
  - **Instrumentation:** How the music is arranged for the instruments.
  - **Timbre:** Sometimes called sound or tonal color, it enables us to distinguish among instruments—for example, a clarinet versus a guitar.
  - **Texture:** "How many parts there are and the way they are put together—a four-piece rock band versus a gospel chorus" (Miles 1997).
  - **Form:** "The structure of a musical piece as determined by the patterns of its phrases, melodies, harmonies, and sections" (Miles). Classical symphonies consist of several movements, each of which might be very different than the others.

As an example of how music can affect action, consider a study in which four German and French wines, all similar in dryness and price, were displayed on the shelves of an English supermarket. On alternate days, German and French music were played at the wine display. When German music was played, 73 percent of the wine purchased was German; when French music was played, 77 percent of the wine purchased was French (Mlodinow 2013). Campbell (1997) cites many similar situations in which the addition of music increased sales in a department store, a supermarket, a restaurant, and a liquor store.

A little closer to the professional work environment, Campbell also provides examples of music increasing performance and productivity at an industrial company, a utility, a book publisher, and a bank. He says these benefits occur because music reduces stress, minimizes irritating sounds, and provides a sense of privacy. The challenge in these kinds of situations is determining the most effective kind of music, with one approach being experimentation.

7.5.2 Examples

Using the preceding basics as a foundation, consider the following three specific and practical ways we can we can use music to work smarter and enhance our creativity and innovation:

1. **Use music to focus your attention.** Recall from Section 3.5 that focusing is one of the three brain-oriented strategies available to those of us who want to be more creative and innovative in addressing an IPO, and as already noted, music accesses both hemispheres, helps us listen more effectively, enhances memories, and affects our mood. Miles (1997) suggests that the music we use in the background to help us focus should have a steady, deliberate tempo; simple and predictive rhythm; sounds we like; no lyrics; a high pitch, such as string instruments; and constant volume. Stated negatively, Miles goes on to say that if we want music to help us focus, we should "avoid unfamiliar sounds, distracting lyrics, deep sounds or heavy bass . . . or selections that stir up strong emotions." Campbell (1997) reinforces the preceding suggestion to favor higher-pitched music (the 2,000 to 8,000 hertz or higher portion of the 16 to 20,000 hertz hearing range) because it activates the brain and enhances attentiveness.

2. **Use music to engage your subconscious in long-term projects.** As you start a new long-term project, such as setting up and conducting an experiment or writing a major report, select a musical piece or type of music that you enjoy. Then, whenever you work on the project, play that music. Also play the music when you are not consciously working on your project. Your subconscious mind will work for you and maybe give you one or more insights or breakthroughs. "The music you heard as you gathered information about your [project] will recall that knowledge at a subconscious level, rearrange it, and allow it to synthesize in new formations," according to Miles (1997). She goes on to say "Stick with your incubation listening until 'aha!' strikes."

3. **Use music to interrupt yourself.** Individual habits, organizational culture, or the Einstellung Effect may stymie you, may limit your ability to think creatively and/or innovatively. Therefore, interrupt yourself with music to help prompt new ways of thinking (Miles 1997). For example, change the radio station, use the shuffle function, play musical pieces you don't normally listen to, go to a performance that you wouldn't normally attend, and/or simply stop working for five or ten minutes and listen to music.

PERSONAL: ENGINEERS ARE INTO MUSIC

Engineers may have a head start over many other professions in using music to stimulate their creativity and innovation. To reiterate and elaborate on a point I made in Section 5.4.1, when I served as an engineering dean, we gathered campus data showing that although engineers made up 10 percent of the student body, they comprised more than 20 percent of the campus musical groups—and more than 20 percent of the campus leadership positions. Faculty at other universities have shared similar observations with me.

Engineering students tend to be more inclined to participate in musical activities than other students, and this probably extends to engineers in general vis-a-vis the population at large. That predisposition to music may enhance your creativity/innovation potential.

7.5.3 Neuroscience Basis

Music is a potentially powerful creativity/innovation tool because it involves many parts of the human brain, such as the left and right hemispheres and our conscious and subconscious minds. Accordingly, music enhances our listening and memories, affects our moods, and more broadly brings many parts of our brain to bear on challenging IPOs.

7.5.4 Positive and Negative Features

The most positive aspects of this creativity/innovation enhancement method are that everyone has easy access to music and most people enjoy some forms of music. Therefore, any student or practicing professional can readily experiment with using music selections to work more effectively. A possible negative aspect of music is that in a group setting, one person's musical preferences could be disagreeable to others. Headphones are one way to address this concern.

7.6 PROCESS DIAGRAMMING

Process Diagramming, which may also be called flow charting or network diagramming, can help you—or better yet, you and your team or group—more fully understand the entire system (the big picture) in preparation for making creative/innovative improvements. The premise is that most repeated processes involve individuals from various departments, offices, and specialties. Examples of engineering processes include site design, in which one task is laying out parking areas, and setting up a manufacturing process, with one task being defining raw materials.

7.6.1 Description and an Example

As suggested by Figure 7.9, although each person knows his or her task, few, if any, see the big picture. They can't see the *forest*, only their *tree*. Therefore, in the absence of systematic interaction among key task leaders, major process improvements, such as elimination of useless tasks, refining tasks, and doing some tasks in parallel, are not likely to occur.

Select a frequently used process that involves individuals or groups from various departments, offices, and specialties, and/or selected by other characteristics, and for which there is some dissatisfaction, or which has occurred for a very long time and warrants a fresh look. The process might be manufacturing a product; preparing a

Figure 7.9
Participants in processes often know their tasks well but usually do not see the big picture (they don't see the forest for the trees); therefore major process improvements are not likely to occur.

(ZaZa Studio/Fotolia)

proposal; planning, conducting, and following up on routine meetings; conducting field reconnaissance; running laboratory experiments; or designing a bridge.

Enlist individuals that represent what are thought to be all of the steps in the process. Collaboratively and visually identify the tasks or steps and their interrelationships. This may be the first time anyone in your organization *sees* and really understands this particular process. Assemble the tasks and their interrelationships into a process diagram, flow chart, network diagram. This is the "As Is" section of Figure 7.10.

Study the highly visual result. Look for tasks that could be eliminated, refined, and combined with or done in parallel with others. The resulting process diagram is the "Could Be" section of Figure 7.10, and it might be deemed the "Should Be." With the development of an action plan, the "Should Be" can become the "Will Be."

Figure 7.10
Process Diagramming first maps the existing process to obtain the "As Is" and then uses it to stimulate thinking that leads to a possible improvement—the "Could Be."

As Is

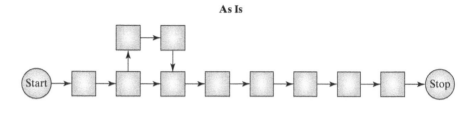

Could Be
(Should Be? Will Be?)

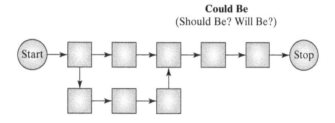

In the illustrated hypothetical case, note that the original ten tasks are reduced to eight tasks, and the elapsed time is reduced partly by doing some tasks in parallel. Software is available to assist with Process Diagramming.

7.6.2 Neuroscience Basis

Process Diagramming is effective because its logical aspect engages the left hemispheres of each participant's brain while its highly visual aspect stimulates the participant's right hemispheres. Contributing individuals are likely to be further motivated when seeing, for the first time in the diagram evolving in front of them, the steps and their interrelationships in an until then somewhat mysterious process, and will be challenged to improve it and begin to see how. If significant breaks are taken when applying the method, that new consciously discovered insight will generate productive subconscious thought.

7.6.3 Positive and Negative Features

A positive aspect of Process Diagramming is its potential long-term cumulative benefit. Given that a process was selected partly because it is frequently used and assuming that the Process Diagramming revealed improvements, those improvements will occur every time the process is used. Every application of the process will benefit from having to do fewer tasks and/or being able to complete all tasks sooner.

A possible negative feature of Process Diagramming is the major effort needed to perform it, mainly in obtaining positive participation by a group composed of individuals, each of whom is familiar with one or more process tasks. Another possible negative is the difficulty of effecting the promising changes identified by the exercise.

7.7 SIX THINKING CAPS

Often, in our team's zeal to resolve an IPO, we individually and as a group jump erratically from logic to emotion to hope and to other aspects of the challenge. We make little progress, rush to decisions because we want to end the chaos, and creativity and innovation suffer in the process. The *Six Thinking Caps Method* resolves this team dilemma by focusing each member of the group on one aspect at a time.

7.7.1 Reducing Confusion While Thinking

De Bono (1999), who was educated in medicine and psychology and is recognized as an authority on teaching thinking, developed the Six Thinking Hats Method. According to de Bono, "The main difficulty of thinking is confusion. We try to do too much at once. Information, emotion, logic, hope, and creativity all crowd in on us. It is like juggling with too many balls." His method enables an individual thinker, or a group of thinkers, to "do one thing at a time." Simply put, symbolically or actually putting on a particular hat calls for a particular, well-defined type of thinking; de Bono believed that the cumulative effect of serially thinking with various hats is quicker and provides better individual and group decisions than less systematic approaches.

De Bono uses hats of various colors as symbols for different types of thinking. The use of hats may reflect headwear customs or perceptions from before or when his book was originally published in 1985. Today, caps—such as in baseball or golf headwear—are very common, worn by children and adults of both genders. Accordingly, in order to strengthen the metaphor, caps are substituted for hats in this chapter, except when quoting de Bono. For purposes of this book, the Six Thinking Hats method becomes the Six Thinking Caps Method (6TCM).

Figure 7.11
Caps are used because of their association with thinking and certain roles and because they can be easily put on and taken off.

(Indigolotos/Fotolia)

7.7.2 Why Caps?

The 6TCM uses colored caps. Before describing and explaining the number of caps and their colors, let's address this question: Why use caps (Figure 7.11) as symbols for a thinking process? Why not stars, gloves, or balloons? "In many cultures," according to de Bono, "there is already a strong association between thinking and thinking caps or thinking hats. The value of a hat as a symbol is that it indicates a role. People are said to be wearing a certain hat." For example, think how you might say that you "put on your manager's cap" when talking to someone about how your organization or your favorite sports team is being managed. In contemplating offering a new course, faculty members might say "let's put on our student caps" to help imagine student views. While discussing a potential service line, a consultant may say "let's put on our client caps," or anyone might say "let's put on our thinking cap."

Edward de Bono goes on to say, "Another advantage is that a hat can be put on or taken off with ease. A hat is also visible to everyone around." As you will soon see, readily available actual caps can be used during the 6TCM process to enhance its effectiveness. Plain, single-colored caps can be purchased for relatively low cost at hobby and craft stores.

7.7.3 Why Six Caps?

Six caps are used to represent six sometimes conflicting and confusing thinking-related functions. Five of the functions have already been mentioned: information, emotion, logic, hope, and creativity/innovation. The sixth is imparting organization and control to a group discussion.

Consider a common situation. A group such as a senior project team, members of an academic department, a business's executive team, or an ad hoc government task force comes together to focus on an IPO or some other challenge. They enthusiastically and positively—or maybe grudgingly and negatively, depending on the situation—begin to think about and discuss the topic. Most of the participants want to resolve the issue, solve the problem, or determine how to pursue the opportunity and do it well and quickly.

However, quick resolution is not easy, as illustrated in Figure 7.12. "The main difficulty of thinking is confusion," as noted by de Bono (1999), who goes on to say: "We try to do too much at once. Emotions, information, logic, hope, creativity, [and the need for organization/control] all crowd in on us." We have to deal with the left-

Figure 7.12
Confusion involving information, emotion, logic, hope, creativity/innovation, and the need for organization and control can frustrate the thinking of a group.

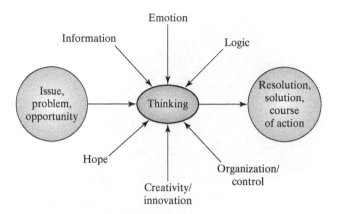

brain person, the right-brain individual, the know-it-all, and the control freak. Furthermore, because of differing personality profiles, some of us dwell on information and logic, others get emotional, some exude great hope, and a few fall into gloom.

6TCM enables an individualist thinker, or a group of thinkers, to "do one thing at a time." Simply put, symbolically or actually putting on a particular cap calls for engaging temporarily in one of the six particular, well-defined types of thinking.

7.7.4 Why the Specific Colors?

De Bono (1999) suggests that although he could have used caps with Greek names, or perhaps numbers, symbols, or shapes, he preferred simple colors to help the thinker visualize the six competing, thinking-related functions. Table 7.1 presents the color selected for each function and the rationale for it.

7.7.5 Does It Work?

De Bono (1999) supports his claim that the 6TCM provides quicker decisions by offering examples. He says that ABB, a Swiss/Swedish power and automation technology company, "used to spend twenty days on their multinational project team discussions. . . . The discussions now take as little as two days." An IBM laboratory "reduced meeting times to one quarter of what they had been." Granted, these claims are anecdotal and may seem extreme. However, given the percent of personnel time in all types of organizations that is invested (or wasted?) in meetings and discussions, the possibility of even small reductions in meeting and discussion time is appealing. For that reason alone, perhaps 6TCM warrants consideration and then experimentation.

Table 7.1 The color of each cap denotes a thinking-related function, with the color selected to suggest the function.

Cap Color	Thinking-Related Function	Rationale for the Color
Blue	Organization and control	Sky; as in overall and above everything else, cool
White	Information: Facts and figures	Neutral, objective; think of paper showing black-and-white facts and figures
Red	Emotion	Anger (e.g., seeing red), warmth, fire
Black	Logic: Caution, skepticism	Somber, serious
Yellow	Hope: Optimism, positive thinking	Sunny, bright, uplifting
Green	Creativity/innovation	Vegetation, fertility, growth

Assume that 6TCM results in quicker decisions, as suggested by the preceding examples. Whether or not the decisions obtained with 6TCM are better is more difficult to document. One might argue that the time savings alone, and the resulting monetary savings (time is money), prove that the 6TCM process is better than what might be viewed as the usual, less systematic approach. However, reducing the cost of the decision-making process, as desirable as that may be, does not necessarily equate to better decisions.

According to de Bono, "the intelligence, experience, and knowledge of all the members of the group are fully used" with 6TCM. He goes on to say, "Everyone is looking and working in the same direction." Alignment of group members and full use of their resources are desirable goals, but can we assume that the resulting decisions are better? After studying 6TCM and facilitating part of a meeting with the tool, I believe that the method, like the others in this chapter and in Chapter 4, is likely to produce decisions superior to those obtained with the usual, less systematic approaches and do so in less time. If you want to experiment with 6TCM, read on for a description of how to use it.

7.7.6 Group Use of the Method

Recognize that 6TCM, like essentially all of the tools described in this text, can be used in addressing a wide variety of IPOs. Thinking—or more specifically, thinking better—in a group setting is a common element in the use of whole-brain tools.

Assume that you are a group leader or a facilitator for a group that is about to take on an IPO. Furthermore, you are intrigued by 6TCM as a means of enabling your group to more thoroughly define the breadth and depth of the IPO and to make more creative/innovative decisions. Finally, assume your group is not familiar with 6TCM. Then, consider the following six suggestions for you and your group's first use of 6TCM:

1. **Provide an introductory overview:** Brief the group about the method, making selective use of the preceding 6TCM materials. Confirm that each person understands the essentials. Then, begin the application of the method as you continue to explain it.
2. **Start with the blue cap:** Always start and end 6TCM with the blue cap—the organization and control cap. Put it on (preferably literally, but if not, then figuratively). As suggested by de Bono (1999), discuss topics such as "why we are here, what we are thinking about, the definition of the situation (or problem), alternative definitions, what we want to achieve, where we want to end up, the background to the thinking, and a plan for the sequence of [caps] to be used." Indicate that information, emotion, logic, hope, and creativity/innovation will be considered as the session proceeds and that results of the ongoing process will be documented. However, for now encourage, everyone to put on their blue caps and engage in the organization/control discussion.

   While the blue cap is in play, no other cap is to be worn. The other functions (information, emotion, logic, hope, creativity/innovation) are off limits. This protocol applies throughout the 6TCM process in that everyone "wears" the currently designated cap. As a result, each person is frequently drawn out of their preferred thinking modes, placing them in a better position to offer more and appreciate and empathize with the thinking of others.
3. **Plan the sequence of caps:** While an ad hoc cap sequence could be used during the 6TCM process, de Bono suggests a preset sequence. For example, you might select this sequence for a situation in which you know participants have strong feelings: blue, red for emotion, white for information, yellow for hope, green

for creativity, black for logic, and then back to blue. With this sequence, the red cap is used after the first use of the blue cap to quickly reveal initial feelings. In the preset mode, all caps do not have to be used. Even if you plan to use all caps, you may instead decide that one or more caps are not needed, based on impressions and information received while moving through the process.

4. **Begin to move through the caps:** Ask each person to put on the next cap. De Bono stresses the need for discipline in using the caps if the process is to be successful. He says: "Members of the group must stay with the [cap] that is indicated at the moment. . . . Only the group leader, chairperson, or facilitator can indicate a change of [caps]." The caps indicate the mode or direction of thinking, not what to think.

    Consider the value of this discipline admonition. When involved in a discussion, we tend to want to make a point, to further our agenda, or to get our way. To do this within 6TCM, we would need to try to dictate the cap to be used. By moving intentionally through a series of caps and focusing on the currently designated cap, each participant is more likely to think broadly, objectively, and maybe creatively and innovatively. Participants are urged by the various caps to stretch themselves—move out of their thinking comfort zone—for the good of the cause.

    The question of how much time to devote to each cap will inevitably arise. "It is much better to set a short time and extend it," according to de Bono, "rather than set a long time and have people sitting around and wondering what to say."

    Some more protocol suggestions:

    - Refer to the caps by their color, not their function. That is, say "let's put on the red cap"; don't say, "let's share our emotional reactions." As explained by de Bono, "If you ask someone to give his or her emotional reaction to something, you are unlikely to get an honest answer because people think it is wrong to be emotional. But the term red [cap] is neutral. Thinking becomes a game with defined rules rather than a matter of exhortation and condemnation." To stress de Bono's point about referring to caps by their color, not their function, do say, "that's enough yellow cap thinking; now let's put on our green caps." Don't say, "that's enough positive thinking; now let's get creative/innovative."

    - Don't use caps to categorize individuals. Why? Because the caps are intended to encourage the entire group, at any given time, to engage in one thinking-related function—that is, organization/control, information, emotion, logic, hope, or creativity/innovation. For example, we might be tempted to think to ourselves or to say, "Jane is a black cap; she's somber and serious. Jose is a green cap; he's creative." Avoid such characterizations. People are much too complex for such simple labels. Furthermore, as emphasized by de Bono, "The [caps] are not descriptions of people, but modes of behavior."

    - Avoid assigning caps to individuals. In our zeal to be effective and efficient, to have a successful meeting, we may be tempted to assign caps to individuals prior to the group meeting or discussion. For example, we'll ask one person to be the white cap thinker (to get the facts) and another to be the red cap thinker (to surface all the emotions). De Bono says you should not do this because it conflicts with the overriding intent of the 6TCM process, which is to have each person eventually wear each cap during the meeting or discussion. In de Bono's words, the point of the method is that "everyone can look in every direction" as a result of eventually wearing every cap during the discussion.

5. **Provide real-time documentation:** For each cap, you might use a whiteboard, one or more sheets of newsprint posted on the wall, or a projection on a screen or wall of text being typed as the discussion progresses. This approach will keep

results of 6TCM in front of everyone while emphasizing the transparency and inclusiveness of the process. Real time, readily viewed documentation engages both hemispheres and recognizes differences and ambiguities so that you and your group can ultimately resolve them.

6. **Conclude with the blue cap:** End the thinking process by returning to the blue cap. As suggested by de Bono, discuss topics such as "what we have achieved, outcome, conclusion, design, solution, and next steps."

Clearly, 6TCM provides a framework for an effective group discussion that, as noted by de Bono, "is much more effective than argument or free discussion." He goes on to say: "The [caps] may also be used by an individual thinking on his or her own. The sequenced framework reduces confusion and ensures that all aspects are fully covered."

7.7.7 Cap-Specific Advice

Let's drill down by considering additional ideas and tips for each of the six caps:

1. **Blue cap:** Like the blue sky above, the blue cap represents overview thinking or, as noted by de Bono, "thinking about thinking." At the beginning of a group discussion, the blue cap encourages the participants to define the IPO to be addressed, what is to be achieved, such as defining the IPO and then resolving it, and how the process will be documented. Cap changes are announced by the blue cap as the session proceeds. While the blue cap is worn most by the facilitator, chairperson, or leader, anyone can put it on, figuratively or literally. As the 6TCM session ends, the blue cap encourages summarizing what has been achieved, or not achieved, and what will be done next.

   In terms of a group or team process, the blue cap is not confined to 6TCM. Other tools (such as those discussed in this chapter and in Chapter 4) could be applied within the 6TCM process. "The blue hat thinker," said de Bono, "customizes the program to fit the situation."

2. **Red cap:** As already suggested, expressing emotions is often unfortunately taboo in business and professional discussions. "The [red cap] provides a unique and special opportunity for feelings, emotions, and intuition to be put forward as such," according to de Bono (1999). He believed that feelings are useful during a discussion and at its conclusion, as when determining how group members feel about the process and their decisions.

   Examples of feelings are confidence, concern, ambivalence, indecision, confusion, doubt, and fear. "There is no need to explain or justify the feelings," according to de Bono. He goes on to say, "If people think they have to validate their feelings, they will put forth only feelings that can be validated."

3. **White cap:** The white hat elicits information—that is, what facts and figures you have or need. "The information can range from hard facts and figures that can be checked, to soft information like opinions and feelings [of others]," according to de Bono.

   Do not offer data or information at a higher level than it actually is. To reinforce this idea, de Bono offers the following what he calls "spectrum of likelihood" descriptors: "Always true—usually true—generally true—by and large—more often than not—about half the time—other—sometimes true—occasionally true—been known to happen—never true—cannot be true (contradictory)."

4. **Yellow cap:** The yellow cap helps participants, according to de Bono, "find whatever benefit there may be in a suggestion." He notes that "People are

forced to solve problems but no one is forced to look for opportunities." Putting on the yellow cap means looking for opportunities and, according to de Bono, "permits visions and dreams"—which, I might add, forms the foundation for creativity and innovation and leads to the next cap.

5. **Green cap:** In describing the green cap, de Bono says, "Think of growth. Think of new leaves and branches. The green [cap] is the creative [cap]." He notes that creativity may be out of the blue or the result of deliberate effort, and states that creativity "involves provocation, exploration, and risk taking," which contrasts with our natural inclination to be secure and right in our thinking. Wearing the green cap gives thinkers "the time and focus"—and, I might add, permission—to be more creative and innovative. De Bono seems to be speaking directly to engineers when he says, "The search for alternatives is a fundamental aspect of green [cap] thinking. There is a need to go beyond the known and obvious and the satisfactory." In other words, avoid the Einstellung Effect trap (Section 3.4).

6. **Black cap:** "The black [cap] is the most used of all the [caps]," according to de Bono, who goes on to say: "The black [cap] is for being careful. The black [cap] stops us [from] doing things that are illegal, dangerous, unprofitable, polluting, and so on." He refers to the black [cap] as the [cap] of survival, the basis of critical thinking, and always logical. We should recognize, as noted by de Bono, that "it is much easier to be critical than to be constructive." Overuse of the black [cap] is not helpful; it can stifle creative and innovative thinking.

7.7.8 Key Points about the Six Thinking Caps Method

Consider the follow principal features of 6TCM:

- **Reduces confusion:** It offers a way to help a group reduce the confusion that occurs when, in the course of a discussion, essentially everyone must deal with six thinking-related functions: information, emotion, logic, hope, creativity/innovation, and organization/control. Claimed benefits include quicker and better decisions. As noted by de Bono, the 6TCM "is much more effective than arguments or free discussion."
- **Rationale:** Caps are used because of the strong association in many cultures between caps or hats and thinking. Six caps are used to correspond to the six thinking-related functions, and the colors are selected to represent the functions.
- **Protocol:** Cap protocol includes referring to caps by their colors, not their functions, and encouraging every person to wear a particular cap when it is designated. Individuals should not be characterized by one or more caps.
- **Process driven by blue:** Wearing the blue cap, a group's facilitator, chairperson, or leader orchestrates the meeting or session. This includes identifying and maybe defining the IPO to be addressed; explaining the expected outcome; announcing cap changes; applying various group processes; and, at the end of the session, summarizing what has been accomplished and is still to be done and making sure that it is documented.
- **Try it:** 6TCM provides a framework for an effective group discussion or individual effort. Therefore, as opportunities arise, consider using 6TCM in order to more fully utilize your group's collective knowledge, experience, and ideas and/or to guide your thinking.

7.7.9 Neuroscience Basis

Recall de Bono's comment, quoted earlier: "The main difficulty of thinking is confusion. We try to do too much at once. Information, emotion, logic, hope, and creativity all crowd in on us." Then, recall the importance of focusing and staying on task (see Section 3.5) if we want to be creative and innovative. By moving from cap to cap, 6TCM forces all members of a group to focus individually on de Bono's "information, emotion, logic, hope, and creativity," thus increasing the likelihood of a broad and deep understanding of a given IPO and a creative/innovative resolution.

7.7.10 Positive and Negative Features

The most positive feature of 6TCM is the use of highly visual colored caps to encourage participants to focus—to not try to do too much at once. On the negative side, the prospect of one or more team members having to put on different colored hats during the course of a serious group discussion may be a deterrent to some individuals. However, experience suggests that most individuals will quickly accept and participate in the process with the hope that it will provide creative/innovative insights.

7.8 SUPPORTIVE CULTURE AND PHYSICAL ENVIRONMENT

Study and work places have widely varying cultural and physical atmospheres when viewed initially by visitors and, more importantly for the purpose of this text, when experienced by students and employees who spend large fractions of their time there. More specifically, student and employee creativity and innovation are likely to be influenced by the physical and cultural settings in which those individuals study and work.

Recall the Section 3.2.2 introductory discussion of whole-brain methods. It noted that some methods, rather than being described as a process, are more of a way of thinking about an IPO, a manner used to approach a challenge, an attitude taken when faced with a complex situation, or an environment in which good things happen. *Supportive Culture and Physical Environment* is one such method. The cultural and physical characteristics of an academic, professional practice, or other organization can be enhanced or markedly changed to encourage creativity and innovation.

7.8.1 Culture and Its Influence

Culture, as used here, means the way things really work in an organization, especially when difficulties arise. As noted by Armstrong (2005), "culture wields great power over what people consider permissible and appropriate. . . . The embedded beliefs, values, and behavior patterns carry tremendous weight. The culture sends its energy into every corner of the organization, influencing virtually everything." Culture is the cumulative effect of an organization's mission and vision, ethical climate, expectations and support, kind of personnel hired and retained, education and training opportunities, and reward system. Effecting change in some cultures is extremely difficult, if not impossible.

7.8.2 Killing Creativity and Innovation

According to professor of business administration Amabile (2011), "When creativity [and/or innovation] is killed, an organization loses a potential competitive weapon: new ideas." After all, "in a world of forces that push toward the commoditization of everything," according to journalist Colvin (2008), "creating something new and different is the only way to survive." Given the pressures faced by engineering practitioners and the many benefits of creativity and innovation, who would obstruct creativity and innovation?

Although some insecure and paranoid individuals will intentionally kill creativity and innovation, most of us would not intentionally frustrate it. However, many acting individually or collectively unintentionally do so. Whether intentional or unintentional, the result is the same: creativity/innovation and all the good it represents dies or is dying. As suggested by Figure 7.13, some organizational cultures

Figure 7.13
Some organizational cultures, intentionally or unintentionally, practice *ideacide* in that creative or innovative ideas are frequently smashed.

(Constantinos/Fotolia)

practice *ideacide* (May 2010), as in germicide, homicide, and herbicide, in that when someone sees the light and offers a creative or innovative idea, it is smashed.

Consider the following dozen ways to frustrate or kill creativity and innovation (Amabile 2011; May 2010; Moon 2014). Think of these as positions taken or attitudes exhibited by people who, as professor of business administration Moon says, "want nothing to do with disruptive change, pie-in-the-sky innovation, or crazy flights of imagination."

1. Let's not stick our necks out or rock the boat. Instead, like cautious turtles, let's pull our necks in or like careful captains, remain in the protected harbor.
2. We know our limitations and know that the unusual idea being suggested is outside of our capabilities. Let's be consistent with our organization's cautious and careful reputation.
3. Before adding more stress, remember that this is just a job. We get paid for doing that job well and not for generating new, potentially disruptive concepts and ideas. Our plates are full!
4. Been there, tried that, and it will never work. We've learned the value of skepticism, and this is another situation in which it should be our guide.
5. Enough of that conceptual, theoretical, pie-in-the-sky, and touchy-feely stuff. This is the real world: Show me the numbers that guarantee your approach will work.
6. Instead of trying to create the future, let's study and then project the past, because that's where we find wisdom and lessons. If we continue to do what we did, we will be successful.
7. Here we go again; this is as foolish as your last big idea. Stop pursuing risky schemes and get back to bill-paying work.
8. No more daydreaming and wishful thinking—instead focus on what we are doing well. That 3-D printing thing is just another fad.
9. You're missing the point and exaggerating the severity of our situation; this is just a short-term dip in the economy. If we all work a little harder, we will get through this.
10. Our clients are not asking for that service, so let's not waste resources to develop it. Our clients know more about the future than we do, and we are client oriented.

11. Let's appreciate humor, but be wary of artsy, creative, free-spirited types. They like to play around and don't understand the work world.

12. What can a new graduate possibly know about our organization? Tell new hires to do as they are told until they understand our operations.

Consider items 6 through 10 in the preceding list, which may be summarized as *everything is fine; this situation will blow over.* In her article titled "Why Companies Fail," columnist McArdle (2012) writes that within many companies, in spite of ominous signs, "Management and workers seem oblivious to their failures. They wait too long before they act . . . even when they do take action, it's often inadequate."

McArdle goes on to note, as elaborated on in Section 5.5.1, that dysfunctional corporate cultures are very efficient at reproducing themselves. Continuing this theme, Kaplan (2011), a consultant, claims that many companies resist changing their mode of operation because the leaders like the current one, and those leaders "want everyone in the organization focused on how to improve its performance."

There seems to be no end to finding ways to if not kill, at least frustrate creativity and innovation and also quickly discredit new concepts and ideas. For example, mechanical and industrial engineer and professor Dhillon (2006) lists the following ways: too academic, against company policy, would need to form a committee, against organizational policy, outside our job description, we are too big, we are too small, not our problem, and may not please our clients/customers.

What happens in the absence of creativity/innovation? Disaster. Examples of organizations that seem to have suffered from lack of creativity and innovation, some of which were previously noted in Section 5.5.1, include Blockbuster, Borders, HP, Kodak (Ante 2012), and various engineering firms, manufacturing companies, university engineering departments, government units, and other entities that are no longer with us or are barely surviving.

7.8.3 Benefits of a Supportive Culture and Physical Environment

On a more positive note, thriving organization-wide creativity and innovation stimulated by a Supportive Culture and Physical Environment yield many benefits for business, government, academic, and other entities. Some examples, drawn from a long list in Table 5.1 (Section 5.1.1) include the following:

- Improved personal/organizational productivity
- Less waste
- New tools/applications
- New services
- Reduced manufacturing, construction, and public works capital and operation and maintenance costs
- Improved public safety, health, and welfare
- Quicker response
- New clients, customers, and stakeholders
- Greater profitability
- Growth and the opportunities it offers
- Reinvigorated staff
- Strengthened reputation
- Enhanced recruitment and retention
- Conquered commoditization
- Less threatened/actual litigation and reduced claim costs
- More awards and other recognition for outstanding projects

Are you and your student or employer organization missing out on these benefits or, more broadly, these kinds of benefits? If so, take a look at your culture and physical environment.

PERSONAL: YOUR SPACE SPEAKS TO YOU AND OTHERS

Blindfold me, walk me into an office building, put me in an elevator, and send me to any floor. As the elevator rises, all you've told me is that the building houses government, architectural, engineering, and law offices on various floors. The elevator door opens on any floor; I step out and take off my blindfold. With a high degree of probability, I will immediately be able to determine where I am. That is, I'm at the entrance to a government agency, an architectural firm, an engineering firm, or a law firm.

I will know where I am not by reading signs, but by the ambience. Typically, an architectural office will proudly display photos, models, videos, and other images of its projects. Conservative order will usually characterize government offices and engineering firms, whereas law firms will exude sophistication often augmented with opulence.

Almost every one of us forms an initial impression of an organization as soon as we see their facilities. More importantly, our student or work performance, including the extent to which we are creative and innovative, is likely to be influenced by our physical surroundings. As visitors or employees, we are also notably impacted by the organizational culture.

7.8.4 Impact of Physical Environment

What constitutes a stimulating physical environment? Although highly subjective, let's consider some possibilities by focusing on the physical environment and starting with academia. Arciszewski (2009), a former engineering professor, offers numerous ideas for establishing a creative physical environment for a successful department within a university in his book *Successful Education: How to Educate Creative Engineers*. His goal is "to present an ideal picture of academic facilities from the perspective of successful education." Examples of his ideas include the following:

- A defined and inviting interior or exterior open space, similar to the agoras or marketplaces in Greek towns, which would serve as a venue for various student, faculty, and visitor interactions.
- Engineering studios whose functions go beyond, but which are located near, workshops with various tools and more traditional laboratories with diverse testing equipment. The studios would "encourage the use of the workshops and building models in the process of problem-solving."
- Professional displays, such as photos of successful graduates and highly accomplished professionals, images of engineering projects, models used in research, and awards received by students and faculty.
- Visual art, such as paintings, pencil drawings, sculpture, and murals.
- Touches of nature, including plants, roof gardens, and aquariums.
- Special places for important events, such as lectures, social events, and award ceremonies.
- Music, such as sounds of nature or classical, distributed through multiple speakers.

Arciszewski offers ideas for enhancing creativity and innovation in an engineering academic setting, but in my view essentially all of his suggestions are equally applicable to an engineering practice setting. Visual aspects of the physical environment, which are prominent in Arciszewski's list, are especially important relative to stimulants for the other senses (Section 2.4), regardless of the type or functions of an organization. "Vision trumps all other senses," and this sense takes up "half of our brain's resources," according to biologist and brain expert Medina (2008).

Innovation expert Kao (2007) stressed the importance of the physical environment by writing, "If [the United States] is to reinvent its innovation capabilities for a new era, we are going to have to rethink and redesign our innovation environments." He goes on to offer diverse ideas that view "our physical spaces as media through which our people can collaborate and learn." Some examples:

- "A flat management structure composed of constantly shifting work groups"
- Informal spaces for conversations, meetings, and refreshments
- A skunk works—a place provided with tools and materials where individuals and teams can build and test prototypes of their ideas
- Setting work stations, other office elements, and laboratory and test equipment on wheels so that personnel can "move their work spaces around in response to the collaborative needs of the moment"
- Huge, wall-sized whiteboards to encourage communication and sharing of results

Perhaps some of the preceding ideas appear different, if not strange. However, as Kao says, organization leaders typically "have no idea how asphyxiating . . . work places can be."

Academic Davenport (2005) argues that special effort is needed to work effectively with knowledge workers. In assessing his ideas, we need to recognize that knowledge workers are not necessarily creative or innovative, and he is not necessarily offering suggestions to encourage creativity and innovation. Davenport concludes that knowledge workers prefer closed offices; like to move around in the course of their work, within their building and traveling; want to both collaborate and concentrate; would rather work in the office—that is, are not into lots of telecommuting; and enjoy communicating with people who are close by. They don't care about facilities he calls *gewgaws*, such as ping-pong tables, office concierges, and conversation pits.

Perhaps some aspects of the physical environment suggested by these preferences of knowledge workers also reflect conditions that stimulate creativity and innovation. Consistent with Davenport's conclusions, two psychology researchers (Haslam and Knight 2010) found that workers are most happy and productive when they control the layout and style of their immediate workspace in contrast with the arrangements and décor being dictated by others.

7.8.5 Examples of Mixing Up the Personnel

As another example of the impact of our physical environment, I and my engineering firm colleagues once had an opportunity to design from scratch how we would use an entire floor in a relatively new office building. Our initial thought was to follow the same logical layout we were used to and that is commonly used—that is, group people with similar functions together: engineers with engineers, administrators with administrators, and so on, as illustrated schematically in the upper part of Figure 7.14.

Figure 7.14
An office arranged heterogeneously with respect to personnel functions provides improved opportunities for staff members to learn more about each other, including expertise.

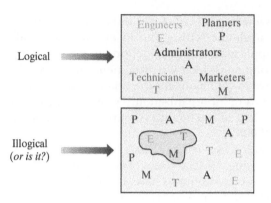

However, we did not pursue our initial impulse. Instead, we innovated. We decided to mix everyone up; this arrangement, heterogeneous with respect to function, would enhance communication and collaboration relative to our traditional homogeneous arrangement. Each of us would have improved opportunities to learn about others and their work and to more fully appreciate the organization's diversity of functions, expertise, projects, and clients/owners. Office conversations would be richer and more varied as a result of the new physical environment and personnel would have more data, information, and knowledge to draw on when addressing issues, solving problems, and/or pursuing opportunities—and it worked.

For example, refer to the circled letters E, T, and M in Figure 7.14. As an engineer (E), I was assigned an office with a technician (T) on one side and a marketing person (M) on the other side. As a result, I talked frequently with each of them, gaining more appreciation for the creative, innovative, and sophisticated field work done by our firm's technicians, and I also received the equivalent of a short course in marketing.

When he led Pixar Animation Studios, Jobs was heavily involved in the design of the company's new office building on a sixteen-acre site between Berkeley and Oakland, California, because he believed that the building could "do great things for a culture." The result was "one huge building around a central atrium designed to encourage random encounters." Jobs believed strongly in face-to-face meetings. "Creativity comes from spontaneous meetings, from random discussions. You run into someone, you ask what they're doing, you say 'Wow,'" according to Jobs, "and soon you're cooking up all sorts of ideas."

The new Pixar building encouraged personnel interaction by forcing people to get out of their offices and go to the central atrium. The building's front doors, main stairs, and corridors all pointed to the atrium. A theater, screening rooms, and windowed conference rooms all opened to the atrium. Finally, all of the buildings bathrooms were accessed through the atrium (Isaacson 2011).

In the middle of the night, a malfunctioning sprinkler flooded the San Francisco, California, offices of Ken Kay Associates, a planning, urban design, and landscape architecture firm. They moved out for one month, gutted the interior, and converted what was one studio with many cubicles into a more open plan that is in effect one large studio. According to office manager Kay (2014), "The effect of this structural change has been nothing short of amazing. . . . Interaction and collaboration happen more organically and more frequently. We strongly believe that this has led to more creativity and innovation with our staff and within our projects." Perhaps your organization can benefit from this firm's disaster-becomes-opportunity experience.

7.8.6 Three Elements of a Supportive Culture

As illustrated in Figure 7.15, a creative/innovative organizational culture results from the intersection of three elements (Amabile 2011; Pink 2009; Walesh 2012b):

- **Varied expertise:** This is the hard-earned, valuable, and largely technical knowledge and skills typically present in engineering and other technically oriented organizations, whether they be private, public, academic, or volunteer entities. Because of this expertise foundation, these organizations have the potential to proactively, creatively, and innovatively address issues, solve problems, and pursue opportunities.

- **Motivation:** The two motivation types are extrinsic and intrinsic, with the former being "carrot" or "stick" external influences, originating mostly with employers, and the latter being each individual's passionate desire to make significant, useful, and often creative/innovative contributions. Extrinsic motivation can improve to a point the productivity of knowledge work, also called algorithmic work, which is defined in Section 1.4.2 as that which can be "reduced to a set of rules, routines, and instructions," the functions of the left brain.

  However, intrinsic motivation is the principal driver of creative/innovative work. Employers can't pour intrinsic motivation into personnel; they have to hire already-motivated personnel. One reason carrots and sticks fail to stimulate creativity and innovation is that they usually have strings attached that greatly narrow the focus of individuals and teams.

- **Whole-brain tools:** These are methods (as discussed in Chapter 4 and this chapter) applied with knowledge of brain basics. They enable individuals and teams to supplement their already strong left-brain capabilities with powerful but different right-brain capabilities, resulting in a whole-brain approach to resolving IPOs. Creative/innovative thinking tools seek to use all the available mental muscles.

The creative/innovative organizational culture created by the intersection of the preceding three elements is likely to generate benefits like and beyond those listed in Section 7.8.3.

7.8.7 The Employer Gathers the Cast and Sets the Stage

Clearly, those who lead and manage organizations can influence the three elements shown in Figure 7.15 that are likely to result in a culture supportive of creativity and innovation. An organization's *expertise*—its breadth and depth—reflects recruiting and retention philosophy, policies, and procedures. For *motivation*, the intrinsic type is a function of the kind of individuals brought into the organization, whereas extrinsic motivation is determined largely by organizational policies and procedures.

Figure 7.15
The intersection of three elements can result in a creative and innovative organizational culture.

Source: Adapted from Amabile 2011 and Walesh 2012b.

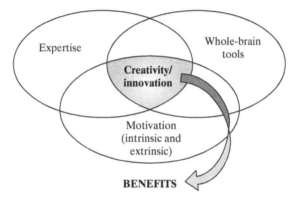

The availability of *whole-brain tools* is determined largely by the employer because such methods, and the foundational brain basics to use them, are typically not included in the formal education of engineers, scientists, and similar professionals. Fortunately, many whole-brain methods are available, and they can be easily taught to, learned by, and then applied by technical professionals, as illustrated by this text.

7.8.8 Suggested Leadership and Management Practices

Assume a business, government, academic, volunteer, or other entity has assembled a great cast. Consider a baker's dozen leadership and managerial practices that can then be used to enable those personnel to perform brilliantly, including creatively and innovatively (based in part on Dyer and Gregersen 2013 and Amabile 2011). I am not suggesting that your student- and work-related organizations do all of these. Instead, think of the list of leadership and management practices as a smorgasbord of ideas that you could choose from or which might stimulate other approaches. Use the list to stimulate discovery of other ideas. The thirteen possible practices are as follows:

1. *Expect creativity and innovation*, especially from the top of the organization, and practice creativity and innovation at the top. This will be difficult in an organization that has not been receptive to creative and innovative efforts. Management guru Drucker (1985) wrote, "Innovation must be part and parcel of the ordinary, the norm, if not the routine." He also stated, "When innovation is perceived as something that goes against the grain, as swimming against the current . . . there will be no innovation."

2. *Conduct education and training* to provide whole-brain tools and underlying brain basics. Help individuals learn more about their most marvelous resource—their brains—and provide tools to help them make better use of it. Education and training can include many elements, such as workshops; access to a library of books and articles; interaction with highly creative/innovative individuals; sharing information about creative/innovative efforts within and outside of the organization; posting IPOs on an internal website and inviting ideas; and supportive actions by organizational leaders. During creativity and innovation education and training events, don't work on hypothetical IPOs; work on actual, high-priority IPOs.

   As an example of broadly interpreting education and training, consider the learning and interaction practice of Ken Kay Associates. A couple of times a year, they invite presenters to speak at their office to a group ranging from thirty-five to 150 people. Some of the presenters are connected to planning, urban design, and landscape architecture, but others are artists, developers, and city officials. The eclectic group provides different perspectives on projects and topics. Often, a problem or obstacle shared during a presentation results in fruitful dialogue within the diverse group and leads to a solution (Kay 2014).

3. Facilitate *Challenges and Ideas Meetings* and acquire *Keystone Habits* (see Section 7.3) when gathering as project teams, departments, disciplines, and for other purposes.

4. *Establish a stimulating physical environment*, as described in Sections 7.8.4 and 7.8.5, including arranging it heterogeneously with respect to the functions of personnel to provide improved opportunities for them to learn about each other and about their expertise.

5. *Ask potential employees*, or potential members of any group committed to creativity and innovation, what they have created, innovated, invented, changed, or

developed. Their response does not have to be some extraordinary product or process, but should suggest that they have a strong inclination to be dissatisfied with the status quo, to seek much better ways of doing things, to think differently, to connect concepts and ideas from widely varying sources, and to proactively and persistently follow through.

6. *Rotate personnel*, at least temporarily, to new functional areas and/or locations.

7. *Challenge individuals and teams* by giving them major issues to resolve, problems to solve, or promising opportunities to exploit, and then get out of the way and let them synergistically tackle the IPOs.

8. *Offer as much autonomy as possible* concerning the means used to address IPOs. In his book, *Drive*, Pink (2009) says that what many of us really want is more latitude to choose what we do or work on, when we do it, how we do it, and who we do it with. That's a big order; however, managers and supervisors can use knowledge of a person's preferences to satisfy some of them. Autonomy can bring individual passion into play. French military theorist Foch said, "The most powerful weapon on earth is the human soul on fire." According to Linkner (2011), an entrepreneur, "With a team full of passion, you can accomplish just about anything. Without it, your employees become mere clock-punching automatons."

9. *Provide adequate resources*, mainly time and money, and establish accountability short of requiring success. Some organizations provide employees with on-the-job time to do whatever they want (Pink 2009). For example, 3M offers many employees 15 percent, Google 20 percent, and Atlassian (an Australian software company) 20 percent. Google claims that the free time generates half of its new ideas.

   I'm not necessarily sold on this free time idea. It seems simplistic and wishful thinking. Sure, some free time for some personnel might be one part of a creativity/innovation culture and program, but it cannot be the program. To be effective, a free time tactic should be preceded by education and training and supported by a system of team formation and support and a means to assess, select, and implement creative/innovative ideas (Heller 2012).

   Resources also mean money. As an example, consider the Memorial Hospital at South Bend, Indiana, which has a comprehensive creativity/innovation program. This is the first US community hospital to have an "innovation research and development budget." It budgets 1 percent of annual revenue, or about $4 million per year. Over a series of several years, "the increase in related operating profit was as much as three times the annual expenditure." The annual expenditure never approached $4 million (Lublin 2008).

10. *Implement a patent policy* that encourages creativity and innovation while striking a balance between personnel recognition and organizational needs. For example, provide monetary compensation to individuals or teams that produce patentable results, or let them own the patent. The latter option might be more appropriate when an organization cannot exploit the creative/innovative outcome (Farid, El-Sharkawy, and Austin 1993). Consider formulating copyright and trademark policies.

11. *Establish a separate group* reporting to a senior-level executive. If your organization decides to form a creative/innovative team, maybe as an experiment, have the team report to a senior-level champion authorized to make major decisions. *Reason:* "The quickest route to failure is slow decision making" (Shapiro 2014). Try to protect the team or group from possible organizational "dysfunction and sluggishness." The team or group could develop an idea database so that "no idea is lost, belittled, or ignored." If an idea doesn't meet a current need, it

might meet a future need. Management should support the team and expect it to perform. The group will grow naturally (Cernasov and Venkatraman 2012).

12. *Celebrate* in-process successes and *tolerate* setbacks.

13. *Walk the talk.* Many of the very busy individuals in your organization are wary of the next hot movement foisted on them by executives and managers who may soon move off to some other popular topic. They are reluctant to invest time and energy in case this is another flash in the pan. They will need to be convinced by the actions of top executives and their lieutenants—which takes us back to the first practice in this list.

Assume that an organization commits to the three element model, gathers a cast, provides motivation, offers education and training, and takes other actions, like some of the thirteen leadership and management practices just listed. Then, because of a supportive culture, the cast will perform creatively and innovatively to the benefit of individual performers, the organization, and those individuals and entities it serves.

7.8.9 Many Organizations Will Resist

For many reasons, such as the seven described in Chapter 5, a large fraction of organizations will not embrace a culture and physical environment supportive of creativity and innovation. The possibility of realizing benefits like those listed in Section 7.8.3 will not sway them. Accidental creativity and innovation, as discussed in Section 3.2.1, will occasionally happen and be appreciated, but the organization's creative/innovative potential will not be realized, to the detriment of personnel, the organization, and those they serve.

However, you and possibly your group, beginning as a student and in student organizations, can at least experiment with creativity/innovation initiatives, even if your organization is not yet supportive. Given the smart people you associate with, you never know what you all might come up with! Creativity and innovation reside within essentially all of us, but we need catalysts to release it. You and your organization can catalyze using principles, information, and tools presented in this book. The knowledge and experience you and others acquire can then be carried into your professional practice.

As individuals, teams, and organizations, we cannot continue to do what we did and expect continued success, to thrive, or even just survive. Fine-tuning or continuously improving principles, policies, processes, and procedures may be the prudent course, but sometimes we need to do much more. As noted by engineer, inventor, and entrepreneur Bonasso (2007), "It is one of life's truths that you can't keep doing the same thing over and over—behaving, functioning, and thinking in the same way—and expect things to really change or be different." British author and statesman Bacon offered this dire warning to those who want to stick with the status quo: "Things alter for the worst spontaneously, if they be not altered for the better." In other words, if we don't effect change, sometimes major, in our increasingly dynamic and globalized world, this thing—this business, this government operation, this university department, this professional society—may blow up in our faces!

7.8.10 Neuroscience Basis

As suggested by my *put me on an elevator* personal view near the beginning of this section, and as evidenced by the discussion itself, our conscious and subconscious minds are likely to quickly detect and be profoundly influenced by our physical surroundings and their connected organizational culture. More specifically, as explained in Section 2.9, our subconscious mind draws on information from our memory and senses and goes to work, without our awareness. Accordingly, if your or my subconscious mind believes by what it sees and hears and senses in the academic or work environment that creativity and innovation are expected, then it will strive to be creative and innovative. The opposite is also likely to be true.

7.8.11 Positive and Negative Features

A negative aspect of establishing a physically and culturally stimulating environment is the major effort and expense required to develop one where it does not exist. For example, how do you or I convince people to fix something if they don't see it as broken? Recall Kao's comment that some organizational leaders "have no idea how asphyxiating . . . work places can be"; this is especially true for their own workplaces, in which they have invested time and treasure in good faith. On the positive side, smaller organizations or small parts of big organizations are more likely to affect physical and cultural changes that stimulate working smarter and being more creative and innovative. Even more positively, some of the most creative and innovative entities attribute their success to their physical and cultural environment.

7.9 THEORY OF INVENTIVE PROBLEM SOLVING (TRIZ)

TRIZ is different from most of the other tools in this book because it is intended primarily for technical IPOs, not nontechnical challenges. *TRIZ* (*Theory of Inventive Problem Solving* in Russian) has a long and successful history (over sixty years) around the globe and therefore warrants treatment in this chapter.

7.9.1 Have Others Faced This Challenge?

When trying to solve a technical problem, have you ever thought that maybe someone else faced this problem, or one like it, and solved it? TRIZ is a tool that recognizes that your problem is unique, but also recognizes that it's probably similar in some important ways to previously solved problems. TRIZ enables you to benefit from those problems and rely less on inefficient trial and error or accidental creativity, as discussed in Section 3.2.1.

HISTORIC NOTE: FINDING PATTERNS IN PATENTS

TRIZ was developed in the former USSR between 1946 and 1985 under the leadership of mechanical engineer, scientist, and author Altshuller (1996). The four letters, pronounced *trees*, are an acronym in the Russian language for *Theory of Inventive Problem Solving*. The method is described "as an international science of creativity that relies on the study of patterns of problems and solutions, not on the spontaneous and intuitive creativity of individuals or groups. More than three million patents have been analyzed to discover patterns that predict breakthrough solutions to problems" (Barry, Domb, and Slocum 2014).

The possible excessive left-brain orientation suggested by the last part of the quote in the Historic Note—the antispontaneous and antiintuitive part—to the possible exclusion of the right brain may concern you. On the surface, it may suggest that TRIZ views creativity and innovation as a rigid, left-brain process.

However, as this book has repeatedly, explicitly, and implicitly indicated, *aha!* moments, as surprising and exhilarating as they may be, are almost always preceded by major efforts, and those efforts are more likely to be successful if they employ some whole-brain processes, such as the tools described in this chapter and in Chapter 4. "It is difficult to invent without having knowledge of inventive methods," according to Altshuller (1996). TRIZ is in effect a whole-brain tool, and accordingly is discussed here for your possible use. Furthermore, as noted by TRIZ expert Mazur (2014b), this method is very likely to lead you to ideas outside of your area of expertise.

The three primary findings of over sixty years of TRIZ use and research are as follows (Barry, Domb, and Slocum 2014):

- "Problems and solutions are repeated across industries and sciences. The classification of the contradictions in each problem predicts the creative solutions to that problem." We may think that our disciplines or specialties have unique problems and solutions, but TRIZ advocates say that our disciplines and/or specialties have much in common with others.
- "Patterns of technical evolution are repeated across industries and sciences." For example, a technology like 3-D printing that is evolving within engineering is also occurring elsewhere, and we can learn from those nonengineering applications.
- "Creative innovations use scientific effects outside the field where they were developed." Under TRIZ, the innovations we need in our discipline or specialty come at least partly from outside our disciplines or specialties.

7.9.2 The TRIZ Process: Conceptual

Barry, Domb, and Slocum (2014) sum up their view of sixty-plus years of TRIZ by saying: "Much of the practice of TRIZ consists of learning these repeating patterns of problems-solutions, patterns of technical evolution, and methods of using scientific effects, and then applying the general TRIZ patterns to the specific situation that confronts the developer." The process they describe, beginning with "our problem," is illustrated in Figure 7.16.

7.9.3 The TRIZ Process: Four Steps

More specifically, application of the TRIZ process to a particular technical IPO may be viewed as consisting of four steps. Each step is discussed in general terms and illustrated with examples.

Step 1: Define the technical IPO. Nothing new here for the conscientious engineer. As noted repeatedly in this book, a problem well-defined is half-solved. As suggested by Domb (1997), the definition of the technical challenge can be aided with Kipling's six (as introduced in Section 4.2.3)—that is:
- *Who* has the IPO?
- *What* does the IPO appear to be?

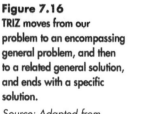

Figure 7.16
TRIZ moves from our problem to an encompassing general problem, and then to a related general solution, and ends with a specific solution.

Source: Adapted from Barry, Domb, and Slocum 2014 and Mazur 2014b.

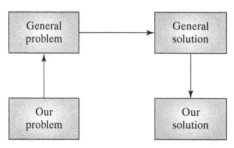

- *When* does the IPO occur—for example, all the time and/or under certain conditions?
- *Where* does the IPO occur?
- *Why* does the IPO occur?
- *How* does the IPO occur?

Step 2: State the technical IPO in terms of contradictions. Improving one feature could cause another feature to worsen. Contradictions are inevitable because "engineers must continue to pursue greater benefits and reduce cost of labor, materials, energy, and harmful side effects" (Mazur 2014b).

"An example of a technical contradiction in civil engineering would be the design of a reinforced concrete beam under bending. In this example, the technical contradiction is obviously rigidity versus weight" (Arciszewski 2009). In automobile design, mechanical engineers are challenged to reduce vehicle weight while not compromising crash resistance. Fogler, LeBlanc, and Rizzo (2014) provide additional examples of the inevitable contradictions we encounter, such as the following:

- Vehicle air bags should activate quickly to protect passengers, but as a result they could harm small, out-of-position individuals.
- A university administration wants to increase wireless Internet access on the campus but not compromise personal information.
- A security devices manufacturer wants to make even better bulletproof vests without adding bulk and weight.

By studying 1,500,000 worldwide patents, Altshuller and others found thirty-nine standard technical characteristics that can cause contradictions. According to Altshuller and others, these characteristics, which are listed in Table 7.2, are common in technical situations, where they appear as desired benefits or unwanted side effects (Mazur 2014b).

Table 7.2 These thirty-nine technical characteristics can cause contradictions.

1. Weight of moving object	14. Strength	27. Reliability
2. Weight of stationary object	15. Durability of moving object	28. Measurement accuracy
3. Length of moving object	16. Durability of nonmoving object	29. Manufacturing precision
4. Length of stationary object	17. Temperature	30. Object-affected harmful (Harmful factors acting on object)
5. Area of moving object	18. Illumination intensity (Brightness)	31. Object-generated harmful (Harmful side effects)
6. Area of stationary object	19. Use of energy by moving object	32. Ease of manufacture
7. Volume of moving object	20. Use of energy by stationary object	33. Ease of operation
8. Volume of stationary object	21. Power	34. Ease of repair
9. Speed of object	22. Loss of energy	35. Adaptability or versatility
10. Force (Intensity)	23. Loss of substance	36. Device complexity
11. Stress or pressure	24. Loss of information	37. Difficulty of detecting (Complexity of control)
12. Shape	25. Loss of time	38. Extent of automation
13. Stability of the object	26. Quantity of substance	39. Productivity

Source: Fogler, LeBlanc, and Rizzo 2014 supplemented with items in parentheses from Mazur 2014b.

For example, you want to increase the length of a bridge that is under design (4: length of stationary object), but this could increase stress (11: stress or pressure). Or, using the previously mentioned design of an automobile, you want to reduce the weight (1: weight of moving object) while not compromising crash resistance (14: strength).

Continuing with TRIZ Step 2, identify as many contradictions as possible, noting their numbers. In searching for conflicting technical characteristics, interpret them broadly. For example, length can refer to various linear dimensions, such as length, width, height, depth, and diameter (Mazur 2014b).

Step 3: Search the relevant inventive principles for potentially applicable principles. In addition to identifying the thirty-nine technical characteristics that commonly contradict each other (Table 7.2), Altshuller and others, as a result of years of patent studies, identified the forty inventive principles listed in Table 7.3. Mazur (2014b) calls these "hints that will help an engineer find a highly inventive (and patentable) solution to the problem." TRIZ's inventive principles are conceptually similar to a more recently developed tool called 77 Cards: Design Heuristics for Inspiring Ideas (Daly et al. 2012; Seifert 2012).

The table names the inventive principles but does not explain or illustrate them; for that, see Mazur (2014b). My hope is that by listing the names, some of which are intriguing, you may be prompted to go to the sources. As a further move in that direction and in order to suggest the richness of ideas included in the inventive principles, let's explore the explanations of some of them, quoting

Table 7.3 These forty inventive principles offer hints for resolving contradictions.

1. Segmentation	21. Skipping (Rushing through)
2. Taking out (Extraction)	22. "Blessing in disguise" (Covert harm into benefit)
3. Local quality	23. Feedback
4. Asymmetry	24. "Intermediary" (Mediator)
5. Merging (Combining)	25. Self-service
6. Universality	26. Copying
7. "Nested doll" (Nesting)	27. Cheap short-living (Inexpensive short-lived for an expensive, durable one)
8. Anti-weight (Counterweight)	28. Mechanics substitution (Replacement of a mechanical system)
9. Preliminary anti-action (Prior counter-action)	29. Pneumatics and hydraulics
10. Preliminary action (Prior action)	30. Flexible shells and thin films
11. Beforehand cushioning	31. Porous materials
12. Equipotentiality	32. Color changes
13. The other way around (Inversion)	33. Homogeneity
14. Spheroidality	34. Discarding and recovering (Rejecting and regenerating parts)
15. Dynamics	35. Parameter changes (Transform physical and chemical states)
16. Partial or excessive actions	36. Phase transitions (Phase transformation)
17. Another dimension	37. Thermal expansion
18. Mechanical vibration	38. Strong oxidants
19. Periodic action	39. Inert atmosphere
20. Continuity of useful action	40. Composite material films

Source: Fogler, LeBlanc, and Rizzo 2014 supplemented with items in parentheses from Mazur 2014b.

from Mazur (2014b). While this exploration will help you further understand TRIZ, it is also valuable apart from TRIZ. That is, the list of forty inventive principles provides a wealth of ideas for your possible use when taking on technical challenges, regardless of the whole-brain tools being used. The following are four inventive principle examples:

- **Asymmetry (4):** "Replace a symmetrical form with an asymmetrical form," such as making "one side of a tire stronger than the other to withstand impact with the curb."
- **Anti-weight (8):** "Compensate for the object's weight by joining with another object that has a lifting force." For example, put airfoils and ground effects on race cars to increase the downforce—that is, the contact between the tires and the track.
- **Color changes (32):** "Change the color of an object or its surrounding." One example is "a transparent bandage enabling a wound to be inspected without removing the dressing."
- **Composite material films (40):** "Replace a homogeneous material with a composite one," such as when military aircraft wings are made of plastic and carbon fiber composites to provide high strength and low weight.

Altshuller keyed pairs of technical characteristic contradictions to inventive principles. That is, he found through his patent studies that each contradiction pair occurred often, and as a result certain inventive principles were frequently used to maximize the benefit and minimize the unwanted effect (Mazur 2014b). Using a matrix format, Figure 7.17 shows the connection between contradiction pairs (columns and rows) and inventive principles (interior of the matrix). Only a portion of the matrix is shown in Figure 7.17 for illustration purposes; see Mazur (2014a) for the entire matrix.

Recall one of our examples, stated in Step 2, to increase the length of a bridge that is under design (4: length of stationary object), but this could

	Undesired technical characteristic →	1	2	3	4	5	6	7	8	9	10	11
Technical characteristic to improve ↓		Weight of moving object	Weight of stationary object	Length of moving object	Length of stationary object	Area of moving object	Area of stationary object	Volume of moving object	Volume of stationary object	Speed of object	Force (intensity)	Stress or pressure
1	Weight of moving object			15, 8, 29, 34		29, 17, 38, 34		29, 2, 40, 28		2, 8, 15, 38	8, 10, 18, 37	10, 36, 37, 40
2	Weight of stationary object				10, 1, 29, 35		35, 30, 13, 2		5, 35, 14, 2		8, 10, 19, 35	13, 29, 10, 18
3	Length of moving object	8, 15, 29, 34				15, 17, 4		7, 17, 4, 35		13, 4, 8	17, 10, 4	1, 8, 35
4	Length of stationary object		35, 28, 40 ,29				17, 7, 10, 40		35, 8, 2, 14		28, 10	1, 14, 35

Note: This is a portion of the matrix for illustration purposes. The total matrix has thirty-nine numbered rows and thirty-nine numbered columns.

Numbers in the body of the matrix refer to the forty inventive principles, which provide hints on how to resolve the contradictions.

Figure 7.17
This matrix keys contradiction pairs to inventive principles.
Source: Adapted from LeBlanc, and Rizzo 2014; Mazur 2012a.

increase stress (11: stress or pressure). When we enter the Characteristic 4/Characteristic 11 contradiction into the contradictions matrix, we are led to these three inventive principles:

- Inventive Principle 1: Segmentation
    a. Divide an object into independent parts.
    b. Make an object sectional.
    c. Increase the degree of an object's segmentation.
- Inventive Principle 14: Spheroidality
    a. Replace linear parts or flat surfaces with curved ones; replace cubical shapes with spherical shapes.
    b. Use rollers, balls, spirals.
    c. Replace a linear motion with rotating movement; utilize a centrifugal force.
- Inventive Principle 35: Parameter changes
    a. Change an object's aggregate state, density distribution, degree of flexibility, or temperature.

Take a moment to recognize what this means. Based on over seventy years of TRIZ development, when engineers and others have been challenged by a Characteristic 4/Characteristic 11 contradiction, they have usually successfully resolved the contradiction via one or more of the three principles just listed. For our bridge example, we might consider multiple spans based on Principle 1 ideas, introduce arches drawing on Principle 14 ideas, and/or use different materials because of Principle 35 suggestions.

Finally, briefly consider the second example mentioned in Step 2—namely, reducing the weight of an automobile (1: weight of moving object) while not compromising its crash resistance (14: strength). Entering the Characteristic 1/Characteristic 14 contradictions into the contradictions matrix (not shown in Figure 7.17) leads us to four inventive principles. They are 1, segmentation; 8, anti-weight; 15, dynamics; and 40, composite material films. Looking at the hints provided by the descriptions of and the examples provided for these inventive principles, I concluded that the most promising way to reduce the weight of the automobile while not compromising its crash performance is to do one or more of the following:

- Design the car in sections that break apart during a crash in a predictable manner to protect passengers
- Enhance energy-absorption aspects of automobile parts interaction during a crash
- Use composite materials that offer high strength and low weight

Step 4: Select a solution. This step, like Step 1, is not new; it is what engineers often do. However, positive and thorough application of TRIZ Steps 1, 2, and 3 will probably provide an unusual number and variety of potential solutions because this tool automatically leverages our thinking and that of our colleagues who have other areas of expertise.

Fogler, LeBlanc, and Rizzo (2014) provide two actual TRIZ applications. The first shows how larger engines were accommodated when increasing the size of the Boeing 737. The necessary ground clearance beneath the engines was achieved by using an unusual asymmetric shape for the engine cowls. The second application involved developing a way to detect undesirable empty soapboxes at the end of a production line in which soap and boxes were merged. Using TRIZ, the team looked at options such as X-raying and weighing the boxes, but decided that "they could just use a fan and blow the empty boxes right off the production line! A small fan was purchased for $20, and the company no longer needed to worry about shipping empty soapboxes."

The asymmetric cowl and the fan solutions may seem simple in retrospect, as is often the case with creative/innovative results, but neither was apparent up front. We often need a collaboration method like TRIZ or one of the others described in this text to fully engage our collective minds.

7.9.4 Neuroscience Basis

TRIZ is neuroscience based in that it draws heavily on the collective cognitive work of many engineers and others. We benefit from the essence of their creative/innovative efforts because the results of their work are concisely captured in the matrix that keys pairs of technical contradictions to inventive principles that were cumulatively developed by others.

Another neuroscience connection is that your or my conscious mind will be challenged by trying to understand and process thirty-nine technical characteristics, any of which might appear as contradictions in our current technical challenge. However, we can be confident that our subconscious minds, on becoming aware of specific contradictions and their past resolutions (as offered in the contradictions matrix), will get to work helping us finding the solutions to our problems.

7.9.5 Positive and Negative Features

The most positive feature of TRIZ is that it answers the questions, "Haven't people faced this technical problem before? Can't I benefit from their efforts?" The answers: "Yes, your kind of problem has been tackled and solved before, and you can benefit from the results." The formal method aside, another benefit of TRIZ is the list of forty inventive principles and explanations of them, which provide a gold mine of ideas for your possible use in addressing a technical challenge, with or without TRIZ. The only negative aspect of TRIZ is the effort needed to understand the underlying principles in order to apply them.

7.10 TAKING TIME TO THINK

As I arrived here in writing this book, I felt the need for a final whole-brain method. Given its position as the last of the text's tools, it should add value for you by reinforcing the previous nineteen methods and by adding some new thoughts. I decided to call it *Taking Time to Think*, or T^4 for short.

Recall the Section 3.2.2 discussion of how some of the methods in this text can be explained and then applied somewhat methodically, in a step-by-step manner. Other methods, rather than being described as a process, are more of a way of thinking about an IPO, a manner used to approach a challenge, or an attitude taken when faced with a complex situation. T^4 is in the latter category.

All of this book's methods were selected, as noted in Section 3.2.1, to stimulate more right-brain activity in order to supplement your left-brain activity and, as a result, enable you to work smarter and be even more creative and innovative. T^4 looks at stimulating more whole-brain thinking simply by thinking more effectively. To do that, we need to take the time.

7.10.1 Why the Focus on Time?

This method adds value for you via its emphasis on time, as in having the discipline to take the time to think. The value of taking the time to think may seem obvious, but although it's within our power to do so, we often don't do it—and then we incur significant individual, team, or organizational costs. For example:

- Some of us routinely, if not habitually, multitask. Without thinking, we jump from task to task, and as explained in Section 2.11, we incur major costs, in that our productivity declines (longer absolute time to complete a task) and the probability of errors increases, as does our organization's liability exposure.
- When in a contentious and emotional situation, we may perceive a personal attack and unthinkingly lash out at someone, or be deeply disappointed and immediately vent our frustration. We may do irreparable damage because although what we said in the heat of the situation was written in sand, the recipient engraved it in rock.

PERSONAL: A LESSON LEARNED ABOUT TAKING TIME TO THINK

Near the end of the first year of my first employment situation, I received a letter indicating my salary increase for the next year. They had to be kidding! Surely I deserved a bigger increase. Without taking the time to think this issue through, I met with my boss and immediately said that if I didn't get more, I would leave. I remember exactly what he said, although it was over five decades ago: "So leave." I did not have a Plan B and had to eat crow. This was a hard way for me to learn this valuable lesson: Take time to think.

A similar situation arose a few years later while in my second employment situation. This time, recalling the preceding incident, I took ample time to think of options and possible outcomes and then asked to meet with my boss. I expressed disappointment, but without anger or threats, even though I now had other employment options. Within a few days, I learned that I would receive a bigger raise.

- Faced with a new challenge, we rashly charge in and either resolve the wrong issue, problem, or opportunity, or create chaos. We fail to take the time to define the IPO, which is one of the uses of many of the tools presented in this book. Remember that your likelihood of creatively or innovatively resolving an IPO increases in proportion to how thoroughly you define it.
- We carefully define an IPO, and then, because of a professor, a boss, the political process, or other pressure, we don't take the time to generate many and varied potential resolutions, which we could have done—perhaps using some of the tools offered in this chapter and in Chapter 4. We rush to judgment and make recommendations. Later, on reflection, we realize that we squandered an opportunity to be creative and innovative.
- An apparently promising personal opportunity arises, and we quickly jump at it even though had we taken the time to think it through, we would have seen what appeared to be an opportunity as inconsistent with our values and goals. The effort fails, and some observers question our character.

Scenarios like the preceding ones with their often negative consequences occur often. They can usually be avoided, assuming you have the discipline to apply T^4. If you work at it using the process described in Section 2.10.5, T^4 could become a powerful habit.

7.10.2 Mindfulness

Increasingly, we hear about meditation, a catchall term for a wide variety of thinking modes. Let's look at one of them: *mindfulness*. This form of thinking means that we are engaged in the present moment. We observe sights, sounds, and other sensations. Our focus is on a challenge at hand without becoming overly occupied with any aspect of it. If our minds drift from the challenge, we notice and refocus (Jha 2013; Ricard, Lutz, and Davidson 2014).

How can you make practical use of mindfulness? Focus for a predetermined period on some IPO, perhaps for fifteen to thirty minutes. Preferably, look at the IPO (e.g., a recurring flaw on products moving through a manufacturing process, a just-collapsed structure). If that isn't feasible, gather images and audio related to the IPO, such as photographs, plotted data, drawings, and video.

Look long enough that you're really seeing; if appropriate, listen long enough that you really hear. This process is similar to the Ohno Circle (Section 4.8) with the big exception that mindfulness seeks to further define an already identified IPO for you. In contrast, the Ohno Circle is more of a fishing expedition seeking to find problems. After fifteen to thirty minutes, or whatever period you use, set mindfulness aside, with the intent to return to the challenge later.

Assuming you resume mindfulness after taking a break from the first session, you will experience at least two benefits. First, you will gain a much better understanding of the IPO. Second, this focused use of your conscious mind will prime and prepare your subconscious mind (Section 2.9) to start working on further defining and eventually resolving the IPO. Each time you return to applying mindfulness to the IPO, expect some new insights and maybe an *aha!* moment.

Another way to practice mindfulness is to use Stream of Consciousness Writing (Section 4.9). Focus on the issue that you want to address, problem you need to solve, or opportunity you are considering. Then, with pen or pencil and paper or at your computer, and in one sitting, write whatever enters your mind without stopping. Expect some fresh and maybe even creative/innovative ideas.

7.10.3 Writing as a Way of Taking Time to Think

Writing is typically viewed as one way we communicate with others. We send texts, emails, memorandums, or reports: This is interpersonal communication. In contrast, we can also apply writing in an intrapersonal communication mode; we can write as means of engaging in T4.

Assume that you are faced with a complex situation, such as a technical or non-technical IPO. The situation is challenging, confusing, and potentially contentious. My advice is to start to write to yourself about the IPO. Begin to describe the symptoms, the causes, potential options, their pros and cons, and a likely course of action. Take breaks during the writing process, let your subconscious mind work on your written thoughts, and then resume writing with the inevitable benefit of your subconscious. This form of writing is more systematic and takes much more time than Stream of Consciousness Writing.

By virtue of the discipline required by writing, you're taking substantial time to think and during the process finding out what you know, don't know, and need to learn. During breaks in the writing, you're likely to go to books, published papers, the Internet, colleagues, and other sources to fill some of the knowledge gaps flagged during your writing.

As succinctly stated by the playwright Albee, "I write to find out what I am thinking" and, I might add, to determine what I know and don't know. Zinsser (1988), a writer, editor, and teacher, said, "Writing is a tool that enables people in every discipline to wrestle with facts and ideas." The thinking stimulated by intrapersonal writing is likely to include creative and innovative ideas.

PERSONAL: WRITING TO LEARN

Years ago, my wife and I stopped at a garage sale and I began rummaging through old books. I thought I saw a book titled *Learning to Write*. On reaching for it, I realized it was titled *Writing to Learn* (Zinsser 1988). The book's thesis, which I wish I had learned earlier in my teaching, education, and training career, is that we should ask students, regardless of the course we are teaching and they are taking, to write as a way to learn.

We have all done that kind of writing in English, literature, and philosophy courses. However, Zinsser also advocates writing in mathematics, science, and engineering courses. Imagine being asked to write a few paragraphs about how calculus enables you to determine the volume of a shape defined by taking an equation describing a relationship in the x-y quadrant and rotating it around the x-axis. That writing experience would deepen your understanding and heighten your appreciation of integral calculus.

Select a topic that interests or fascinates you and start writing about it. Write long enough and in a disciplined manner and you will become an expert on the topic. That expertise will flow from writing as you find out what you know, don't know, and want to learn. I often use this process, usually beginning with Mind Mapping, to help me identify some relevant topics. That process enabled me to write many parts of this book.

7.10.4 Neuroscience Basis

T^4 explicitly leverages the powerful conscious mind–subconscious mind interplay. When you take the time to consciously think about anything, you send messages to your subconscious mind. The former plants seeds in the latter. The subconscious mind learns about an IPO you want to define and resolve because you sent it detailed information; it believes the IPO can be defined and resolved; and it gets to work doing so. The planted seeds sprout. Your conscious mind sees reality, the way things seem to be. In what often turns out to be a fruitful contrast, your subconscious mind cannot differentiate between what is real and imagined. Therefore, it may provide you with a potential new reality.

7.10.5 Positive and Negative Features

On the surface, the most positive feature of mindfulness is its apparent ease of application. That is, what could be difficult about taking the time to think or, more specifically, to focus on an IPO for fifteen to thirty minutes? However, this kind of attentiveness may be challenging given the ever-quickening pace of our lives (even as students) and the need for immediate results. T^4 requires self-discipline, at least until it becomes a habit; intrapersonal writing can provide the necessary discipline.

I introduced mindfulness as a means of working smarter and being more creative and innovative, but scientists also claim or suggest other benefits. Exploration of those possible positives is beyond this text's scope. However, you may want to explore other possible benefits of mindfulness, such as reduced stress, rewired brain circuits, generation of more neurons, pain control, reduced depression, and strengthening the brain's ability to pay attention (Jha 2013; Ricard, Lutz, and Davidson 2014).

7.11 MANY MORE WHOLE-BRAIN METHODS

The practical considerations of penning a book meant that although I searched far and wide for whole-brain methods, I needed to select a workable subset. Factors considered in selecting methods include personal experiences with them, observing students and practitioners using tools, trying to imagine processes used by many creators and innovators (such as many mentioned in this book), and a bias toward visualization because neuroscience tell us that sight is our dominant sense (Section 2.4.2).

Some readers may want to learn about and experiment with additional whole-brain methods. Therefore, here is a list of starter sources that I've discovered and reviewed, each of which describes some methods not included in this book: Adams 1986; Arciszewski 2009; Bailey 1978; Beakley, Evans, and Keats 1986; Dhillon 2006; Fogler, LeBlanc, and Rizzo 2014; Gelb 2004; Herrmann 1996; Koberg and Bagnall 1991; Lumsdaine and Binks 2007; McKim 1980; Michalko 2001; and Wolff 2012.

7.12 CONCLUDING THOUGHTS ABOUT ADVANCED WHOLE-BRAIN METHODS

Adding to the eleven basic whole-brain methods described in Chapter 4, this chapter offers you nine more advanced methods. Although you are more likely to use the basic methods during your undergraduate studies, you can also draw on them and on the advanced methods during graduate studies and while in engineering practice.

Assume that you study the whole-brain methods in these two chapters so that you are generally aware of their features. Then, you will have the means in your individual and team efforts within your studies, in your personal life, and in professional practice to engage in many creative/innovative endeavors and to enable others to do the same. You and those that join you will generate many ideas for successfully resolving issues, solving problems, and pursuing opportunities.

7.13 REVISITING BRAIN BASICS

Brain basics are essential to understanding, appreciating, and applying the twenty whole-brain methods presented in this chapter and Chapter 4. Each method is accompanied by an explanation of its neuroscience basis. As stated early in Chapter 2, if you want to work smarter, live smarter, replace some bad habits with good habits, and/or be more creative and innovative, then an understanding of brain basics will help you. The text referred to the brain as an amazing instrument that will play the tune you want if you understand how it works.

Let's revisit the brain basics introduced in Chapter 2 and note their practical applications, which include, but go beyond, supporting the twenty whole-brain methods. Table 7.4 lists thirteen of those basics in the first column and notes their practical applications in the second column. Entries in both columns are keyed to many different parts of the text for ease of reference.

Table 7.4 is another way of communicating a major theme of this text. That is, if you take the time to learn how your brain functions, you will be more effective in your studying, professional work, and beyond. When I say *learn*, I don't mean learn

Table 7.4 This text demonstrates why and how an understanding of brain basics yields many practical results, like those listed here.

Brain Basics (Related book sections shown in parentheses)	Practical Applications (Related book sections shown in parentheses)
1) One-fifth of the blood (and the glucose, nutrients, and oxygen it carries) pumped by the human heart (up to sixteen gallons per hour) goes directly to the brain (2.3.1).	Regularly engage in aerobic exercise and eat smart (2.16.1, 2.16.2).
2) Vision trumps all other senses (2.3.1).	Make extensive use of images when learning and when communicating (2.4.2, 9.3).
3) The brain and mind are different. The former is an organ, and the latter is what we do with it (2.5).	You, as defined by your mind—your thoughts, beliefs, memories, aspirations, and plans—are unique. Celebrate and practice good stewardship with your uniqueness (2.5).
4) Memories of events change with time. Our recall is selective and not totally reliable (2.5).	Be cautious about what you think you remember. At least in the professional world, be meticulous about documentation of meetings, conversations, site visits, and so on (2.5).
5) Asymmetry—that is, some very different left- and right-hemisphere capabilities, such as, respectively, verbal vs. visual, logical vs. intuitive, literal vs. emotional, and symbolic vs. actual (2.7.1).	Further engage the right hemisphere to supplement your already heavily engaged left hemisphere by placing additional emphasis on processes and environments that have visual, intuitive, emotional, and experiential elements (2.7.1, 2.7.2).
	Apply the whole-brain methods in Chapters 4 and 7 because many use the brain's asymmetry. Enjoy more creative/innovative results and the associated personal and organizational benefits, such as reduced cost and risk, increased profit, saved lives, enhanced communication, personal satisfaction, and more (see Table 5.1 for a long and varied list of example benefits).
6) Neuroplasticity (2.8.1).	You can continue to develop your brain if you challenge and care for it (2.8.2, 2.16.1–2.16.4).
7) The conscious mind can only think of one topic or thing at a time, whereas the subconscious mind works 24-7 on many topics and things at the same time. The conscious mind gives thinking tasks to the much more cognitively active subconscious mind (2.9).	Increase productivity by reducing multitasking (2.11.1, 2.11.5, 3.5).
	Reduce errors and therefore liability exposure by reducing multitasking (2.11.1, 2.11.2, 3.5).
	Reduce stress and increase awareness by reducing multitasking (2.11.4).
The conscious mind sees reality, whereas the subconscious mind cannot differentiate between what is real and imagined (2.9.2, 2.9.3).	Work on tasks and projects intensely, but intermittently, to engage the subconscious mind (2.9.3).
	Apply the whole-brain tools presented in Chapters 4 and 7 because many use the conscious mind–subconscious mind interplay, and enjoy more creative/innovative results and associated personal and organizational benefits, such as reduced cost and risk, increased profit, saved lives, enhanced communication, personal satisfaction, and many more (see Table 5.1 for a long and varied list of example benefits).
8) Habits—what we automatically think, say, and do—may dominate our lives in that we are on automatic pilot at least half the time (2.1.1).	Create new habits or replace bad habits with good ones and be more effective (2.10.3, 2.10.5–2.10.8).
9) Negativity bias (2.12.1–2.12.3).	Realize more personal and organizational opportunities by offsetting your likely negativity bias (2.12.4).
10) Left- and right-handedness (2.13.1).	Left-handers have a slight edge with language, music, mathematics, and creativity (2.13.2).
	Right-handers are less likely to experience learning difficulties, dyslexia, and stuttering, and customs tend to favor right-handers (2.13.3).

Table 7.4 (*Continued*)

Brain Basics (Related book sections shown in parentheses)	Practical Applications (Related book sections shown in parentheses)
11) Gender differences (2.14.1–2.14.5).	Men, consider being a little more expressive, working at reading voice and facial signals, thinking more before reacting, appreciating the emotional part of women's memories, and leveraging your three-dimensional capability (2.14.6, 2.14.7).
	Women, consider appreciating men's under-expressed emotions, setting more self-discipline examples, reminding men of the emotional aspect of memories, and persisting in developing more three-dimensional capability (2.14.6, 2.14.5).
12) Although human brains generally look similar, each of us has a unique knowledge-skills-attitude set, personality profile, and other characteristics (4.6.2, 4.6.3, 4.6.8).	Form heterogeneous teams because they tend to be more creative than homogeneous teams (4.6.1, 4.6.4– 4.6.8).
13) Listening to or making music involves essentially all of the human brain (7.5.1).	Use music to focus attention, enhance listening, assist memory, and elevate mood (7.5.2, 7.5.3).

about the brain in depth and breadth like a neuroscientist or brain surgeon. Instead, I mean learn like an intelligent layperson—an inquisitive, open-minded individual—and use that knowledge to enhance your success and significance.

> An invasion of armies can be resisted, but not an idea whose time has come.
>
> —*Victor Hugo, French author*

CITED SOURCES

Adams, J. L. 1986. *The Care and Feeding of Ideas: A Guide to Encouraging Creativity.* Reading, MA: Addison-Wesley Publishing Company.

Altshuller, G. 1996. *And Suddenly the Inventor Appeared: TRIZ, the Theory of Inventive Problem Solving.* Translated by Lev Shulyak from the original 1984 Russian version. Worcester, MA: Technical Innovation Center, Inc.

Amabile, T. M. 2011. "How to Kill Creativity." In *The Innovator's Cookbook: Essentials for Inventing What Is Next,* edited by S. Johnson. New York: Riverhead Books.

Anft, M. 2012. "Aping Nature." *Johns Hopkins Magazine,* Summer: 48–55.

Ante, S. E. 2012. "Avoiding Innovation's Terrible Toll." *The Wall Street Journal,* January 7–8.

Arciszewski, T. 2009. *Successful Education: How to Educate Creative Engineers.* Fairfax, VA: Successful Education LLC.

Arciszewski, T., E. Grabska, and C. Harrison. 2009. "Visual Thinking in Inventive Design: Three Perspectives." In *Soft Computing in Civil and Structural Engineering,* edited by B. H. V. Topping and Y. Tsompanakis, 179–202. Stirling, Scotland: Saxe-Coburg Publications.

Armstrong, S. C. 2005. *Engineering and Product Development Management: A Holistic Approach.* Cambridge: Cambridge University Press.

Bailey, R. L. 1978. *Disciplined Creativity for Engineers.* Ann Arbor, MI: Ann Arbor Science Publishers.

Bar-Cohen, Y. 2012. "Introduction: Nature as a Source for Inspiration and Innovation." In *Biomimetics: Nature-Based Innovation*, edited by Y. Bar-Cohen, 1–34. Boca Raton, FL: CRC Press.

Barry, K., E. Domb, and M. S. Slocum. 2014. "TRIZ: What Is TRIZ?" *TRIZ Journal*. Accessed November 19, 2014. http://www.triz-journal.com/archives/what is triz/.

Beakley, G. C., D. L. Evans, and J. B. Keats. 1986. *Engineering: An Introduction to a Creative Profession*. New York: Macmillan Publishing Company.

Benyus, J. M. 1997. *Biomimicry: Innovation Inspired by Nature*. New York: Harper Perennial.

Berra, Y. 1998. *The Yogi Book*. New York: Workman Publishing.

Bonasso, S. G. 2007. "Inquiry, Discovery, Invention, and Innovation: The Personal Experience of Technology Generation and Transfer in Engineering and Scientific Research." *Leadership and Management in Engineering*, ASCE, October: 141–150.

Campbell, D. 1997. *The Mozart Effect: Tapping the Power of Music to Heal the Body, Strengthen the Mind, and Unlock the Creative Spirit*. New York: Avon Books.

Cernasov, A., and L. Venkatraman. 2012. "Culture of Innovation." *PM NETWORK*, January: 20–22.

Churchill, W. 2013. *Painting as a Pastime*. London: Unicorn Press.

Colvin, G. 2008. *Talent is Overrated*. New York: Portfolio.

Czyzewski, A. 2011. "Nature Inspires New Methods of Making Porous Materials." *The Engineer*, e-newsletter, August 3.

Daly, S. R., S. Yilmaz, J. L. Christian, C. M. Seifert, and R. Gonzalez. 2012. "Uncovering Design Strategies." *Prism-Magazine.Org*, December.

Davenport, T. H. 2005. "The Physical Work Environment and Knowledge Worker Performance." In *Thinking for a Living: How to Get Better Results from Knowledge Workers*, 165–185. Cambridge, MA: Harvard Business School Press.

de Bono, E. 1999. *The Six Thinking Hats*. Boston: Little, Brown and Company.

de Bono, E. 2010. "Finding the Motivation for Creativity." *Management Issues*, August 2. Accessed November 18. 2014. http://www.management-issues.com/opinion/6005/finding-the-motivation-for-creativity/.

Dhillon, B. S. 2006. *Creativity for Engineers*. Hackensack, NJ: World Scientific.

Dim, J. M. 2013. "Richard Sears Catalog Turned a Page in Retail." *Investor's Business Daily*, May 29.

Domb, E. 1997. "How to Help TRIZ Beginners Succeed." Paper presented at the Invention Machine User's Group Conference, New Orleans, LA, February 3–4.

Drucker, P. F. 1985. *Innovation and Entrepreneurship*. New York: Harper Business.

Duhigg, C. 2012. *The Power of Habit: Why We Do What We Do in Life and Business*. New York: Random House.

Dyer, J., and H. Gregersen. 2013. "The Secret of Innovative Companies: It Isn't R&D." *Innovative Solutions*, April 18. Accessed November 19, 2014. http://www.innovationmanagement.se/2013/04/18/the-secret-of-innovative-companies-it-isnt-rd/.

EarthSky 2012. "Sunni Robertson on How a Kingfisher Inspired a Bullet Train." June 29. Accessed November 19, 2014. http://earthsky.org/earth/sunni-robertson-on-how-a-kingfisher-inspired-a-bullet-train.

Edwards, B. 1999. *Drawing on the Right Side of the Brain*. New York: Jeremy P. Tarcher.

Farid, F., A. R. El-Sharkawy, and L. K. Austin. 1993. "Managing for Creativity and Innovation in A/E/C Organizations." *Journal of Management in Engineering*, ASCE, October: 399–409.

Finn, H. 2012. "A Cure for the Age of Inattention." *Wall Street Journal*, June 2–3.

Floating Island International. 2014. Accessed November 18. http://www.floatingislandinternational.com.

Fogler, H.S., S. E. LeBlanc, and B. Rizzo. 2014. *Strategies for Creative Problem Solving*, 3rd ed. Upper Saddle River, NJ: Prentice-Hall.

Gelb, M. J. 2004. *How to Think like Leonardo da Vinci: Seven Steps to Genius Every Day*. New York: Delta Trade Paperback.

Haslam, S. A., and C. Knight. 2010. "Cubicle, Sweet Cubicle." *Scientific American Mind*, September/October: 30–35.

Headley, T. R., and C. C. Tanner. 2008. "Floating Treatment Wetlands: An Innovative Option for Stormwater Quality Applications." Paper presented at the 11th International Conference on Wetland Systems for Water Pollution Control, Indore, India, November 1–7.

Heller, R. 2012. "Who's Hindering Innovation in Your Firm?" *Management Intelligence*, e-newsletter, May 31.

Herrmann, N. 1996. *The Whole Brain Business Book*. New York: McGraw-Hill.

Hill, N. 1960. *Think and Grow Rich*. New York: Fawcett Crest Books.

Isaacson, W. 2011. *Steve Jobs*. New York: Simon & Schuster.

Jha, A. P. 2013. "Being in the Now." *Scientific American Mind*, March/April: 26–33.

Kao, J. 2007. *Innovation Nation: How America Is Losing Its Innovation Edge, Why It Matters, and What We Can Do to Get It Back*. New York: Free Press.

Kaplan, S. 2011. "Five Reasons Companies Fail at Business Model Innovation." *HBR Blog Network-Harvard Business Review*, October 21.

Kay, C. 2014. Business manager, Ken Kay Associates, San Francisco, California, pers. comm., October 1.

Klatt, B. 2011. "Bruce '75: Floating a Sustainable Idea." *On Wisconsin Magazine*, Fall. Accessed November 18, 2014. http://onwisconsin.uwalumni.com/departments/bruce-kania-75-floating-a-sustainable-idea/.

Koberg, D., and J. Bagnall. 1991. *The Universal Traveler: A Soft-Systems Guide to Creativity, Problem Solving, and the Process of Reaching Goals*. Lanham, MD: National Book Network.

Levitin, D. J. 2006. *This Is Your Brain on Music*. New York: Penguin Group.

Linkner, J. 2011. "Seven Steps to a Culture of Innovation." *Inc*, June 16. Accessed November 19, 2014. http://www.inc.com/articles/201106/josh-linkner-7-steps-to-a-culture-of-innovation_Printer_Friendly.html.

Lublin, J. S. 2008. "A CEO's Recipe for Fresh Ideas." *WSJ.com*, September 2. Accessed November 19, 2014. http://online.wsj.com/article/SB122030336412088091.html.

Lumsdaine, E., and M. Binks. 2007. *Entrepreneurship from Creativity to Innovation: Thinking Skills for a Changing World*. Victoria, British Columbia: Trafford Publishing.

Lumsdaine, E., M. Lumsdaine, and J. W. Shelnutt. 1999. *Creative Problem Solving and Engineering Design*. New York: McGraw-Hill.

Marcus, A. M. 2015. "Healing Arts: Doctors Diagnose Paintings." *Wall Street Journal*, January 2.

May, M. E. 2010. "Ideacide, or 14 Ways to Kill Creativity," *The World: American Express Open Forum*, August 10.

Mazur, G. 2014a. "Altshuller's Table of Contradictions." Accessed November 19, 2014. http://www.mazur.net/triz/contradi.htm.

Mazur, G. 2014b. "Theory of Inventive Problem Solving (TRIZ)." Accessed November 19, 2014. http://www.mazur.net/triz.

McArdle, M. 2012. "Why Companies Fail." *The Atlantic*, March: 28–32.

McKim, R. H. 1980. *Thinking Visually: A Strategy Manual for Problem Solving*. Belmont, CA: Lifetime Learning Publications.

Medina, J. 2008. *Brain Rules: Twelve Principles for Surviving and Thriving at Work, Home, and School.* Seattle: Pear Press.

Michalko, M. 2001. *Cracking Creativity: The Secrets of Creative Genius.* Berkeley, CA: Ten Speed Press.

Miles, E. 1997. *Tune Your Brain: Using Music to Manage Your Mind, Body, and Mood.* New York: Berkley Books.

Mlodinow, L. 2013. *Subliminal: How Your Unconscious Mind Rules Your Behavior.* New York: Vintage Books.

Moon, Y. 2010. *Different: Escaping the Competitive Herd.* New York: Crown Business.

Moon, Y. 2014. "My Anti-Creativity Checklist." Video. Accessed November 19, 2014. http://vimeo.com/10175915.

Nagle, J. G. 1998. "Seven Habits of Effective Communicators." *Today's Engineer,* Summer.

Pink, D. H. 2009. *Drive: The Surprising Truth about What Motivates Us.* New York: Riverhead Books.

Ricard, M., A. Lutz, and R. J. Davidson. 2014. "Mind of the Mediator." *Scientific American* 311 (5): 39–45.

Roam, D. 2008. *The Back of the Napkin: Solving Problems and Selling Ideas with Pictures.* New York: Penguin Group.

Sarkisian, M., E. Long, C. Doo, and D. Shook. 2011. "Learning from Nature." *Civil Engineering,* ASCE, June: 60–65.

Seifert, C. 2012. "Seventy-Seven Cards: Design Heuristics for Inspiring Ideas." *YouTube,* August 1.

Shapiro, A. 2014. "Stop Blabbing about Innovation and Start Actually Doing It." *FastCompany.com.* Accessed November 19, 2014. http://www.fastcompany.com/1833190/stop-blabbing-about-innovation-and-start-actually-doing-it.

Shlain, L. 2014. *Leonardo's Brain: Understanding da Vinci's Creative Genius.* Guilford, CT: Lyons Press.

Tischler, L. 2010. "The Idea Lab at Stanford's d.school," *Fast Company,* May 5.

Vanderbilt, T. 2012. "Better Living through Imitation: Biomimicry Engineers Are Finding the Designs of the Future in the Greatest Field Laboratory of the Past: The Natural World." *Smithsonian,* September: 50–53.

Walesh, S. G. 2012a. "Developing Relationships." In *Engineering Your Future: The Professional Practice of Engineering,* 123–126. Hoboken, NJ/Reston, VA: John Wiley & Sons/ASCE Press.

Walesh, S. G. 2012b. "Staging a Creative Culture." *Leadership and Management in Engineering,* ASCE, October: 338–340.

Wallace, R. 1966. *The World of Leonardo 1452–1519.* Alexandria, VA: Time-Life Books.

Wolff, J. 2012. *Creativity Now.* Harlow, UK: Pearson.

Zinsser, W. 1988. *Writing to Learn.* New York: HarperResource.

EXERCISES

Notes:

1. The goal of the exercises is to provide students, usually and preferably working in diverse groups, the opportunity to use all of this chapter's tools and also some from Chapter 4.

2. However, many circumstances and corresponding teaching/learning opportunities may arise. For example, a team could use a different tool

or more than one tool, or the stated issue may be altered to meet specific concerns or needs. Rather than work with the largely hypothetical situation described in a particular exercise, a team may wish to take on an actual issue, problem, or opportunity facing the team or one or more of its members. These and similar variations are encouraged, subject to the concurrence or direction of the instructor.

3. Recall the facilitation discussion in Section 3.8. Each of the team exercises provides opportunities for individual students to apply pre-, during-, and post-facilitation advice. Even if your instructor does not require facilitation, you may want to practice it for two reasons. First, your group will get better results. Second, students who provide the facilitation will gain valuable knowledge and skills.

7.1 FROM HARD TO SOFT LANDING (BIOMIMICRY OR TRIZ): A former champion high diver, who is now a college diving coach, encourages members of the diving team to experiment with ever more complicated dives. However, as the dives get more complex, the frequency of hard collisions with the water and possible injuries increases. The coach is torn between enhancing the difficulty of the dives and protecting the divers (adapted from Altshuller 1996). What do you suggest? You might apply Biomimicry and/or TRIZ to meet this challenge.

7.2 YOU SET THE AGENDA (CHALLENGES AND IDEAS MEETINGS): This exercise assumes that you are an officer of an organization and in a position to influence the agenda for one or more meetings. Maybe the organization is a student engineering society, a campus club, a local branch or section of a professional society, or an ad hoc task force at your place of employment.

Conduct an experiment intended to increase your group's interest, intensity, creativity, and innovation. Use the Challenges and Ideas Meetings tool (Section 7.3) to do this. More specifically, select one of the three agenda-connected items in that section (challenges, ideas, or habits) and insert it into the agenda for the next meeting or agendas for several meetings. Evaluate the pros and cons of your experiment. In a related matter, for seventeen practical, road-tested tips that you can draw on to plan, conduct, and follow up on a meeting, see Chapter 4, "Developing Relationships," in my book *Engineering Your Future: The Professional Practice of Engineering* (Walesh 2012a).

7.3 STRONG BUT LIGHT BULLETPROOF VESTS (TRIZ): Consider a conflict. A bulletproof vest should be robust enough to protect the wearer from bullets, shrapnel, and other objects but sufficiently light and flexible so as not to be uncomfortable. Apply TRIZ to generate one or more ways to resolve this contradiction (adapted from Fogler, LeBlanc, and Rizzo 2014).

7.4 ACCURATE DRILLING IN A RUBBER HOSE: The design of a manufacturing process includes finding a way to accurately drill many small holes in a length of rubber hose. Early experimentation reveals that when the drill is applied, the hose compresses and bends so that the holes are not properly located or drilled. Burning the holes with a heated iron rod improves accuracy but produces ragged edges (adapted from Altshuller 1996). What would you do? Select and apply one or more of the Chapter 4 or Chapter 7 tools.

7.5 MEASURING THE TEMPERATURE OF TICKS (TRIZ): An environmental engineer is part of an interdisciplinary team studying ways to reduce the disease-carrying capacity of ticks, small insects that do not jump or fly. The team needs to determine the body temperature of the insect. To illustrate the challenge, the group visits the lab, sees one of the insects in a glass beaker, and starts to Brainstorm ways to measure its body temperature. They begin to think of developing a new thermometer suited to the size and physical characteristics of the insect. Then another, simpler idea is suggested by the environmental engineer (adapted from Altshuller 1996). What might it be? Use TRIZ to generate ideas.

7.6 FIXING A TROUBLED BUSINESS (PRODUCT + SERVICE DESIGN): You work for a small-scale packaging-machine manufacturer, who sells their machines to supermarkets for packaging food - meat, cheese, milk, bread. Due to a change in their business model, supermarkets have decided to stop packing food on their premises. Your company did not anticipate this change and is now completely out of business. Your company had been a well-known player and is known for the quality of its products. The firm's top executives call an emergency meeting with its top executives from the service line: human resource, finance, marketing and sales. In the meeting, a team is formed which can fix the situation with a quick and low-budget yet profitable solution for the firm. You are part of this team.

Your team applies some of this text's problem-definition tools (eg., Ask-Ask-Ask, Mind Mapping, Process Diagramming). Since developing a new product is not an option considering the time and budget frame assigned to the team, the team decides to innovate on alternate service design and a new market launch as prospective alternatives. It then brainstorms on alternative creative solutions using the tools mentioned in the book (Six Thinking Hats, Borrowing Brilliance, Ohno Circle, Stream of Consciousness Writing, What if).

With an alternative service plus product (existing mostly) design in mind, conduct the sessions. Use at least one problem definition and one idea generation whole-brain tool. Write a report describing how your team went about forming the team, defining the problem and generating ideas. You can use case examples of small-scale packaging-machines to get inspired for your exercise.

7.7 FIXING A TROUBLED CONSULTING BUSINESS (IT'S OUR MARKETING): This situation begins as described in the first two paragraphs of Exercise 7.6— but then there is a fundamental difference.

Your TC meets, applies some of this text's problem-definition tools(e.g., Ask-Ask-Ask, Mind Mapping, Process Diagramming), and concludes that the principal problem is the need for greatly enhanced marketing.

Using Borrowing Brilliance, your team conducts some far-reaching research and assembles the following list of companies and descriptions of their highly diverse marketing strategies (from Moon 2010 unless noted otherwise):

- IKEA: The customer assembles it and the resulting product is not expected to last long
- Apple: Know what's best for their customers, which was articulated by Steve Jobs as "customers don't know what they want until we've shown them" (Isaacson 2011)
- Mini Cooper: real small and proud of it
- Google: Homepage has a single element, a text box with two search buttons
- Birkenstock shoes: Comfortable but ugly

- Sears, Roebuck, and Company: About a century ago, made its catalog (called the *Wishing Book*) a little smaller than the Montgomery Ward catalog so that the former would most likely sit atop the latter on a coffee table (Dim 2013)

You each share some of the marketing strategies/tactics of your favorite restaurants, sports team, car model, hotel, travel agency, and similar product/service organizations.

What marketing strategies/tactics used by the companies you identified might your firm consider?

7.8 HAND SANITISING IN NEONATAL ICU: A neonatal ICU houses extremely critical newly born babies. Inside the ICU, 10-15 babies can be kept in separate incubators. A critical part of the care is avoiding any potential source of infection for the babies. To achieve this, a doctor or nurse is supposed to first use a hand sanitizer before opening the incubator lid and performing the requisite activities. Once the incubator is closed, the doctor or nurse should reuse the hand sanitizer. A hand sanitizer bottle is placed near each incubator. But during busy days, when the number of babies is high, it has been observed that the hand sanitizing is not followed very strictly. Your team has been assigned to design a foolproof solution so that hand sanitizing is followed strictly.

Remember, a technologically sophisticated solution is not always the best solution. Can your team come up with a low cost and maybe low-tech solution which works on the habit-building part of the problem? Can you work on a reward-based encouragement mechanism rather than a penalty based mechanism? Use one of the idea-generation tools presented in the text and come up with as many creative ideas as possible.

7.9 FANTASY ANALOGY: Fantasy analogy is based on the notion that creative thinking and wish fulfillment are strongly related. For example, my fantasy for cleaning clothes is: I throw the garment in a box and get a perfectly clean, crease- and lint-free folded garment out from the other side. In order to fulfill this wish, I can start thinking of a new type of washer-dryer which might clean using ultrasound waves rather than detergent and dry using a vacuum.

Think of a typical daily activity or need. Try using fantasy analogy to do a wishful thinking on how you would like to achieve it. Then, use one of the idea-generation techniques presented in this text to identify possible ways to achieve it

7.10 ENERGISING YOUR ENVIRONMENT: Assume that you have been assigned to create an Ideation Corner in your school campus. This corner can be a physical and/or a combination of a physical and a virtual space where anyone from the school can come and work in. This environment should not only be conducive to creative/innovative work but should also be capable of inspiring creative thoughts through all possible human-to-human and human-to-non-human interactions built into it. Consider the points mentioned in Section 7.8.

7.11 ENHANCING YOUR CULTURE: Briefly think about the culture of an organization in which you study, work, or otherwise participate. After reviewing the culture portions of Section 7.8, think deeply and widely about your culture. Does it support creativity and innovation? If not, identify and briefly describe three prioritized changes that you would like to make so that your culture would be even more conducive to creative/innovative work for you and those you interact with. Comment on the feasibility of making the cultural changes, including what you could do unilaterally.

7.12 CREATING A PLAN FOR ONE OF YOUR GOALS: Recall the Section 1.2 discussion of success and significance and consider your unique interpretation of the specifics and relative value of success versus significance. Select one of your goals that, if achieved, would move you toward your definition of success and significance. Maybe the goal is to hold an advanced position, visit an exotic place, earn an advanced degree, write a book, master a musical instrument, research a topic of special interest, design a skyscraper, run for political office, or start your own business.

Then, create a plan to achieve that goal. Notice that I said *create*; your goal is unique to you and you will need your own special way to achieve it. The following are some suggested items to include in your written plan: dates, resources, learning, contacts, places, and sacrifices (Adams 1986). Consider using Mind Mapping, Stream of Consciousness Writing, and/or What If to stimulate your creative thinking.

You or I cannot have or do everything we sort of want to have or do, but we can have or do almost anything that we *really* want, provided that we have a plan and the discipline to achieve it. That is the powerful message in Hill's (1960) classic book.

7.13 REFLECT ON HOW YOU ONCE DID IT (PROCESS DIAGRAMMING): Recall how you had selected your current study program. Many students find it difficult to make a well- thought-out decision regarding their study program. Assume that you want to start a study-program-selection counseling service. First analyze the process as you and your friends had handled it, search for ways to resolve it, and create a creative process diagram for your counseling service. Consider using before and after Process Diagramming to guide your analysis.

7.14 REFLECT ON HOW YOU PREVIOUSLY RESOLVED ISSUES, PROBLEMS, AND OPPORTUNITIES: Chapters 4 and 7 introduced you to many whole-brain tools intended to improve your ability to define and resolve IPOs. Via assigned exercises and perhaps your unilateral experimentation, you've now had the opportunity to use most of the tools. Assuming you have found at least some of the whole-brain methods useful, reflect on the following and summarize your results in writing:

1. What were your previous individual and/or team approaches? What was in your toolbox?
2. How do your previous approaches differ from this course's and the text's tools, and most importantly, which are more effective and why?

7.15 FRESH LOOK AT AN OLD CHALLENGE (PROCESS DIAGRAMMING): Procrastination is a challenging problem and little professional help is available to a habitual procrastinator. Even before one seeks professional help, the first step will have to be recognizing the problem and kindling the desire to come out of it. Also, most procrastinators can be helped to self-recover. Take a blue sky approach, which in the context of this book means to be creative and innovative, to come up with a solution for students who are habitual procrastinators. Describe the environmental, social, cultural, economic, psychological and/or physiological challenges; state the type of procrastinators that you will target; state the assumptions made and theories used; and then describe, in bulleted form or using Process Diagramming, the steps that you would take to make a difference in the situation.

7.16 **DRAW A PICTURE (FREEHAND DRAWING):** Select an object, process or service that you think you understand well. Now you want to explain this to a 10-year old. Study the object, process or service again and then develop freehand sketch or sketch series, annotated with brief notes, to describe how it works. The goal is to communicate the essentials, not to produce a formal drawing. Notice that as you begin to sketch, you become aware of gaps in your understanding of the device, process or service; as a result, you have to probe deeper. You have to also take care that the drawings and annotations are meaningful for the child. Take care not to over-simplify the sketches. Some potential examples, to get you thinking are as follows:

- Making and receiving a phone call
- The water cycle in Nature
- The digestion of food
- The logarithmic scale
- Vortex based cleaning of water
- The El Niño effect
- Ozone depletion

7.17 **MUSIC THAT SUPPORTS THINKING:** This chapter (Section 7.5.2) indicates that music can help focus your attention. This raises the practical question of what kinds of music enhance studying. For example, is it classical, instrumental jazz, country, rock, or some other category? Organize your team to explore this question by interviewing students and asking them what kind of music they prefer when they want to do some serious studying. Emphasize the studying part to separate that use of music from their overall music preferences. Prepare a brief report that indicates the number and types of students you contacted and summarizes their studying music preferences.

7.18 **TAKING ON A CONTROVERSIAL CAMPUS ISSUE (SIX THINKING CAPS):** Form a diverse team, and then collectively scan your campus scene looking for IPOs. Select one, preferably a controversial one. Consider acquiring six caps with the dominant colors described in Section 7.7.4. Using actual caps, not just images of caps, will help your group understand and use the method.

Starting with the blue cap, apply Six Thinking Caps to your chosen IPO, generally following the guidance offered in Section 7.7.6. Throughout the process, be very firm about "what cap everyone is wearing right now" because the resulting group focus at any point in your discussion is key to the success of this collaboration tool. First, seek a broad and deep definition of the IPO. Then, possibly using some the tools described in this text, generate many potential resolutions, with hopefully some of them being creative or innovative. Finally, recommend a course of action. You will probably find yourself going through the six caps and then returning to some of them before wrapping up with the blue cap. Write a report that describes your IPO, indicates your potential options for resolving it, and presents your recommended course of action.

8

Creativity and Innovation Examples From Various Engineering Specialties

> We recognize that we cannot survive on meditation,
> poems, and sunsets. We are restless.
> We have the irresistible urge to dip our hands into the stuff
> of the earth and do something with it.
> —*Samuel C. Florman, engineer and author*

Objectives:

After studying this chapter, you will be able to:

- Use six engineering specialties to illustrate the diversity of creativity and innovation in the engineering profession
- Describe lessons learned from the creative/innovative cases

- Give examples of other opportunities to be creative and innovative
- Discuss the importance of engineering relative to many other professions

8.1 MORE EXAMPLES TO ENGAGE YOU

Now that you've studied twenty whole-brain methods in Chapters 4 and 7, you are likely to see their potential for helping you and teams you serve on be much more creative and innovative. Perhaps you are even anxious to use some of the tools to address real challenges—and of course you can, because each of us is surrounded, whether we are students or practitioners, by real engineering and other challenges.

Over eighty examples of creative/innovative approaches to technical and non-technical IPOs are at least briefly described in the preceding chapters of this book, as summarized in Table 5.1. Building on those examples and on your exposure to many whole-brain methods and as further support for your creative/innovative urges, this chapter presents a sampling of creative/innovative results drawn from widely varying engineering specialties in more depth.

Although I cannot usually link one or more of the whole-brain methods to the processes used in these examples, you can safely assume that the essentials of some of those tools were employed. The products and processes produced in each of the examples presented in this chapter clearly used the input of engineers, scientists, and others. However, for simplicity and because engineers are my primary audience, I am focusing on engineering specialties. For your benefit, each description concludes with a Lessons Learned section. The lessons relate mostly to creativity and innovation, but some also address wider realities of engineering practice.

8.2 AEROSPACE ENGINEERING: LANDING A ROVER ON MARS

Early in this century, a team of US National Aeronautics and Space Administration (NASA) engineers and scientists was challenged to transport a one-ton robot 352 million miles to Mars. Once it entered the Mars atmosphere, the robot, which would be called the Curiosity rover, was to be gently set down so that it could move about, gather images, monitor the environment, and drill into the planet's surface.

8.2.1 How They Did It

After nine years of persistent creative-innovative effort, which began with a three-day brainstorming session in 2003, they thought they knew how to meet the challenge and were ready to go. They were prepared to take Curiosity, the six-wheeled robot illustrated in Figure 8.1, to Mars.

The team's persistence, creativity, and innovation paid off. Curiosity began its work on Mars in August 2012. This is how the amazing feat was accomplished (Ouellette 2013, Wall 2012):

1. Beginning with a November 2011 blast off from Cape Canaveral, Florida, a rocket traveled for eight months at up to 13,200 miles per hour and took the payload to the Mars atmosphere.
2. The rocket ejected the space capsule, which carried landing gear with the robot attached to the landing gear's underside.
3. The capsule deployed a supersonic parachute that slowed the descent of the two components to two hundred miles per hour.
4. Bolts exploded, releasing the parachute, and then rockets on the landing gear fired to slow the descent to two miles per hour.
5. The landing gear/robot combination hovered sixty feet above Mars' surface while cables lowered the robot to the planet's surface. The landing gear, appropriately, was called the *sky crane*.

Figure 8.1
This artist's concept shows how the Curiosity rover might look as it explored Mars.

(SergeyDV/Shutterstock)

6. Cable cutters severed the cable links when, on August 2, 2012, the robot was safely on the Mars surface, and the landing gear moved away and intentionally crashed—its mission accomplished.

7. Curiosity went to work, as shown in the self-portrait in Figure 8.2, which is a mosaic of dozens of images taken in April and May 2014. The composite image does not show the rover's arm.

Figure 8.2
Nine years of persistent creativity and innovation enabled Curiosity, the robot, to travel 352 million miles in eight months so it could work on Mars.

(JPL-Caltech/MSSS/NASA)

The process summarized in the preceding seven steps was appropriately called *Audacity*. Successfully dealing with the radio delay between Earth and Mars meant the engineers and scientists knew they could not control the system in real time. Therefore, they had to exercise control autonomously, and they did so, assisted by five hundred thousand lines of computer code.

8.2.2 Lessons Learned

Landing the Curiosity rover certainly illustrates the creative/innovative power of persistence. It also demonstrates collaboration, as captured by mechanical engineer Steltzner, who led the effort and said, "That is one of the beautiful things about engineering. It is a collaborative art" (Ouellette 2013). Returning to persistence, recall President Coolidge's "persistence and determination alone are omnipotent" comment, quoted in Section 6.8. We engineers can confidently be persistent partly because our education, experience, and observations enable us to understand fundamental physical, chemical, and biological principles and use them to do what needs to be done.

8.3 AGRICULTURAL ENGINEERING: PRECISION AGRICULTURE

Creativity and innovation are a common thread in the almost 250-year history of US agriculture, and engineers have played a major role. The following are a few examples of many and varied technical and nontechnical agriculture accomplishments (Taylor and Whelan 2014; USDA 2014):

- Invention of the cotton gin by Eli Whitney in 1793. This machine revolutionized cotton production by speeding up the process of removing seeds from cotton fiber. The word *gin* was derived from *engine*.
- Passage of the federal Morrill Land Grant College Act in 1862, which gave added impetus to formal agricultural education by granting land to states for establishing colleges that would teach agriculture and what was referred to as the *mechanic arts* (and now would be primarily engineering).
- Work by George Washington Carver at Tuskegee Institute from 1900 to 1910 to develop ways of diversifying southern agriculture by finding new uses for peanuts, sweet potatoes, and soybeans.
- Development of precision agriculture, beginning in the 1990s, with the first substantial workshop held in Minneapolis in 1992.

One indication of US agriculture's success is that today's farm population, which is about 1 percent of the US population, produces ample food for the nation and beyond (Alston et al. 2010). Let's examine precision agriculture, one of this discipline's innovative achievements.

8.3.1 Elements of Precision Agriculture

Precision agriculture may be defined as "a management system that is information and technology based, is site specific, and uses one or more of the following sources of data: soils, crops, nutrients, pests, moisture, or yield, for optimum profitability, sustainability, and protection of the environment" (McLoud, Gronwald, and Kuykendall 2007). From a farmer's perspective, the building blocks for successful application of precision agriculture are as follows (Downey, Giles, and Slaughter 2004; McLoud, Gronwald, and Kuykendall 2007; Taylor and Whelan 2014):

1. **Data-collection process:** Data needs include, but are not limited to, soil type, temperature, moisture, nutrients, and organic matter; crop biomass; weed type

and location; crop yield; and land elevation. Examples of data sources include soil maps; topographic maps; soil sampling; ground-based platforms; and satellite, aerial, and drone imaging. All data collection must include temporal and spatial recording, with the latter usually being performed with GPS to facilitate later analysis and decision making.

2. **Data-management system:** Given the voluminous amount of necessary data, a farmer must have a system for organizing and processing data so that it's available for making decisions. Commercial and public domain software is available to manage data, including producing maps and other images that present inter- and intrafield spatial and temporal changes in crops and conditions that affect them.

3. **Analysis and decision-making process:** Data are used to recognize and solve problems and meet goals. Because analysis and decision making are complex and require significant hands-on time, consultants are often used to set up and manage the process.

4. **Specialized implementation equipment:** The purpose of this high-tech building block is twofold: (1) spatially apply crop inputs, such as seeds, fertilizers, herbicides, and pesticides at variable rates determined by current and expected site-specific field conditions; (2) measure crop yields spatially and temporally in order to assess results. Examples of specialized equipment include GPS guidance systems, auto-steer tractors, yield monitors, electrical conductivity and moisture-measuring devices, weed imagers, variable-rate applicators (Figure 8.3), variable center pivot irrigators, biomass sensors, and yield monitors. Considering the range of technologies used, precision agriculture nicely demonstrates Borrowing Brilliance, the whole-brain tool described in Section 4.3.

5. **Evaluation and improvement:** Using the extensive and growing data base, the precision agriculture process is assessed, and changes are identified and scheduled.

The prime benefit of precision agriculture is potential cost reduction through more effective and efficient use of resources, with a resulting improved economic return for farmers. It also reduces the farmer's risk, consistent with the idea that knowledge used is power. Precision agriculture can provide improved data recording and retrieval for food safety and environmental protection purposes. Soil and

Figure 8.3
Light-reflectance sensors on the front of this applicator measure nitrogen deficiency so that nitrogen can be automatically applied at the optimum rate.

(Newell Kitchen/USDA)

Figure 8.4
Five essentially simultaneous steps, all sharing a common spatial and temporal reference, define precision agriculture.

Source: Adapted from Taylor and Whelan 2014.

water quality benefits may occur because of reduced or more targeted application of nutrients, pesticides, herbicides, and irrigation (McLoud, Gronwald, and Kuykendall 2007, Taylor and Whelan 2014).

8.3.2 The Process: A Continuous Improvement Cycle

Using the building blocks just discussed, the precision agriculture process is illustrated in Figure 8.4. In its simplest form, the process is viewed as consisting of the following five steps: data collection, data management, data analysis and decision making, spatial and temporal implementation, and evaluation and improvement, all conducted with respect to a common spatial and temporal reference. In actuality, although one step may be emphasized at any given time, all steps essentially occur simultaneously in a dynamic fashion. Given the wealth of spatial and temporal data, the precision agriculture process enables classic continuous improvement.

8.3.3 Lessons Learned

As an outsider looking in at the agricultural engineering discipline, I marvel at how so few (the agricultural community enabled by that engineering discipline) can do so much in that only 1 percent of the US population provides food for the entire US population and beyond. The discipline's history of continued efforts to be more effective and efficient is admirable and offers a continuous improvement lesson. Another lesson learned, as exemplified by precision agriculture's adoption of an array of technologies, such as drones, satellites, GPS, and robotics, is that any engineering discipline can borrow brilliance from various engineering and other disciplines.

8.4 BIOMEDICAL (ELECTRICAL AND MECHANICAL) ENGINEERING: BIONICS

Five hundred or more people in the United States have one or more limbs surgically amputated each day. These limbs are lost for a variety of reasons, such as diabetes, heart disease, cancer, accidents, war, and various illnesses. Limb loss is expected to increase in an aging (and maybe less health-conscious) society. Prostheses—that is, artificial devices that augment or replace a missing or impaired body part—are highly valued by most amputees (Platt 2012). In addition to loss of limbs, some individuals suffer partial or complete loss of hearing and vision.

HISTORIC NOTE: PROSTHETICS GO WAY BACK

As one indication of human creativity and innovation, prosthetic devices first appeared three thousand years ago. For example, in 2000, archeologists working in Cairo, Egypt, discovered a very real-looking prosthetic toe fashioned from wood and leather and attached to the foot of the three-thousand-year-old mummified remains of a wealthy Egyptian. In the Middle Ages, some armored knights were equipped with prosthetic limbs crafted by armorers, probably more for appearance than function. And of course, pirates had wooden peg legs and artificial hands with metal hooks. In the fifteenth and sixteenth centuries, European doctors added hinges, locking joints, and improved means of attaching prostheses.

In more recent times, newer, lighter, and stronger materials, such as plastics and carbon-fiber composites, have been used. The socket, the portion of a prosthesis that interfaces with the limb's stump, has been improved, as has the joint mechanism, all of which are suggested by Figure 8.5.

Figure 8.5
Prosthetic devices have advanced through use of lighter materials, better interfaces, and improved joint mechanisms.
(Belahoche/Fotolia)

Physical therapy accompanies a new prosthesis so that the device performs well in everyday activities. Functional devices also have appeared—that is, those that can be controlled mechanically by cables connected to other parts of the body, such as a prosthetic arm connected to a healthy shoulder. Motor-powered prostheses are controlled by the patient using switches or buttons. The most recent, exciting, and creative/innovative development that takes prosthetics up to the next level, as discussed next, is bionics (Clements 2014; Herr 2014).

8.4.1 Bionics: Taking Prosthetics to the Next Level

Within the medical field, *bionics* means the study and use of mechanical and electronic systems that function like living organisms (or part of them), with the systems being controlled by the organism. This approach is potentially powerful in prosthetics because even when flesh and bone are damaged or missing, nerves and related brain parts continue to function. Therefore, in bionics, a person's damaged or missing body parts are replaced with devices connected to the individual's nervous system, and the devices respond to commands from the person's brain.

The prosthetic device, a machine that may be called a neural prosthesis or robotic prosthesis, is linked to the brain (Fischman 2010; Herr 2014). As you can imagine, many specialists contribute to advancing bionics, including medical doctors, neuroscientists, physical therapists, and, certainly not least, biomedical engineers. For our purposes, *biomedical engineers* are primarily electrical and mechanical engineers.

Linking the Brain and the Prosthesis

From a system perspective, what are the scientific principles and engineering challenges behind neural prostheses? How does bionics work? The challenge in linking the brain and a prosthesis is that although nerves activated by the brain conduct electricity, those nerves cannot be directly spliced and wired to the prosthesis. Even if connections could be made, the connections between nerves and wires would invite infections. Furthermore, those nerve signals are very weak, and regardless of how the brain–prosthesis connection is made, those signals have to be detected so they can be used.

The answer was found to be in muscles: "When muscles contract, they give off an electrical burst strong enough to be detected by an electrode placed on the skin." As suggested by Figure 8.6, biomedical engineer and physician Kuiken "developed a technique to reroute severed nerves from their old, damaged spots to other muscles that could give their muscles the proper boost" (Fischman 2010). Those nerves start in the brain and extend into what remains of the lost limb.

After the intricate operation, the patient eventually begins to feel parts of the *phantom* (no longer there) limb, the presence and function of which were mapped into his or her brain. Then, the patient is fitted with the bionic limb, which, as also shown in Figure 8.6, has electrodes embedded in the interface (the cup that fits around the stump), with the idea that the electrodes will sense the muscle signals.

The prosthesis contains one or more electric motors and a microprocessor, and is intended to mimic the action of its natural counterpart. Working with a technical

Figure 8.6

The brain–prosthesis connection begins with an operation to connect residual nerves to muscles, which in turn transmit signals to electrodes in the prosthesis.

Source: Adapted from Fischman 2010.

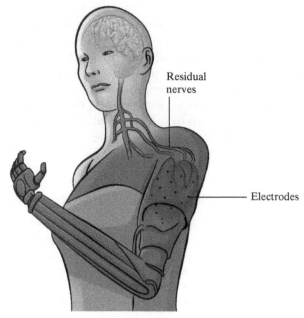

Residual nerves

Electrodes

The Bionic Body

expert, the patient learns to convert those signals to desired movements of the artificial limb. The microprocessor in the prosthesis is gradually programmed to look for the correct signals from the brain via the muscles and activate the appropriate motors. From then on, conscious and subconscious thinking activate the prosthesis (Fischman 2010).

More Innovation

As we might expect within such a creative/innovative environment, other improvements are underway. For example, biomedical engineers are adding more motors to the prostheses for more functions and developing pressure-sensitive figure pads to aid patients. Other biomedical engineers are using bionics to give new life to a limb that although it is still basically intact, does not function because of nerve damage between the brain and the limb (Fischman 2010). Exoskeleton neuroprostheses—that is, devices that wrap around limbs—are being developed for use by paraplegics and people with muscular disabilities and to generally enhance people's physical capabilities (Herr 2014).

Retinal implant neuroprostheses help to restore vision. They consist of a retinal implant, a camera to capture light, and a processor to convert incoming video signals into electrical signals for transmission to the cortex. A similar neuroprosthesis, called a cochlear implant and named after the coil in the inner ear, is available to restore hearing (Gibb 2012).

These vision and hearing neuroprostheses remind us, as nicely stated by scientist Gibb, that "in reality, hearing, vision, and other sensory impressions occur inside the brain, created from variations in the chemicals, light, air, and physical forces we're exposed to." Our ears don't hear, and our eyes don't see: They are visible sensory receptors that convert sound waves and light to electrical signals that are sent to the brain for processing, enabling us to hear and see. Replacing or repairing the natural sensor function continues to hold great promise for collaboration between engineers and medical professionals.

Figure 8.7
Kitts' bionic prosthesis, which is controlled with her thoughts, enables her to perform just about any activity with the five-year-old children in her day-care center.

(Clay Owen/Knoxville News Sentinel)

8.4.2 Bionics Examples

Amanda Kitts, a Knoxville, Tennessee, day-care center operator, lost her left arm from just above the elbow in a 2006 car accident. She benefits from the creative/innovative efforts to restore the links between the brain and the mind (see Figure 8.7).

Her neuroprosthesis consists of three motors, a metal frame, an electronics network, and a white plastic cup that fits over her biceps. After the operation to reroute nerves to muscles, the nerves grew deeper into the muscles. At four months, Kitts began to feel different parts of her phantom hand. Working with a research engineer, she gradually learned how to use her thoughts to control her prosthesis; it wasn't easy. When asked how it works, she said, "I don't really think about it. I just move it" (Fischman 2010).

Thirty years ago, mechanical engineer and biophysicist Hugh Herr lost both legs in a mountain-climbing accident. Severe frostbite required the amputation of both his limbs below the knee. Now he heads the biomechatronics group in the MIT Media Lab, where he led the development of two robotic prostheses that let him not only walk, but also run.

Ballroom dancer Adrianne Haslet-Davis lost her left leg as a result of the 2013 Boston Marathon terrorist bombing. Under the creative/innovative leadership of Herr, and with the participation of many experts, a robotic prosthesis was designed and built for Haslet-Davis: Its intended purpose went way beyond walking. About two hundred days after losing her left leg, Haslet-Davis and a partner danced beautifully during a TED (Technology, Entertainment, and Design) Talk (Herr 2014).

PERSONAL: TRY TED

TED Talks, although formally addressing technology, entertainment, and design, go beyond such topics into science, business, the arts, and global issues. Each audiovisual presentation lasts eighteen minutes or less, is well prepared, and is professionally presented.

> Whenever you view a TED Talk, you will simultaneously learn about an interesting topic of your choice and receive a lesson in effective speaking. TED Talks are closely aligned with this book because both value innovation. If you want to learn more, go to the following website, launched in 2007, where you can view any of the talks at no cost: www.TED.com.

8.4.3 Lessons Learned

What immediately comes to my mind, no pun intended, as a result of this bionics introduction is that if creative/innovative minds conceive something, they can probably make it happen. With bionics, creative/innovative individuals conceived using minds to control prostheses and made it happen with the potential to vastly improve the quality of life for many. As with other creations and innovations described in this chapter, the bionics story is one of collaboration among many specialties, with two of the leading ones being electrical and mechanical engineering. You could be one of those collaborators and help improve the quality of life for many people around the globe.

8.5 CHEMICAL ENGINEERING: DESALINATION

Consider the world's supply of water. Only 2.5 percent is fresh water; two-thirds of that is frozen in glaciers and ice caps. A growing global population increasingly wants to draw on the 97.5 percent of Earth's water—salt water—in the oceans (IDA 2014). However, that water will kill humans. When the body senses salt in its systems, cells expel water molecules through the process of osmosis to dilute the salt. This depletes the cells of moisture, which impedes kidney function and damages the brain.

Recall the line "water, water, everywhere, nor any drop to drink" in English poet Coleridge's "The Rime of the Ancient Mariner." Many of Earth's inhabitants are surrounded by water, whether seawater or otherwise undrinkable water, but don't have "any drop to drink" (Dove 2014). The chemical engineering profession is taking the lead in meeting this challenge by creatively and innovatively developing and continuing to improve desalination.

8.5.1 Introduction to Desalination

Desalination is the process by which dissolved salts are removed from seawater to produce potable water for domestic and municipal purposes. Desalination occurs naturally in nature in the form of the hydrologic cycle. Water evaporates from the oceans and from lakes and streams via the sun's energy, leaving dissolved minerals and other substances behind. The water vapor condenses and forms clouds that produce rain, which restores freshwater sources, and the cycle continues. Engineered desalination seeks to augment this process in site-specific locations to meet human needs (IDA 2014; USGS 2014).

The US Geological Survey defines *freshwater* as having a dissolved salt concentration by weight of one thousand parts per million (ppm) or less. In contrast, the oceans contain about 35,000 ppm (USGS 2014). Therefore, the engineering challenge of desalination is to economically remove at least 97 percent of the salt in an environmentally sensitive manner.

HISTORIC NOTE: CENTURIES OF DESALINATION

The need for freshwater, coupled with human creativity and innovation, led humans through two millennia of desalination. According to the International Desalination Association (2014), Aristotle wrote about seawater distillation in 320 BC, the Romans distilled seawater using condensation on fleece, the Greeks distilled with sponges, and seafaring explorers desalinated seawater during long voyages. Until the end of World War II, thermal evaporation followed by condensation was the most common form of distillation. In the postwar years, scientists and engineers began to investigate other desalination approaches, such as osmotic processes developed in the 1950s and described in this section.

As of 2009, about fourteen thousand desalination plants were operating in over 120 countries. The freshwater they were producing accounted for less than 1 percent of the world's freshwater consumption. Approximately 70 percent of the globe's desalination capacity is in the Middle East; California and Florida are the principal users of desalination in the United States. The process's cost has restrained its global use. Today, about 90 percent of desalination plants use either the reverse osmosis or multiflash process, with the former being the most common because it is usually less costly (Dove 2014; USGS 2014).

8.5.2 Osmosis

As is the case in essentially all creative/innovative efforts within engineering, the design and operation of desalination plants around the globe draws on fundamentals, those concepts and theories you begin to study as a first-year engineering student. These basics, most of which are taught and learned throughout your undergraduate engineering program, include osmosis. Let's discuss osmosis principles; depending on where you are as a student or practitioner, this will be either an introduction to the topic or a review of it.

Osmosis is the spontaneous net passage or diffusion of molecules of a solvent, such as water, through a semipermeable membrane from a place of lower solute concentration to a place of higher concentration, while blocking passage of the solutes, until the solute concentration is equal on both sides. Consider the left side of Figure 8.8, which shows a container of water at time zero with a low concentration of salt on the left side of the semipermeable membrane and high concentration of salt on the right side.

Osmosis begins as soon as the container and its contents are prepared. The system will seek equilibrium—that is, equal salt concentration on both sides of the membrane—and will achieve that state due to water moving from the left side to the right side, as shown on the right side of Figure 8.8. Water and not salt moves through the membrane because water is composed of much smaller molecules than salt. The driving force—the net movement to the left of water molecules through the membrane—is called *osmotic pressure* and is indicated by the final difference in water levels (Dove 2014; Kershner 2014).

Although our primary interest is understanding osmosis so that we can get on with further exploration of desalination, consider the vital and broad application of osmosis within the human body, including the brain. As noted in Section 8.5.1,

Figure 8.8
Osmosis is the natural process by which a solvent-solute system partitioned by a semipermeable membrane seeks equal solute concentration by, in this case, having water move from left to right, driven by osmotic pressure.

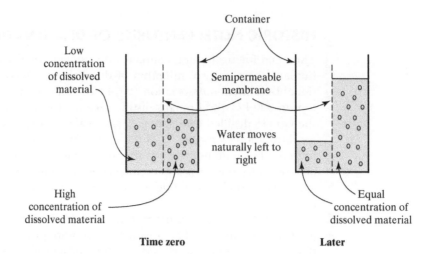

when the body senses salt in its systems, its cells expel water molecules through the cell membranes to dilute the salt. If that osmotic action continues unabated, it threatens the kidneys and the brain. More generally, osmosis is used throughout the body to regulate the flow of certain substances, such as water and gases, into and out of cells (Baggaley 2001).

Returning to desalination, understanding it requires understanding osmosis, but that is not enough. Desalination uses osmosis but reverses it, as described in the next section.

8.5.3 Reverse Osmosis

Reverse osmosis capitalizes on one of the natural or "forward" osmosis features. More specifically, if we are considering two saltwater solutions of different concentrations separated by a semipermeable membrane, water, but not salt, moves through the membrane because water is composed of much smaller molecules than salt. This fact is the key to reverse osmosis.

For an illustration of reverse osmosis, assume saltwater is placed on one side of a semipermeable membrane and pure water on the other side, as shown in Figure 8.9. Then, a large pressure, greater than the opposing left-to-right osmotic pressure, is applied to the liquid in the left side of the container. Freshwater flows

Figure 8.9
Reverse osmosis is the engineered process by which a solvent-solute system, partitioned by a semipermeable membrane, uses externally imposed pressure to force water from a high-salt concentration supply to create an acceptably low-salt supply.

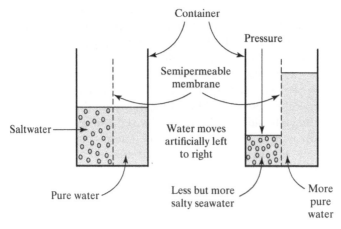

from left to right through the membrane, adding to the freshwater supply on the right side of the membrane (Dove 2014; Kershner 2014).

Reverse osmosis became operational in the 1960s as a result of the work of chemical engineers Loeb and Sourirajan. They developed membranes from cellulose acetate, a polymer used in photographic film, that markedly improved the water diffusion rate. In 1965, that key innovation led to the world's first, although small, reverse osmosis desalination plant, which went into operation in Coalinga, California (Economist 2008). Pores used in today's reverse osmosis membranes are one hundred thousandth the diameter of a human hair (ACS 2014).

8.5.4 An Example: Tampa

A brief review of the Tampa Bay Seawater Desalination facility in Florida introduces us to the water supply achievements of chemical engineers and others (Tampa Bay Water 2014). This reverse osmosis facility can provide twenty-five million gallons per day (mgd) of drinking water, which meets about 10 percent of the region's needs.

The plant's principal sequential processes, when producing 25 mgd of drinking water, may be summarized as follows:

- Withdraw 44 mgd from the cooling water being discharged from Tampa Electric's Big Bend Power Station, which, along with the reverse osmosis facility, is on Tampa Bay.
- Filter out debris (e.g., shells and wood) greater than one-quarter inch in size using screens.
- Settle out particles in sedimentation tanks.
- Remove smaller particles using sand filters.
- Capture microscopic particles in diatomaceous earth filters.
- Remove remaining particles by pumping the water through cartridge filters.
- Separate the water from the salt by pumping the seawater through reverse osmosis membranes, leaving 19 mgd twice-as-salty seawater to be mixed with the discharge from the power station and returned to Tampa Bay.
- Post-treat the remaining 25 mgd of drinking water to stabilize it.
- Pump 25 mgd of drinking water to a regional facility, blend it with treated drinking water from other sources, and deliver the water to users.

8.5.5 Building on Positives to Meet Challenges

Clearly, the principal benefit of desalinization, regardless of the process used, is the ability to draw on the vast ocean source of water. We can get at some of that 97.5 percent of Earth's water that is undrinkable and provide a basic human necessity.

Challenges of the reverse osmosis approach to desalination include high construction and operation and maintenance costs relative to more traditional water supply treatment methods. These costs reflect in part having to engineer environmentally sound ways to deal with the leftover salt—that is, the brine that has twice the salt concentration of seawater. Higher maintenance costs occur in part because membranes must be protected by pretreatment unit processes and cleaned frequently and because of energy usage. Distillation plant inflows and outflows also can adversely affect marine life. (IDA 2014; Kershner 2014).

These negatives pose creativity/innovation challenges for chemical engineers and other engineering and scientific professionals. These challenges will be met, as suggested by the following recent and current research and development efforts:

- Use of solar and wind energy to power the desalination process (Harrington 2013; IDA 2014)

- Biomimetic membranes (see Section 7.2) inspired by those in human kidneys and red blood cells, which exhibit high water permeability and favorable solute-trapping selectivity (IDA 2014)
- Lessening the impact on marine life during a distillation plant's intake and outfall processes (IDA 2014)
- Using fully submerged buoys to extract wave energy and use it to pump water to onshore hydroelectric turbines that will send water through reverse osmosis membranes in a desalinization plant (Harrington 2013)

8.5.6 Lessons Learned

As the engineering profession continues to create and innovate, as illustrated by reverse osmosis desalination, valuable advancements draw on science and engineering science topics taught and learned early in the engineer's formal education. As engineering students, when we are introduced to fundamentals such as Newton's laws of motion, conservation of energy, or osmosis, we may question the value of what appear to be esoteric, theoretical principles. However, as illustrated by the preceding desalination discussion and by the other creative/innovative developments described in this chapter, those basics are the foundation of creativity and innovation; they define what is possible. It is up to us to make it happen—and maybe, for some of us, to discover additional fundamentals.

Another lesson learned from desalination is the idea that when engineers resolve a societal or environmental challenge, they inevitably produce additional related challenges. The amazing global benefits of desalination illustrate this phenomenon. As suggested by the previous section, engineers will creatively and innovatively resolve the new issues.

8.6 TRANSPORTATION ENGINEERING: TEMPORARY USE OF A BRIDGE

In 2009, civil engineers faced a challenge involving two bridges over the Capilano River near Vancouver, British Columbia. As shown in Figure 8.10, the river is crossed

Figure 8.10
The two-lane bridge needs to be replaced with a three-lane bridge.

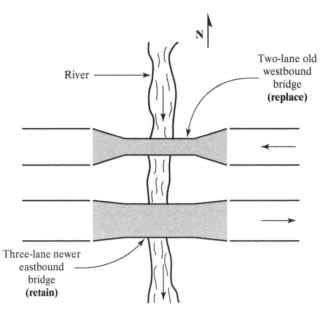

Figure 8.11
The old two-lane bridge consists of a two-span steel truss structure.

(British Columbia Ministry of Transportation and Infrastructure)

by two bridges owned by the British Columbia Ministry of Transportation and Infrastructure. One was a relatively new, three-lane, eastbound bridge served by a three-lane highway, and the other, as shown in Figure 8.11, was an old, two-lane, westbound bridge constructed in 1929 to serve two lanes of opposite traffic but now serving the volume of three lanes of one-way traffic. The two-lane bridge needed to be replaced by a three-lane structure consistent with the three-lane highway it serves (Johnson, Queen, and Sandhu 2012).

8.6.1 Options and the Solution

Because of high traffic demands and lack of practical alternative routes, a temporary detour bridge would be required for westbound vehicles during construction. The temporary detour bridge would have to be temporarily constructed as close to the old bridge as possible while allowing space to construct the wider westbound three-lane bridge. This initial concept is illustrated in Figure 8.12.

Review of that conventional approach led to the development of an innovative second option (Figure 8.13). The old bridge would be moved to the north—slid onto a newly constructed temporary central pier and two temporary abutments—to serve as a temporary detour bridge. Then, the new westbound bridge would be constructed and put into service and the old bridge removed. This bridge-sliding option was selected.

Moving the old bridge to its new temporary location caused minimal traffic interference. Highway traffic was disrupted for only seventeen hours (from 6:00 p.m. on Saturday, June 19, 2010, to 10:30 a.m. on Sunday) while the old bridge was pushed to its temporary new location. The sliding operation used the following four steps:

1. Lift the bridge with vertical hydraulic jacks at the west and east abutments and the center pier.

Figure 8.12
The first option considered was to build a temporary westbound detour bridge, remove the old westbound bridge, construct the new westbound bridge, and remove the temporary bridge.

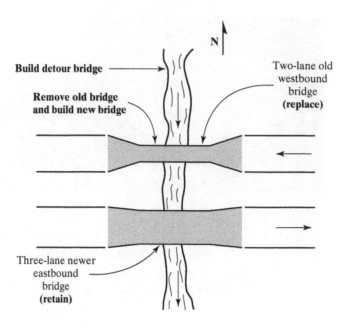

2. Attach sliding shoes to the bottom of the bridge at the intended contact points and install and grease the underlying steel sliding tracks.
3. Lower the bridge so that the sliding shoes rest on the tracks.
4. Use horizontal jacks to slide the bridge to its new location on the just-constructed and temporary central pier and two temporary abutments.

Looking from west to east, Figure 8.14 shows the old bridge in its new temporary location serving as a detour during construction of the new westbound, three-lane bridge. The completed project, with the new westbound bridge in place and the old bridge removed, is presented in Figure 8.15.

Besides the benefit of minimal traffic interference, the owner saved about $500,000 because moving the old bridge to a temporary new location was less costly

Figure 8.13
The first option led to the innovative second idea, in which the old westbound bridge would be moved to the north to serve as a temporary westbound detour while the new westbound bridge was constructed.

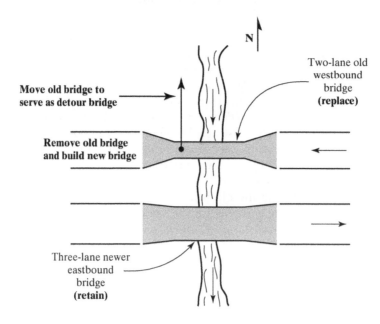

Figure 8.14
Contractors slid the old bridge to its temporary new location to carry westbound traffic so that the new wider westbound bridge could be constructed.

(British Columbia Ministry of Transportation and Infrastructure)

than constructing a new temporary bridge. Furthermore, the selected option had minimal impact on the local salmon runs in the Capilano River. How might this innovative concept apply elsewhere? How might we slide, lift, lower, turn, tip over, or turn around something to serve a temporary function during construction?

Jones (2012) describes a 2012 Nevada Department of Transportation project referred to as *accelerated bridge construction* (ABC). In this case, bridge slides

Figure 8.15
The complete project with the new westbound bridge in place and the old bridge removed.

(British Columbia Ministry of Transportation and Infrastructure)

somewhat like the one described previously were used for both the northbound and southbound lanes of Interstate 15. The two new bridges were constructed next to the existing bridges; as soon as the existing bridges were removed, the new bridges were slid into place with minimal traffic disruption.

ABC and other sliding approaches are transitioning from being innovative to becoming common, as is often the ultimate result of innovation and how the engineering field moves forward. As a student or practitioner, you can help the profession advance and provide even better service to society by being open to new ideas and creative and innovative approaches in your studies and work.

8.6.2 Lessons Learned

First ideas are often not the best ideas. They tend to reflect the Einstellung Effect discussed in Section 3.4. That is, as in the case described here, when faced with a well-defined challenge, we first tend to recall a past similar challenge and how it was resolved. Although that line of thinking is prudent and may ultimately be fruitful, we should parallel it with a creative/innovative process using one or more of the tools described in this text. Allow for major divergent thinking to generate many options; then, and only then, move to convergent thinking to sort them out.

Another lesson learned from this case study is the value of collaboration during planning and design between engineers and contractors. Although each ultimately has specific project responsibilities, sharing knowledge early on enhances the probability that creative/innovative ideas will be discovered and successfully implemented.

8.7 WATER RESOURCES ENGINEERING: MULTIPURPOSE STORM WATER FACILITY

For this example, let's consider the design, financing, and construction of a multipurpose urban storm water management facility (American Society of Civil Engineers and Water Environment Federation 1992; Donohue and Associates 1984). The project and related 2.96 square mile watershed were within and near the city of Valparaiso, Indiana, as shown in Figure 8.16. At the time of the project (the 1980s), Valparaiso had a population of twenty-two thousand. Serious flooding had occurred in recent years, as shown by the flood-prone areas in Figure 8.16, even though the watershed included two storm water detention facilities.

Therefore, the city retained an engineering firm to prepare a comprehensive flood control plan for the watershed and ultimately to design the major recommended facility. This provided an opportunity for the consultant, the client, and others to explore some innovative technical, financial, and other approaches that could benefit the community.

8.7.1 Engineering Guidelines Set the Stage

The engineering firm prepared engineering guidelines, which were supported by the client, to set the stage for taking a comprehensive, innovative approach to solving the flooding caused by medium to large storms. The guidelines are summarized as follows:

- Size and configure storm water storage facilities to store or convey runoff from the one hundred-year recurrence interval, six-hour rainfall occurring under future land use conditions. The six-hour duration was selected using watershed-modeling sensitivity analyses.

Figure 8.16
Serious flooding occurred within one of the watersheds lying wholly or partly within Valparaiso, Indiana.

Source: Adapted from American Society of Civil Engineers and Water Environment Federation 1992.

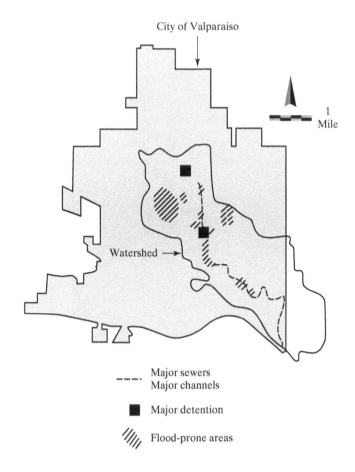

- Resolve flood problems as close as possible to their origin and avoid transferring problems from one location within or outside of the watershed to another.
- Address extensive and serious surface flooding problems with an eye toward beginning to resolve sanitary and combined sewer backup problems.
- Favor gravity inflow and outflow for detention/retention facilities.
- Give preference to a few large, publicly owned and maintained detention/retention facilities and try to avoid many small, privately owned facilities.
- In addition to flood control, consider potential recreational and aesthetic aspects of all detention/retention facilities.

The details will vary, but preparing or assembling planning, design, or other guidelines somewhat like the preceding example is advisable on the front end of or early on into any potentially complex engineering project. Sometimes, such guidelines are included in the engineer and client contract or are prescribed by state, federal, or other entities. However, do what you can to define the depth and breadth of the subsequent engineering as early as possible, especially if you want to set the stage for possibly exploring creative/innovative options. Get everyone on the same page in terms of expectations and craft the guidelines so as to encourage creativity and innovation in addition to conventional approaches. Don't presume the solution.

8.7.2 Analysis and Recommendations

Diagnosis of the watershed hydrologic–hydraulic system using simulation revealed that the existing detention facilities were undersized and that major channels and

Figure 8.17
The engineering firm recommended new and modified detention facilities and channel clearing.
Source: Adapted from American Society of Civil Engineers and Water Environment Federation 1992.

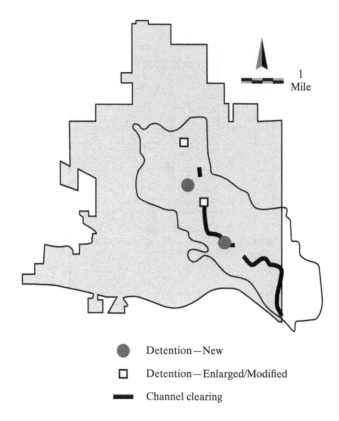

●   Detention—New

☐   Detention—Enlarged/Modified

▬   Channel clearing

conduits through built-up areas had insufficient conveyance capacity. Future urbanization would worsen flooding in scattered locations throughout the watershed. Various alternative structural flood control facilities and nonstructural measures were evaluated. The recommended major improvements, shown in Figure 8.17, include construction of two new detention facilities (one of which will soon be discussed in detail), modification of two existing detention facilities, and extensive channel cleaning and maintenance.

The firm also recommended that the city prepare a program for operation and maintenance of sewers and channels; that owners or renters of residential or commercial property purchase flood insurance; that the city review and upgrade its storm water management regulations; and that the city, perhaps in cooperation with the county, develop a storm water management plan for all watersheds in the Valparaiso area.

Since issuance of the plan, the recommended channel cleaning was completed, the two existing detention facilities enlarged as recommended, and the two recommended new detention facilities constructed. In order to illustrate some creative/innovative aspects of this project, let's focus on the northernmost and largest of the two recommended new detention facilities.

8.7.3 Design of the Major Detention Facility

Figure 8.18 shows the twenty-seven-acre site then available. Although it was in the city, it was owned by the county because it was the recent home of the annual county fair and other outdoor events. Also shown is the initial idea for a single-purpose, offline, rectangular detention facility that would occupy the eastern 41 percent of the site so that the city would not have to purchase all twenty-seven acres or so that the remainder

Figure 8.18
The initial idea was to construct a single-purpose storm water detention facility on the eastern eleven acres of the twenty-seven-acre site.

Source: Adapted from American Society of Civil Engineers and Water Environment Federation 1992.

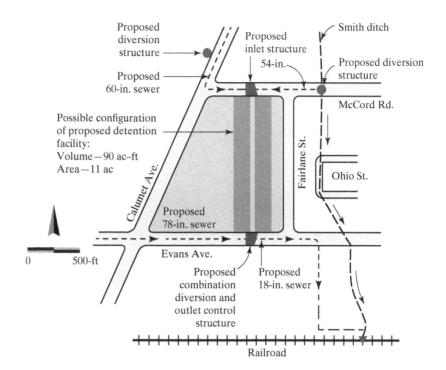

of the available land could be used for other purposes. This is the point at which the engineering group, in keeping with What If (Section 4.12), asked, "What if we used a new point of view?" Instead of moving to the design step, the engineering team stepped back and asked what else was occurring in and near the city.

Coincident with the need to solve the flooding problems, the recreation needs of the city were receiving attention. The park and recreation board contracted preparation of a citywide park master plan. Because that recreation planning effort was carried out approximately parallel to the flood control planning effort, the flood control and park professionals began to collaborate on possible flood control and recreational use of the twenty-seven acres available.

Figure 8.19 presents the initial concept for a flood control/recreation development. The eastern approximately one-third of the site would be excavated to provide the necessary ninety acre-feet, one-hundred-year recurrence interval flood storage when needed, as well as supporting three soccer fields and two softball fields. An additional two softball fields and other athletic fields would occupy the remaining nonflood control portion of the available land, along with a restored building in the southwest corner that would serve as a large park shelter.

Further collaboration and the opportunity to remove an old concrete grandstand on the west center portion of the site resulted in the final site configuration shown in Figure 8.20. A set of terraces would cover the site, and the originally flat site would now have a total relief of thirteen feet, with the lowest area at the outlet in the southeast corner. The least used portions of the facility, such as one of the overflow soccer areas, would be on the lowest levels. In contrast, frequently used areas, such as lighted softball fields, would occupy the highest terraces.

A network of four- to eighteen-inch diameter perforated and corrugated polyethylene pipe would provide subsurface drainage of recreation areas. Recreation surfaces would have a surface slope of at least 1 percent to encourage rapid drainage after rainfall or flooding. Because of these design features, even the lower recreation

Figure 8.19
Collaboration of engineers and park planners led to this initial multipurpose concept.

Source: Adapted from American Society of Civil Engineers and Water Environment Federation 1992.

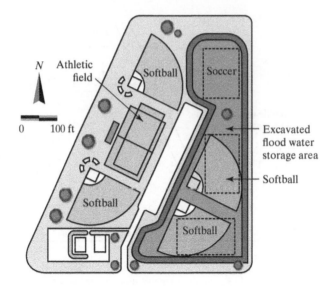

facilities on this site would probably be available for use more often than other single-purpose facilities scattered around the city. The final design provided numerous and varied active and passive recreation opportunities and included onsite provision for service and maintenance facilities and equipment. The value of the constructed project was about $2.4 million then, or about $5 million today.

8.7.4 Finance and Construction of the Facility

After completing the design, the project team turned to financing the multipurpose facility. Major public works projects like this are typically financed through sale of bonds. Again, the team applied the What If approach and, although a bond issue was used to finance much of the cost of the facility, other innovative means of finance were also used. The engineering and park and client group took the thirty-thousand-foot view and asked what else was going on in the Valparaiso area. This perspective led to several cost-saving finance innovations:

- In the summer of 1985, the city and its park and recreation department committed to proceed with the multipurpose project. After obtaining an appraisal

Figure 8.20
Further collaboration produced the final multipurpose design.

Source: Adapted from American Society of Civil Engineers and Water Environment Federation 1992.

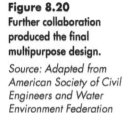

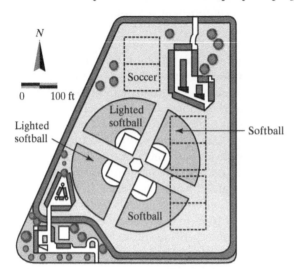

for the twenty-seven-acre fairgrounds site, the city negotiated with the county for site acquisition. The city purchased the site in August 1985 for $300,000, which would be paid in six annual amounts of $50,000 at zero interest. The negotiations included the city agreeing to give the county first right of refusal on a city-owned parking lot close to the county courthouse.

- Negotiations then proceeded with the city and the Valparaiso community schools, with the result that the school system would give the city 11.3 acres of land elsewhere in the city, valued at $254,000. The Valparaiso community schools held this land to meet anticipated future education needs. In return for the land, the city agreed to provide certain recreation facilities at the new fairgrounds facility or elsewhere for use by the school system. This innovative exchange offset most of the cost incurred by the city in purchasing the fairgrounds because the city could sell the land acquired from the school system as a means of recovering the flood control/recreation facility land purchase price or other costs incurred in providing the additional recreation services. With some major financial matters resolved, construction began while innovative financing continued.
- Construction of a bypass highway in the vicinity of Valparaiso, which was underway when the construction began on the flood control/recreation facility, generated a strong demand for fill material. The fill areas were 1.6 miles or more away from the flood control/recreation site, suggesting that a long haul would cause high excavation costs. However, the city began to investigate the possibility of providing fill for the highway project because site excavation costs were a large part (about one-third) of the total cost of the project. The city advertised the availability of up to 210,000 cubic yards of material at its project site and received six bids, with the lowest being submitted by a contractor involved in the bypass highway project. That contractor won the contract and eventually removed 180,500 cubic yards from the site to the highway project for $1.02 per cubic yard ($184,100). Assuming that the original estimate of $4.20 per cubic yard for excavation in 1985 costs would have applied in absence of the tie-in to the highway project, the city saved $574,000 by moving innovatively and quickly, integrating its detention facility construction with the bypass highway construction.
- In exchange for a time extension, the contractor who was excavating and hauling material agreed to provide additional services at no cost to the city. These services included stripping and stockpiling topsoil at the site, rough grading, placing topsoil on the steeper side slopes, seeding and mulching those slopes, and demolishing and removing the previously mentioned concrete grandstand. These services amounted to an additional savings of at least $20,000 to the city.
- Before planning and design of the flood control/recreation project, and completely unrelated to it, the city, state, and federal government had been designing and preparing financing for improvements to a portion of the busy street bordering the west side of what now would be a multipurpose facility. The drainage component of the street improvement project was altered to direct runoff into the flood control/recreation facility. Because this innovation reduced the cost of the street-improvement project, $90,000 of federal and state transportation funds were directed to the city to pay for some of the design and construction costs associated with the outlet control.

Figure 8.21 illustrates some features of the site. The facility functions year-round as a popular place for active and passive recreation. The facility occasionally performs its flood control function, as shown in Figure 8.22.

Figure 8.21
These photos suggest the active and passive recreation activities available within the flood control/recreation facility.

(Stuart Walesh)

Figure 8.22
When needed, the facility provides downstream flood control, as it did in August 2014.

(Stuart Walesh)

Figure 8.23
Offsetting the hydroillogical cycle, representing the likelihood of public apathy, may require creative/ innovative communication and other measures.

Source: Adapted from Cyre and Shearer 1987.

8.7.5 Offsetting the Public's Short Memory

Reflect on an added benefit of a multipurpose project: Experience indicates that interest in flood control facilities rises and falls with the flood waters. If the detention facility described here had been for the single purpose of flood control, community interest may not have been sustained, in spite of the public information efforts, at a high enough level to see the project through to implementation.

During and shortly after a flood or similar rare and disastrous natural event, political leaders with public encouragement are willing to take action, at least in the form of engineering planning and design efforts. However, months later, when the engineering is completed and costly recommendations are made, political and public interest often wanes and little or nothing is done (Walesh 1989). This common aspect of flood-related public works projects is summarized as the "hydroillogical" cycle (Cyre and Shearer 1987), illustrated in Figure 8.23; offsetting it may require creative/innovative means. In the case of the previously described project, the detention facility's recreation features, some of which would be available year-round, were publicized and helped to broaden and sustain community interest, including finding ways to finance the project. Therefore, the project moved promptly ahead and, in fact, is used every day.

8.7.6 State Legislation

Partly because of a suggestion by the project's consulting engineer, the city engineer and a local state legislator took the lead in seeking state legislation to provide any Indiana municipality or similar entity with the option of establishing a storm water management utility. This type of utility enables a community to charge a fee for storm water management services, as it does for water, wastewater, and other services, and to use such funds to solve existing flooding problems and prevent development of new ones. Typically, the fee is based on some indicator of the amount of runoff generated by each property. The legislation, innovative for Indiana and prompted by engineers, was adopted in 1988. As of 2015, Indiana had thirty-nine storm water management utilities, including Valparaiso.

8.7.7 Lessons Learned

The preceding description of the planning, design, finance, and construction of a multipurpose storm water management facility offers the following insights for an engineering student or practitioner, especially one inclined to be creative and innovative:

- Apply your creative/innovative instincts to all aspects of your project, not just the technical aspects, as important as they always are. The described project included innovative engineering, innovative finance and, the frosting on the cake, innovative legislation.
- Don't assume others share your inclination to explore creative/innovative options; most don't. Accordingly, do what you can early on in any project to set the stage for possible creativity and innovation, as was done with the engineering guidelines on the storm water project. Try to dispel a *business as usual, let's do it as we always have* project atmosphere by what you say, write, and do.
- Recognize and value your knowledge and experience, and use it to initiate and influence creative/innovative local, state, and national policy and legislation.
- Anticipate the public's short memory and creatively and innovatively keep elected officials, community leaders, and the public at large engaged with an appropriate strategy, such as favoring multipurpose projects.

8.8 CONCLUDING THOUGHTS: WHAT PROFESSION DOES MORE FOR HUMANITY?

From the beginning of this book-writing project, I committed to finding and including many examples of creative/innovative products, processes, structures, facilities, and systems and noting their benefits. The examples were drawn from within and outside of engineering and include both technical and nontechnical developments. As explained in the Preface, "This strong examples/benefits thread is intended to inspire you to work smarter and to achieve even higher levels of creativity and innovation in all aspects of your current studies and later in your professional, personal, family, and community lives, as well as other activities."

However, as I approached the end of the book-writing effort, I gradually realized that something was missing: this chapter. To drive home my message about the need to be even more creative and innovative and how to do it, I needed to provide you, the engineering student or practitioner, with some more in-depth accounts of technical and nontechnical creativity and innovation drawn from a wide spectrum of engineering specialties. After all, this is mostly a book about engineering for engineers.

I have always been proud to be an engineer, especially in the *we will figure out a way to do it* sense. However, after what I learned by researching and writing this chapter—and it presents only the tiniest part of the tip of the engineering creativity/innovation iceberg—I am even more proud of our profession. Engineer, humanitarian, and thirty-first US president Hoover said: "It is a great profession. There is the fascination of watching a figment of the imagination emerge through the aid of science to a plan on paper ... Then it elevates the standards of living and adds to the comforts of life. That is the engineer's high privilege." What profession does more for humanity?

It is not very important whether engineering is called a craft, a profession, or an art; under any name this study of man's needs and of God's gifts that may be brought together is broad enough for a lifetime.

—*Hardy Cross, engineering professor*

CITED SOURCES

ACS. 2014. "Fresh Water from the Sea." American Chemical Society. Accessed October 14, 2014. http://www.acs.org/content/acs/en/pressroom/podcasts/globalchallenges/freshwater.html.

Alston, J. M., M. A. Andersen, J. S. James, and P. G. Pardey. 2010. "A Brief History of U. S. Agriculture." In *Persistence Pays: U. S. Agricultural Productivity Growth and the Benefits from Public R&D Spending*, 9–21. New York: Springer.

American Society of Civil Engineers and Water Environment Federation. 1992. "Case Study of a Multipurpose Flood Control Facility." In *Design and Construction of Urban Stormwater Management Systems*, 697–714. New York: ASCE.

Baggaley A., ed. 2001. *Human Body: An Illustrated Guide to Every Part of the Human Body and How It Works*. London: Dorling Kindersley Limited.

Clements, I. P. 2014. "How Prosthetic Limbs Work." *How Stuff Works*. Accessed September 4, 2014. http://science.howstuffworks.com/prosthetic-limb1.htm/printable.

Cross, H. 1952. *Engineers and Ivory Towers.* Edited by R. C. Goodpasture. New York: McGraw-Hill.

Cyre, H., and J. S. Shearer. 1987. "Stormwater Management Financing." Paper presented at the 14th Annual Water Resource Planning and Management Conference, ASCE, Kansas City, MO, March.

Donohue and Associates. 1984. *Smith Ditch Lagoon No. 1 and Hotter Lagoon Investigation— Valparaiso, Indiana.* Sheboygan, WI: Donohue and Associates.

Dove, L. L. 2014. "How Desalination Works." *How Stuff Works.* Accessed October 8, 2014. http://science.howstuffworks.com/environmental/earth/oceanography/desalination1.htm/printable.

Downey, D., D. K. Giles, and D. C. Slaughter. 2004. "Weeds Accurately Mapped Using DGPS and Ground-Based Vision Identification." *California Agriculture,* October–December: 218–221.

Economist. 2008. "Tapping the Oceans." *The Economist-Technology Quarterly,* Q2 2008, June 5. Accessed October 14, 2014. http://www.economist.com/node/11484059.

Fischman, J. 2010. "Bionics." *National Geographic Magazine,* January.

Gibb, B. J. 2012. *A Rough Guide to the Brain: Get to Know Your Grey Matter.* London: Rough Guides Ltd.

Harrington, K. 2013. "World's First Wave-Powered Desalination Plant." *ChEnected,* American Institute of Chemical Engineers, September 10. Accessed November 20, 2014. http://chenected.aiche.org/energy/worlds-first-wave-powered-desalination-plant/.

Herr, H. 2014. "The New Bionics that Let Us Run, Climb, and Dance." TED Talks, March 24. Accessed November 20, 2014. https://www.ted.com/talks/hugh_herr_the_new_bionics_that_let_us_run_climb_and_dance.

IDA. 2014. "Desalination: An Overview." International Desalination Association. Accessed October 8, 2014. http://idadesal.org/desalination-101/desalination-overview/.

Johnson, M., D. Queen, and N. Sandhu. 2012. "Moving Bridges." *Civil Engineering,* ASCE, February: 64–79.

Jones, J. 2012. "Spanning the Nation." *Civil Engineering,* ASCE, March: 56–78.

Kershner, K. 2014. "How Reverse Osmosis Works." *How Stuff Works.* Accessed October 8, 2014. http://science.howstuffworks.com/reverse-osmosis.htm.

McLoud, P. R., R. Gronwald, and H. Kuykendall. 2007. "Precision Agriculture: NRCS Support for Emerging Technologies." Agronomy Technical Note No. 1, National Resources Conservation Service, US Department of Agriculture, East National Technology Support Center, Greensboro, NC, June.

Ouellette, J. 2013. "Mars Attack." *Smithsonian,* December: 36–41.

Platt, J. R. 2012. "Prosthetics: A Career That Changes Lives." *IEEE-USA Today's Engineer,* July. Accessed September 4, 2014. http://www.todaysengineer.org/2012/jul/career-focus.asp.

Tampa Bay Water. 2014. "Tampa Bay Seawater Desalination Plant." Accessed October 14, 2014. http://www.tampabaywater.org/tampa-bay-seawater-desalination-plant.aspx.

Taylor, J., and B. Whelan. 2014. "A General Introduction to Precision Agriculture." Australian Centre for Precision Agriculture, Sydney, Australia.

Walesh, S. G. 1989. "Preparation of a Master Plan." In *Urban Surface Water Management,* 453–496. New York: John Wiley & Sons.

Wall, M. 2012. "Touchdown! Huge NASA Rover Lands on Mars." *Space.com,* August 6. Accessed November 20, 2014. http://www.space.com/16932-mars-rover-curiosity-landing-success.html.

Wilson, D. H. 2012. "Bionic Brains and Beyond." *The Wall Street Journal*, June 2–3.

USDA. 2014. "A Condensed History of American Agriculture 1776–1999." US Department of Agriculture. Accessed November 20, 2014. http://www.usda.gov/documents/timeline.pdf.

USGS. 2014. "Saline Water: Desalination." USGS Water School, US Geological Survey. Accessed October 8, 2014. http://water.usgs.gov/edu/drinkseawater.html.

EXERCISES

Notes:

1. The goal of the exercises is to provide students, working alone or as a team, the opportunity to think about and use the ideas, principles, and information offered in the chapter.
2. However, many circumstances and corresponding teaching/learning opportunities may arise. For example, a stated situation may be altered to meet specific concerns or needs.

8.1 **ORIGINS OF A CREATION/INNOVATION IN YOUR SPECIALITY:** This chapter describes in some depth a sampling of creative/innovative results drawn from six widely varying engineering specialties. Maybe your chosen or potential specialty was omitted, or perhaps you related to one of the specialties, but the creative/innovative entity did not resonate with you and others. Regardless, here is an opportunity to explore some aspect of your, or your group's, chosen or potential specialty. The purpose of this exercise is to enable you or you and your group to further explore that specialty while learning more about creative/innovative processes.

Suggested tasks are as follows:

a. Select a structure, facility, system, product, or process from within your chosen or potential specialty that you admire and that at least seems to reflect creativity or innovation. Perhaps it drew you to the study of engineering.
b. Conduct research and then write a report that cites all sources (e.g., websites, reference books, published articles or papers, experts) and answers questions such as the following:

- Why do you admire what you selected?
- Who (individual or team) is credited with the original idea?
- What motivated the creative/innovative effort? That is, what were the circumstances? Stated differently, what issue, problem, or opportunity (IPO) was being addressed?
- How did the creative/innovative idea arise? For example, can you discover that the individual or team followed some systematic process (like those described in Chapters 4 and 7 of this book), is the process unknown, or did the idea simply "appear"?
- What obstacles were encountered and how were they overcome?
- What was the duration of the effort from concept to completion?
- What kinds of experts participated?
- What other resources were required (e.g., finance, legal, prototyping, testing) to implement the creative/innovative idea?
- What lessons did you learn?

8.2 **FROM DISABLED TO SUPERABLED:** Neuroprostheses (Section 8.4), now in their infancy, offer marvelous enhanced quality-of-life possibilities for individuals with various physical disabilities. As with most new technologies, neuroprosthetic applications will expand exponentially, as will the number of beneficiaries. One of the likely results is that some individuals or groups of similar individuals will transition from disabled to "superabled" (Wilson 2012). Working as a team, discuss possible superabled situations and their societal implications. For example, consider superabled athletes and superabled scholars. Use Mind Mapping to get started on this exercise. As you discover possible conflicts and controversies, generate potential resolutions using tools such as Brainstorming, the group form of Stream of Consciousness Writing, and What If.

9
Moving On: The Next Move Is Yours

> Do not be too timid and squeamish about your actions.
> All life is an experiment.
> —*Ralph Waldo Emerson, schoolmaster, minister,*
> *lecturer, and writer*

Objectives:

After studying this chapter, you will be able to:

- Relate the text's purpose and the means used to achieve it
- Analyze the degree to which the book's purpose was fulfilled
- Employ up to eleven tactics for implementing your

idea for an improved or new structure, facility, system, product, or process
- Demonstrate that you now have the knowledge and skill to work smarter and be more creative and innovative

9.1 THE END OF THIS TEXT

As my work began on this chapter, I searched for a metaphor to help define and communicate the chapter's message. In fact, I happened to be at a social event at the time, and I explained what I was doing and asked for metaphor ideas. I received none; I was on my own. My first thought was to use a simple stop sign; simple can be good. If you, the reader, made it this far, you're on the last chapter and can soon stop reading and using this book. However, I hope you do not stop reading and thinking about and working with the ideas and tools presented in this book.

The failed stop sign metaphor somewhat naturally led to a traffic signal. We've been on green for eight chapters, and now we see yellow, warning us that change is occurring in the form of slowing down to reflect. This chapter begins on red and ends on green. It stops to reflect on the text's message and then offers you ideas and advice for where to go next. This chapter is my last chance to influence you to make even better use of that marvel between your ears—to use what we know about it to work smarter, including being more creative and innovative.

9.2 REFLECTING ON THE TEXT'S PURPOSE AND THE MEANS USED TO ACHIEVE IT

The purpose of *Introduction to Creativity and Innovation for Engineers*, as stated in the Preface and summarized in Section 1.1, is to help you acquire creativity/innovation knowledge, skills, and attitudes (KSAs) so that you can work smarter and achieve more individual and organizational success and significance in our rapidly changing world. Those KSAs will enable you to generate and begin to develop ideas for improved or new structures, facilities, systems, products, processes, or services.

I set out to accomplish that purpose for you by performing the following tasks:

- Suggesting six reasons why *you should learn more about creativity and innovation* and describing the *historic and linguistic connections* between engineering and creativity (Chapter 1).
- Providing you with a *brain primer* because understanding brain basics, and then using them to learn and apply whole-brain tools, will empower you and your team to work smarter and be more creative and innovative when you take on technical and nontechnical challenges (Chapter 2).
- Introducing, describing, and illustrating *twenty whole-brain methods* designed to stimulate you and, more powerfully, your group, such as a project, planning, design, research, experimental, marketing, or other team, to think more deeply and widely. For convenience purposes, Table 9.1 presents a summary of the tools covered and their neuroscience foundations. These neuroscience-based methods will help you generate more ideas, analyze them, explore many and varied optional courses of action, and select from among them (Chapters 3, 4, and 7).
- Warning you about the *obstacles* that most of your and your team's creative/innovative efforts will inevitably encounter and offering ideas for how to surmount them (Chapter 5).
- Identifying some *characteristics of creative/innovative individuals*, with the hope that you would see many of them within you or within your reach (Chapter 6).
- Offering more in-depth descriptions of creative/innovative results drawn from seven widely varying engineering specialties. These stories are intended to broaden and deepen your appreciation for how the process works and to inspire you to make similar contributions (Chapter 8).

The preceding eight chapters collectively included three themes: First, an issue, problem, or opportunity (IPO) well-defined is half-solved. Second, that marvelous three-pound entity between your ears works best when you engage all of it. Third, we can learn from and be inspired by the creative/innovative efforts of others. To that end, ninety creative/innovative structures, facilities, systems, products, processes, and approaches were introduced in this book for your possible benefit, with some covered in depth.

Table 9.1 Summary of whole-brain methods and their neuroscience bases.

Method	Brain basic(s) applied
1) Ask-Ask-Ask	The interactive and reflective process of asking and answering questions engages both hemispheres.
	Stimulates the subconscious mind, after the interaction, to elaborate on the questions and the answers.
2) Borrowing Brilliance	If consciously stimulated, by searching broadly, the human mind is likely to make new connections.
	Energized by possibilities inherent in new connections, the subconscious mind will energetically generate more connections and their potential implications.
3) Brainstorming	A diverse group combined with moderate visual stimulation will generate and exchange ideas.
	Initiates post-process subconscious thinking and its inevitable benefits.
4) Fishbone Diagramming	Highly visual and non-linear features engage the right hemisphere to complement the left.
	The subconscious mind generates additional bones and elements of bones if the method is applied in a series of sessions.
5) Medici Effect	Left- and right-brain individuals, who are also different in many other ways, offer widely varying views.
	Those views, while at time contentious, can produce surprisingly original results.
6) Mind Mapping	Highly visual and nonlinear features, stimulated by the open-ended process, engage both hemispheres.
	Intense conscious thought engages subconscious minds if used in a series of sessions.
7) Ohno Circle	Capitalizes on vision, the dominant sense.
	The long time period characteristic of the method stimulates conscious–subconscious interaction.
8) Stream of Consciousness Writing	The time requirement forces the individual to draw on all cognitive resources.
	The effort may help to offset a person's limited thinking attributed to his or her negativity bias.
9) SWOT (Strengths-Weaknesses-Opportunities-Threats)	Highly visual and partly emotional aspects engages both hemispheres.
	Generates subconscious activity if applied over multiple sessions.
	Required balance of positives and negatives stimulates thinking.
10) Taking a Break	The focused conscious mind primes the subconscious mind.
	The relaxed conscious mind gradually learns from the now stimulated and always active subconscious mind.
11) What If	Frees, at least temporarily, the conscious mind from well-intended left-brain constraints.
	Explicitly challenges natural negativity bias.
	Typically unusual ideas prime the subconscious mind to work and then share the resulting expanded ideas.
12) Biomimicry	The focused conscious mind stimulated by nature begins to see new possibilities.
	The subconscious mind naturally expands on the initial nature-driven ideas.

Table 9.1 (*Continued*)

Method	Brain basic(s) applied
13) Challenges and Ideas Meetings	Brain-numbing routine reporting is diminished.
	Encourages, via explicit high expectations, creative/innovative conscious and subconscious thinking prior to meetings.
	Plants a desire to resolve challenges and develop ideas in the subconscious minds of informed participants.
14) Freehand Drawing	Engages the right hemisphere to supplement the left hemisphere out of necessity.
	Relies heavily on the dominant sense of sight.
15) Music	Leverages the listening sense in that it accesses both hemispheres and the conscious and subconscious minds.
	Recalls memories that can lead to current and potential applications.
16) Process Diagramming	Highly visual nature enables focused minds to finally see the forest, not just the trees.
	Enhanced understanding of the system combined with possible subsequent subconscious thought generates improvement ideas.
17) Six Thinking Caps	Group members concentrate serially and collaboratively on each of six often competing thinking functions.
	Highly visual nature clarifies understanding of a challenge and stimulates thinking about resolving it.
18) Supportive Culture and Physical Environment	Increases productive interaction among very diverse individuals.
	Employs the dominant visual sense.
	Engages conscious and subconscious minds, with the latter believing what it sees and hears about expectations.
19) TRIZ (Theory of Inventive Problem Solving)	Systematically draws on the successful creative/innovative approaches of many others.
	Contradictions and inventive principles provide a broad and deep source of ideas for consideration by conscious and subconscious minds.
20) Taking Time to Think	The focused conscious mind plants seeds in the active subconscious mind.
	The subconscious mind, which cannot differentiate between what is real and what is imagined, generates ideas in the realm of the latter.

PERSONAL: YOU BE THE JUDGE

You are in the best position to determine the degree to which this text's purpose was accomplished. If you find that *Introduction to Creativity and Innovation for Engineers* is true to its purpose and was and probably will be useful to you, please let me know (stuwalesh@comcast.net). Equally important, if you think that the book fell short of its purpose and/or was of little value, your critique and ideas for improvement would be most welcome.

9.3 IMPLEMENTATION: THE OTHER PART

As noted in Section 9.2, this text focuses on creativity/innovation KSAs and the resulting generation of ideas for improved or new structures, facilities, systems, products, or processes. In the engineering world, idea generation and initial development must be followed by implementation. Potentially fruitful thoughts must be executed if they are to have practical value. Implementation of creative or innovative ideas is frequently alluded to and sometimes discussed in this text. For example:

- Electrical engineer de Mestral's ten-year effort to commercialize Velcro (Section 1.3.2)
- Goodyear devoting ten years to experimentation and other tasks to obtain his vulcanization patent (Section 3.6.2)
- The twenty-six-year effort initiated by Bernard Silver to operationalize the bar code (Section 4.11.2)
- The three-decade, on-again, off-again engineering and construction project culminating in the 1914 opening of the Panama Canal (Section 4.12.5)
- Joseph Strauss's two-decade effort, in the face of widespread skepticism, to plan, design, finance, and build the iconic Golden Gate Bridge (Section 6.4.1)
- NASA's nine-year effort to land the Curiosity rover on Mars (Section 8.2)

The preceding examples represent major implementation efforts, requiring many of the personal characteristics described in Chapter 6 and ongoing creativity and innovation. However, this is not an idea-implementation text. That topic, as important as it is, goes beyond this text's scope and is treated in other books, such as the entrepreneurship book by Lumsdaine and Binks (2007) and the creative problem-solving strategies book by Fogler, LeBlanc, and Rizzo (2014).

HISTORIC NOTE: DA VINCI'S POOR IMPLEMENTATION RECORD

As a student and admirer of da Vinci, I have extolled the creative and innovative ideas flowing from this marvelous Renaissance man, a remarkable artist, scientist, and engineer (Section 6.3.2). However, one of his faults was that he often did not implement his ideas, which we engineers must do if our creative/innovative efforts are to have practical value. As one of his biographers (Wallace 1966) explains, "Leonardo always seemed to go on to other things before he took the final step of bringing his projects to concrete, functioning reality." We too can fall into that trap.

Bringing projects to "concrete, functioning reality" is what engineering is all about. As I've elaborated on elsewhere (Walesh 2012), design, which may be creative and innovative, is the root of engineering; the fruit that grows from that root is a useful structure, facility, system, product, or process. I hope you will be somewhat like da Vinci by being creative and innovative. In contrast, I hope that you will be unlike him in that you and your team will see your ideas through to implementation. May you set down some roots and then see them bear fruit.

If the message and content of *Introduction to Creativity and Innovation for Engineers* engaged you, then you are likely to be interested in implementation. To be helpful, at least in a modest, get-you-started way, I am offering some preliminary idea-implementation suggestions. This confidently assumes that you and maybe a core group of colleagues have or someday will have a creative or innovative idea for an improved or new structure, facility, system, product, or process. Your idea, which may be technical or nontechnical, appears to have great potential. You have begun to engineer, test, and otherwise develop it, and now want to move to full implementation. Eleven implementation-oriented tactics follow:

- Perform an *overall reality check* by answering the twenty questions listed in Section 5.10. Among other things, you'll be advocating change, which is usually challenging, so make sure you are doing the right things for the right reasons.
- From a commercial perspective, ask and answer the following three *specific reality check* questions (Section 5.8.2): 1) Who do we serve? Every organization serves someone, otherwise it would not exist. 2) What is the greatest current or near-future unmet need among those we serve and would like to serve? 3) How will we meet that need?

    Then, get on with applying the concepts and tools in this text to proactively, and hopefully creatively/innovatively, meet that need. However, recognize (as presumptuous as it may sound) that maybe those you serve don't know what they need or want, but you think you do and want to go in that direction. When asked after making a presentation about a potential project if market research should be used to determine what customers want, Apple's Jobs said, "No, because customers don't know what they want until we've shown them" (Isaacson 2011).
- Consistent with the Medici Effect (Section 4.6), if you don't have a *diverse team*, then evolve one. You may have developed a brilliant idea on your own, but you are unlikely to implement it alone. The variety of complex technical and non-technical tasks typically required for implementation requires the KSAs of many diverse individuals. As you assemble or augment your team, be guided in part by the characteristics of creative/innovative individuals, as described in Chapter 6.
- Work at developing *intra-team trust*; with *diversity* and *shared vision*, together they are three qualities that lead to productive collaboration. As discussed in Section 6.7.3, each team member must earn the trust of the others, mainly by practicing honesty and integrity.
- Learn about and know how to selectively use the *legal means* available to protect and advance your creative/innovative idea, such as copyright, trademark, and patent.
- Prepare a *business plan* as appropriate that describes your structure, facility, system, product, or process and indicates how it will be prototyped, tested, legally protected, financed, and marketed. Indicate if a patentability search and opinion will be needed and how that will be accomplished (Keefe 2012; Witters 2010).
- As you move forward with various implementation steps, be open to frequently applying the Chapters 4 and 7 *whole-brain tools* to those steps. Don't limit use of those tools to initial definition of the motivating issue, problem, or opportunity (IPO) or to potential resolutions of it; continue to use the tools during implementation. For example, invoke Ask-Ask-Ask during many of the steps, thoroughly assess various attributes of your idea with SWOT, identify possible marketing approaches using Borrowing Brilliance and Mind Mapping, and apply Process Diagramming to develop the overall implementation process.
- Revisit the seven *obstacles to creativity and innovation* described in Chapter 5, recall the possible remedies offered, and prepare to use some of them if needed. Expect resistance because creativity/innovation and change are two sides of the same coin. Both sides mean new directions, suggest uncertainty and risk, and raise anxiety and fear. That coin may eventually lead to joy, excitement, celebration, and many other benefits that, unfortunately, may not be evident at this point in the implementation process (Adams 1986).

- Assess your group's *communication resources*—namely, which person or persons are most adept at listening, writing, speaking, and using visuals—and make optimum use of them. If you don't have at least one good to great communicator, add one to your team.
- Your creative/innovative structure, facility, system, product, or process will move forward only if you effectively impart its various features, with emphasis on benefits, to stakeholders. The most exciting vision, the most thoughtful insights, or the most elegant resolution of an IPO are all for naught unless they are communicated. Communicating to make things happen is a broad and deep subject, and one that has long interested me. If you are looking for advice, refer to my book *Engineering Your Future* (Walesh 2012) for a pragmatic treatment of listening, writing, and speaking.
- View your implementation effort as a formal project—that is, a temporary effort that must satisfy deliverable, schedule, and budget requirements. Apply proven *project management fundamentals* (e.g., see Walesh 2012) to enhance the probability of success.

PERSONAL: COMMUNICATE IN A CREATIVE/INNOVATIVE MANNER

As you move forward to implement your creative/innovative structure, facility, system, product, or process, communicate creatively and innovatively. We don't always have to use PowerPoint! I've used white boards, newsprint, and props.

Consider props. I've spoken to professional society and student groups on topics such as "Engineering Your Future in a Down Economy: Ten Tips" and "Ten Tips for Success and Significance." These are some of what I call my Ten Tips presentations, and I use a specific set of ten props for each presentation.

After I'm introduced, I place a plain-looking box, as shown in Figure 9.1, on a table in front of the audience while stating that I welcome the opportunity to offer ten tips for consideration. Then, one at a time, I pull out items like those shown in Figure 9.1 and use each to stress a tip. After I've offered all of the tips, the props remain on the table in front of the audience. As part of my summary, I pick them up, one at a time, and place them back in the box. While doing that, I ask what tip each prop represents and always get accurate answers quickly.

Having done about a half-dozen variations on these Ten Tips presentations using props, I offer the following observations: 1) The box gets the audience's attention; audience members seem to welcome something other than another PowerPoint presentation. 2) The audience members stay connected because they wonder, "what will he pull out next?" 3) Participants get the message, as evidenced by the quick recall of the meaning of each prop near the end of my talk as I put them back in the box.

Try prop-based or other creative/innovative presentations to advance the implementation of your creative/innovative idea. As you prepare your oral and written presentation, keep in mind the neuroscience observation presented in Section 2.4.2: "Vision trumps all other senses."

Figure 9.1
The box and examples of props used in Ten Tips presentations.
(Stuart Walesh)

9.4 MY HOPE FOR YOU

Perhaps you read this far into the text and this chapter at least partly because you wanted to. The content, themes, and flavors resonated with you and with the levels of success and significance (Section 1.2) you want to achieve professionally and beyond. Whether a student or practitioner, you see connections between this text and realizing your career and life goals. If these assumptions are at least roughly correct, allow me to offer the following thoughts that may help you continue to move forward:

- Practice good stewardship with the intellectual and work ethic edge you are likely to possess as an engineering student or practitioner (Section 1.4.5).
- Proactively and continuously apply this text's brain basics and whole-brain tools, or at least frequently experiment with them, in your career and beyond.
- Continue, whether formally or on your own, to study the human brain, and use that knowledge to work smarter and be more creative and innovative. Keep up with what will be a continuously expanding body of practical neuroscience knowledge.

Best wishes for achieving success and significance.

> Far better it is to dare mighty things, to win glorious triumphs, even
> though checkered by failure, than to take rank with those poor spirits
> who neither enjoy much nor suffer much, because they
> live in the gray twilight that knows not victory nor defeat.
>
> —*Theodore Roosevelt, twenty-sixth US president*

CITED SOURCES

Adams, J. L. 1986. *The Care and Feeding of Ideas: A Guide to Encouraging Creativity.* Reading, MA: Addison-Wesley Publishing Company.

Fogler, H.S., S. E. LeBlanc, and B. Rizzo. 2014. *Strategies for Creative Problem Solving.* 3rd ed. Upper Saddle River, NJ: Prentice-Hall.

Isaacson, W. 2011. *Steve Jobs.* New York: Simon & Schuster.

Keefe, S. L. 2012. "Patent Eligibility: An Open Field for Civil Engineering." *Civil Engineering,* American Society of Civil Engineers, January: 70–73.

Lumsdaine, E., and M. Binks. 2007. *Entrepreneurship from Creativity to Innovation: Thinking Skills for a Changing World.* Victoria, British Columbia: Trafford Publishing.

Walesh, S. G. 2012. *Engineering Your Future: The Professional Practice of Engineering.* Hoboken, NJ/Reston, VA: Wiley/ASCE Press.

Wallace, R. 1966. *The World of Leonardo 1452–1519.* Alexandria, VA: Time-Life Books.

Witters, S. A. 2010. "Steering Engineering Efforts through the Patent Maze." *PE,* National Society of Professional Engineers, August/September: 18.

EXERCISES

Notes:

1. The goal of the exercises is to provide students, sometimes working alone and sometimes as teams, the opportunity to think about and use the ideas, principles, and information offered in this chapter.

2. However, many circumstances and corresponding teaching/learning opportunities may arise. For example, a stated situation may be altered to meet specific concerns or needs. Such variations are encouraged, subject to the concurrence or direction of the instructor.

9.1 **IMPLEMENTATION CASE STUDY:** Select, as an individual or a team, a creative or innovative structure, facility, system, product, or process that interests you. Research, describe, and document the process used to implement it. Include contact (face-to-face or otherwise) with the leader of the effort or a key player. Ask about setbacks and how they were managed, and summarize what you learn. Determine the dominant characteristics of the leader/principal player and describe them. Identify and describe creative/innovative tactics used to move forward with implementation.

9.2 **LEGAL MEANS FOR PROTECTING YOUR IDEA:** Take one of your creative ideas and research three means of protecting it: copyrights, patents, and trademarks. Describe how and where each can be used for the protection of your idea.

9.3 **PRIORI SEARCH FOR PATENT:** Before applying for a patent, you need to find all existing, "priori", to your idea. For the idea used above, do a priori search and document the results. On which exact features can you apply for a patent?

9.4 **COMMERCIAL BENEFIT CALCULATION:** Conduct a simple Excel-based calculation for your idea using the following heads: cost of manufacturing, assembly, transportation, advertisement, servicing and disposal.

9.5 **BUSINESS PLAN SEMINAR:** Assemble, in a manner that embraces the Medici Effect (Section 4.6), a diverse team that includes one or more business students. Prepare presentation notes, visuals, and handouts for a seminar that your team will present to students who are interested in implementing their creative/innovative ideas. Your team will be the experts in the seminar, and participants will look to you for facts and guidance. Therefore, be prepared to identify and describe each part of a business plan and to provide examples of actual business plans. Select presenters, practice the presentation, and then deliver it.

9.6 **CROWDFUNDING:** *Crowdfunding* means raising funds to finance a project by using the Internet to obtain contributions from a large number of people. Perhaps crowdfunding could be used to finance your current or future creative/innovative idea. With that possibility in mind, study crowdfunding and write a brief report that explains how the process works and describes its positive and negative features.

APPENDIX

A Abbreviations

ABC	Accelerated bridge construction
ACEC	American Council of Engineering Companies (formerly American Consulting Engineers Council)
AD	From the Latin anno Domini, meaning in the year of the Lord
AIChE	American Institute of Chemical Engineers
ASCE	American Society of Civil Engineers
ASEE	American Society for Engineering Education
ASME	American Society of Mechanical Engineers
AWWA	American Water Works Association
BC	Before Christ
BIM	Building information modeling
CADD	Computer-aided design and drawing
CAE	Certified Association Executive
CEBOK	Civil Engineering Body of Knowledge
CEO	Chief Executive Officer
CPA	Certified Public Accountant
DGPS	Differential global positioning system
DIP	Ductile iron pipe
DWYSYWD	Do what you say you will do
EBOK	Engineering Body of Knowledge
EEG	Electroencephalography
fMRI	Functional magnetic resonance imaging
FUD	Fear, uncertainty, doubt
GPS	Global positioning system
HP	Hewlett-Packard
IEEE	Institute of Electrical and Electronic Engineers
IPO	Issue, problem, opportunity
IQ	Intelligence quotient
KSA	Knowledge-skills-attitudes
MEG	Magnetoencephalography
mgd	Million gallons per day
MIT	Massachusetts Institute of Technology
MRI	Magnetic resonance imaging
NAE	National Academy of Engineering
NASA	National Aeronautics and Space Administration
NIH	National Institutes of Health
NCR	Current name for the former National Cash Register Company
NSF REU	National Science Foundation Research Experiences for Undergraduates
NSPE	National Society of Professional Engineers
PE	Professional Engineer
PET	Positron emission tomography
PMI	Project Management Institute
ppm	Parts per million, by weight
PVC	Polyvinyl chloride pipe
PYWAWYP	Plan your work and work your plan

R&D	Research and development	TI	Texas Instruments
RCA	Radio Corporation of America	TINO	Team in Name Only
6TCM	Six Thinking Caps Method	TRIZ	Theory of Inventive Problem Solving (TRIZ is an acronym for *Theory of Inventive Problem Solving* in Russian)
SOP	Standard operating procedure		
SPECT	Single photon emission computed tomography	USDA	US Department of Agriculture
STC	Size-Time-Cost	USGS	US Geological Survey
SWOT	Strengths-Weaknesses-Opportunities-Threats	WEF	Water Environment Federation
TC	Technical committee	WTP	Water treatment plant
TED	Technology, Entertainment, and Design		

B Glossary

Introduction to Creativity and Innovation for Engineers presents ideas and information drawn from a variety of disciplines, such as engineering, business, science, art, neurobiology, and medicine. Accordingly, the following glossary offers readers who are primarily engineers and generally not familiar with the other disciplines a means to more effectively work through the book's content. The twenty whole-brain methods included in this text are not included in this glossary; they are clearly featured and defined in the text.

Algorithmic work: Work following a set of rules, routines, and instructions that are mainly functions of the brain's left hemisphere.

Amygdale: Almond-shaped and sized element in the second or middle major part of the human brain that regulates emotions such as fear, rage, pleasure, and memories of the same.

Asymmetry: Refers to the fact that the two sides of the brain, in contrast with lateralization, are specialized with respect to certain capabilities.

Axon: Also called a nerve fiber, this is the portion of a neuron that transmits chemical signals to other neurons.

Billable time: The hours engineers and others work for professional service firms that can be billed to clients in order to generate income, in contrast with those hours that are not billable.

Bionics: The study and use of mechanical/electronic systems that function like living organisms (or parts of them), with the systems being controlled by the organisms.

Brain: Organ of the human body located within the skull and composed of cells, water, chemicals, and blood vessels. The brain is the organ, and the mind is what we do with it.

Brain stem: The third and lowest part of the human brain, the brain stem manages basic body functions such as breathing, heart rate, blood pressure, sleeping, and wakefulness.

Carbohydrates: Organic compound used by the body to make glucose, the fuel that provides energy.

Cerebellum: A major part of the brain stem, or lowest part of the brain, and responsible for involuntary movement.

Civil Engineering Body of Knowledge (CEBOK): The aspirational necessary depth and breadth of knowledge, skills, and attitudes required for an individual entering the practice of civil engineering at the professional level (licensure as a professional engineer) in the twenty-first century.

Clairvoyance: Gathering information about an object or place using abilities beyond our six senses of vision, hearing, smell, taste, touch, and proprioception.

Commissurotomy: Surgery in which the corpus callosum is severed as a last resort to help individuals severely disabled by epileptic seizures involving both hemispheres.

Conscious mind: Where cognitive processing occurs that we are aware of, such as using information from our memories and senses to makes decisions and convert them to actions. We are thinking and we know it.

Corpus callosum: A system of two hundred million nerve fibers that connect the human brain's left and right hemispheres.

Cortex: A sheet of neural tissue on the brain's surface that is folded so that a large area fits within the confines of the human skull. Nerve centers for thinking, voluntary movement, the senses, and personality reside in the cortex.

Create: Originate, make, or cause to come into existence an entirely new concept, principle, outcome, or object.

Culture: The way things really work in an organization, especially when challenges arise.

Decibel: The loudness or volume of sound, with each ten-decibel increase in loudness being twice as loud as the previous level.

Dendrite: Portion of a neuron that detects and receives chemical signals from neighboring neurons.

Design fixation: Unintentionally adhering to a set of ideas or concepts that limit the creativity and innovation of the result. A similar term for this habitual behavior is the *Einstellung Effect*.

Drawing: Converting what you see into a visually recognizable form.

Einstellung Effect: Resolving issues, problems, and opportunities only by using approaches that have worked in similar situations, rather than looking at each situation on its own terms and at least considering new approaches. A similar term for this habitual behavior is *design fixation*.

Engineering Body of Knowledge (EBOK): The aspirational depth and breadth of knowledge, skills, and attitudes necessary to enter practice as a professional engineer in responsible charge of engineering activities that potentially impact public health, safety, and welfare.

Exoskeleton neuroprosthesis: A neural prosthesis that wraps around limbs for use by paraplegics and people with muscular disabilities and that also generally enhances people's physical capabilities.

Glucose: The brain's source of fuel that interacts with oxygen and nutrients to provide energy to brain cells. Also called *blood sugar*.

Habit: An involuntary behavior controlled by the subconscious mind.

Hemisphere, left: The left half (oriented according to your left) of the human brain. It exhibits valuable verbal, logical, literal, temporal, symbolic, and linear processor capabilities.

Hemisphere, right: The right half (oriented according to your right) of the human brain. It exhibits valuable nonverbal, intuitive, emotional, non-temporal, actual, and parallel processor capabilities.

Hertz: The frequency of sound waves expressed as number of cycles per second.

Hippocampus: Located in the second or middle major part of the brain, it aids with learning and converts our short-term memories into long-term forms.

Hormones: Chemicals produced by glands and transported by the body's circulatory system to produce effects on cells and organs remote from the point of origin.

Ideacide: Intentionally or unintentionally killing creativity or innovation within an organization.

Innovate: Make something new by purposefully combining different existing principles, ideas, and knowledge.

Lateralization: Each of the brain's hemispheres interacts with the opposite side of the body.

Mind: The way a human thinks, believes, hopes, wants, and remembers. The mind is what we do with the organ called the *brain*.

Mindfulness: Engaged in the present moment, observing sights, sounds, and other sensations.

Multitasking: Frequently jumping, in grasshopper fashion, from task to task.

Neural prosthesis: A prosthesis that is linked to the brain. Also called a *robotic prosthesis*.

Neurons: Nerve cells that receive and send electrochemical signals stimulated by neurotransmitters.

Neuroplasticity: Refers to the changeability of the human brain; through most of life, new connections can be made among neurons and new neurons can be developed.

Neurotransmitter: A chemical released from a neuron that helps to amplify or modulate a signal that passes from one nerve cell to another or to a muscle.

Osmosis: The spontaneous net passage or diffusion of molecules of a solvent, such as water, through a semipermeable membrane from a place of lower solute concentration to a place of higher concentration while blocking passage of the solutes, until the solute concentration is equal on both sides. See also *reverse osmosis*.

Parapraxis: A misunderstanding that enables your subconscious mind to speak to your conscious mind. Three ways in which this can happen are (1) you say something you didn't mean to say, (2) you hear something incorrectly, or (3) you read or see something incorrectly.

Precision agriculture: An information- and technology-based management system that is site specific and uses soil, crop, nutrients, pest, moisture, yield, and other data for optimum profitability, sustainability, and protection of the environment.

Prefrontal cortex: The brain's CEO, which resides behind our foreheads.

Proprioception: Sensing body position, posture, and movement.

Protein: Complex molecules that are the building blocks of body tissue; they are used for cell growth, repair, and function.

Reduced cognitive filtering: The ability of some individuals to benefit from the cognitive processing that occurs in their subconscious minds, which can lead to more exceptional insights flowing from their subconscious into their conscious minds.

Retinal implant neuroprosthesis: A retinal implant, a camera to capture light, and a processor to convert incoming video signals into electrical signals for transmission to the cortex.

Reverse osmosis: The engineered process by which a solvent-solute system, partitioned by a semipermeable membrane, uses externally imposed pressure to force water from a high-salt-concentration supply to create an acceptably low-salt-concentration supply.

Senses: Sight, hearing, smell, taste, touch, and proprioception; the last item refers to sensing of the body's position, posture, and movement.

Subconscious mind: Where cognitive processing occurs that we are not aware of, such as habitual actions, dreaming, and reacting. We are thinking and we don't know it.

Subconscious thinking: Brain processes that are below the level of awareness.

Telepathy: Mind-to-mind communication.

Thalamus: Egg-shaped element in the second or middle major part of the human brain that receives and processes signals sent from the senses and routes them to various parts of the brain.

Triune Brain Model: Based on function, physiology, and evolutionary development, describes the overall three-part structure of the human brain.

Whole-brain method: A process, approach, attitude, and/or environment used to stimulate you and, more powerfully, your group or team to think more deeply and widely as you generate more ideas, analyze them, explore many and varied options, select from among them, and implement the best choice.

Index